The Pilot's Guide to Weather Reports, Forecasts & Flight Planning

TAB
PRACTICAL
FLYING SERIES

Other Books in the TAB PRACTICAL FLYING SERIES

ABCs of Safe Flying—2nd Edition *by David Frazier*

The Pilot's Radio Communications Handbook—3rd Edition
by Paul E. Illman and Jay Pouzar

Aircraft Systems: Understanding Your Airplane
by David A. Lombardo

The Art of Instrument Flying *by J.R. Williams*

The Aviator's Guide to Flight Planning
by Donald J. Clausing

Mountain Flying *by Doug Geeting and Steve Woerner*

Avoiding Common Pilot Errors: An Air Traffic Controller's View
by John Stewart

The Beginner's Guide to Flight Instruction—2nd Edition
by John L. Nelson

The Pilot's Air Traffic Control Handbook
by Paul E. Illman

Ocean Flying—2nd Edition *by Louise Sacchi*

Mastering Instrument Flying
by Henry Sollman with Sherwood Harris

The Pilot's Guide to Weather Reports, Forecasts & Flight Planning

Terry T. Lankford

TAB Books
Division of McGraw-Hill, Inc.
Blue Ridge Summit, PA 17294-0850

FIRST EDITION
FIFTH PRINTING

© 1990 by **TAB Books.**
TAB Books is a division of McGraw-Hill, Inc.

Printed in the United States of America. All rights reserved. The publisher takes no
responsibility for the use of any of the materials or methods described in this book,
nor for the products thereof.

Library of Congress Cataloging-in-Publication Data

Lankford, Terry T.
    The pilot's guide to weather reports, forecasts & flight planning
 / by Terry T. Lankford.
        p.   cm.
    Includes index.
    ISBN 0-8306-7582-5   ISBN 0-8306-6582-X (pbk.)
    1. Meteorology in aeronautics.   I. Title.
TL556.L36   1990
629.132′4—dc20
                                                    90-38955
                                                    CIP

Acquisitions Editor: Jeff Worsinger
Book Editor: Norval G. Kennedy
Director of Production: Katherine G. Brown
Book Design: Jaclyn J. Boone

Contents

Preface   ix

Introduction   xi

1 Surface Observations (SA)   1
Sky Cover • Ceiling • Visibility • Atmospheric Phenomena • Atmospheric Data • Automated Weather Observing System (AWOS)

2 Pilot Reports (UA, PIREPs)   39
PIREP Format • Turbulence • Icing • Remarks

3 Forecasts   53
Accuracy • Specificity • Expectations

4 Advisories   59
AIRMETs and SIGMETs • Convective SIGMETS • Alert Weather Watch • Center Weather Advisories • Dissemination

5 Area Forecasts (FA)   71
Hazards • Synopsis • Icing and Turbulence • Icing and Freezing Level • Turbulence and Low-Level Wind Shear • Significant Clouds and Weather • Outlook • Area Forecast Amendment Criteria • A Day on the FA Desk • Using the Area Forecast • The High Altitude Significant Weather Prog • Using the High Altitude Significant Weather Prog

6 TWEB Forecasts   99
Synopsis • Significant Clouds and Weather •
Local Vicinity Forecasts • Amendment Criteria • Using the TWEB
Route Forecast

7 Terminal Forecast (FT)   111
Body and Remarks • Outlook • Amendment Criteria •
Terminal Aerodrome Forecasts (TAF) • Using the Terminal Forecast

**8 Winds and Temperatures
Aloft Forecasts (FD)   133**
Tabulated Forecasts • Forecast Charts • Amendment Criteria •
Using the FD Forecast

9 Radar and Convective Analyses   145
Radar • Stormscope • Radar Weather Reports (RAREPs) •
Radar Summary Chart • Using RAREPs, RRWDS, and the Radar
Summary Chart • Convective Outlook and Severe Weather Outlook
Chart • Composite Moisture Stability Chart • Microbursts and
Low-Level Wind Shear

10 Air Analysis Charts   177
Surface Analysis Chart • Weather Depiction Chart •
Upper Air Analysis Charts • Observed Winds Aloft Chart •
Vorticity • Upper Level Weather Systems

11 Pilot Briefings   213
Standard Briefing • Abbreviated Briefing • Outlook Briefing •
In-Flight Briefing • FAA's Pilot Weather Briefing Service •
Commercial Weather Briefing Services /DUAT

12 Updating Information   237
Flight Service Station Communications •
Airport Advisory Frequency • En Route Flight Advisory Service
(Flight Watch)

13 Notices to Airmen (NOTAMs)   247
Terminology • NOTAM (D) • NOTAM (L) • FDC NOTAMs •
Class II Notices to Airmen • Using the NOTAM System

14 **VFR Flight Planning**   259

Flight Plan Information • Flight Plan Filing • FSS Flight Plan
Procedures • Search and Rescue • Using VFR Flight Plan Service •
Special VFR • Using Special VFR • Flight Assistance Service

15 **IFR Flight Planning**   273

Flight Plan Information • Flight Plan Filing and Processing •
Composite Flight Plans • Obtaining and Canceling IFR Clearances •
Using IFR Flight Plan Service

Appendix A: Abbreviations   287

Appendix B: Forecast and Report Locations   335

Appendix C: Plotting Identifiers   341

Appendix D: Area Designators   351

Appendix E: Weather Products   353

Glossary   361

Index   367

Preface

I OBTAINED A PRIVATE PILOT CERTIFICATE IN 1967 THROUGH AN AIR FORCE aero club in England: certificate because the FAA cannot spell license. Back in the states, with the G.I. Bill, I obtained the commercial certificate and flight instructor rating along with an instrument rating. Subsequently, as a full-time flight instructor I earned a Gold Seal. I have owned two airplanes, both Cessna 150s that have taken me across the country twice. I have also flown in Canada and Mexico. I don't fly as much as I'd like, but manage to keep my instrument and instructor ratings current.

A commercial pilot certificate and instrument rating qualified me for my present position with the Federal Aviation Administration (FAA) as an Air Traffic Control Specialist (Station), although I prefer Flight Service Station (FSS) specialist.

Only once as flight service specialist did I become an air traffic controller. While at the Lovelock, NV, FSS a call came in from a VFR pilot caught in clouds at 13,000 feet. In such cases the control facility (approach control or center) usually provides assistance. Coordinating with Oakland Center, the controller replied: "OK, you've got 14 and below, keep me advised." Instant air traffic controller.

I've been an FSS specialist for 15 years, which has brought together two interests: aviation and weather.

With all the books and articles written about aviation weather it might seem everything has been said. As a flight instructor, however, I discovered that very little practical information was available for pilots on the subject of meteorology. Certain texts and periodicals contain excellent points and suggestions. Most merely paraphrase government manuals. Some actually include incorrect and misleading information. Many say nothing.

I find it exasperating to read an article with meteorological terms that espouses the need to understand weather then fails to include a definition or explain application of a term. Virtually none have an understanding of information available from, or the requirements and responsibilities of, the FSS weather briefer. Nor do they present practical ways of translating, interpreting, updating, and applying information.

As an FSS specialist I've become aware of requirements and procedures that the FAA seems to want to keep secret. Most requirements and procedures have to do with how FSS specialists and air traffic controllers do their jobs. Much of this book is dedicated to points glossed over, or ignored altogether, in the *Airman's Information Manual*.

Pilots, especially within the general aviation community, have a close relationship with the FSS specialist. The FSS specialist, whether during preflight or in-flight, has at his or her fingertips a wealth of information. The pilot, for whom the FSS exists, is an integral part of the aviation weather system. He or she provides feedback in the form of pilot reports (PIREPs), essential for the meteorologist to verify the forecast, and optimum system operation. When the pilot or specialist forgets, or does not understand, the requirements and responsibilities of the other, the system can fail, sometimes with fatal results.

Aviation weather-related accidents continue to take their toll; analysis often reveals an inadequate, misinterpreted or misunderstood weather briefing. With FSS automation, Automated Weather Observation Systems (AWOS), and increased availability of Direct User Access Terminals (DUAT) and other commercial weather information systems, pilots will be required to read, interpret, and apply weather information on their own. A sound background in meteorology, and the products available to aviation, are essential to safety.

I am greatly indebted to many people for their generous help, guidance, and advice, too numerous to be listed in full. Among them are the meteorologists of the National Weather Service (NWS) at the FAA Academy in Oklahoma City, and local and regional NWS offices plus flight service station specialists that I have been privileged to know, especially at the Oakland, CA, FSS. And, the pilots who have allowed me to assist them and in turn provided me with the best education possible. This book is dedicated to these people.

Introduction

W EATHER AFFECTS A PILOT'S FLYING ACTIVITY MORE THAN ANY OTHER physical factor. Most pilots agree that weather is the most difficult and least understood subject in the training curriculum. Surveys indicate that many pilots are uneasy with, or even intimidated by, weather. In spite of these facts, or because of them, weather training for pilots consists of bare bones, only enough to pass the written test, while weather-related fatal accident statistics remain unchanged.

Air Force pilot training contains a mere 15 hours of formal weather instruction, as compared to 50 or 60 hours in the past. Navy pilot weather training has been reduced by 25 percent to 30 hours, with no refresher. Army aviator weather training consists of about the same number of hours. My own FAA certificated primary ground school included a mere nine hours of weather. Ironically, Federal Aviation Regulations (FAR) perpetuate this trend. Student, private, recreational, and commercial airplane pilots are only required to obtain and use weather reports and forecasts, recognize critical weather situations, and estimate ground and flight visibility. An additional requirement of forecasting weather trends on the basis of information received and personal observations is required for an instrument rating. Only the airline transport pilot certificate requires the applicant to have serious meteorological knowledge.

A major revision to the practical test standards in 1984 required that applicants exhibit "knowledge of aviation weather information by obtaining, reading, and analyzing . . ." reports and forecasts, and make ". . . a competent go/no-go decision based on the available weather information. The practical test standards do reference AC 00-6 *Aviation Weather* (basic meteorological theory) and AC 00-45 *Aviation Weather Services* (a basic discussion of weather reports and forecasts), but neither reference relates weather to flight situations or application of go/no-go decision. Most flight tests are given during good weather, and pilots requesting check ride briefings, all too often, have little idea of the information required or the presentation format of the FSS briefer; this requirement would seem to have little practical consequence.

This situation evolved because when regulations were originally written, virtually all flying, except military and airline, was visual. The aircraft of the day had neither the performance nor the instruments to take on weather. When weather was encountered, pilots simply landed in the nearest field. Regulations are extremely difficult to change; take the aeronautical experience of 40 hours required for the private pilot. These hours have been woefully inadequate for years with the constant increase of additional requirements. Many of the people who write regulations and perform flight tests are former military pilots with minimal weather training, because after graduation they were under direct control of older, more experienced pilots and gained experience in a controlled environment.

Accident reports and commentaries frequently refer to a pilot's poor judgment, namely the failure to reach a sound decision. Pilot judgment is based on *training* and *experience*. *Training* is knowledge imparted during certification, flight reviews, seminars, and literature; *experience* can be best defined when the test comes before the lesson. Unfortunately, failure can be fatal. Pilot applicants have only their instructor to prepare them to make competent go/no-go decisions.

Odds are, little if any judgment training occurred unless situations were actually encountered. General aviation training runs the entire gamut from the flight school that prohibits its instrument students and instructors from flying in the clouds, to the instructor in a Cessna 182 who requested to be vectored into icing conditions to demonstrate the effects of ice to his student. (Neither instance seemingly exhibits sound judgment.) The fact remains that the least experienced pilots have minimum weather training. Following certification there is no requirement for additional or refresher weather instruction.

An essential part of flight preparation concerns the weather. No matter how short or simple the mission, Federal Aviation Regulations place the responsibility for flight preparation on the pilot, not the NWS forecaster, not the FSS briefer. To effectively use the available resources, a pilot must understand what weather information is available, how it is distributed, and how it can be applied to a flight situation.

This book provides information, not only required to pass written and practical examinations, but to prepare the dispatcher as well as the pilot—from student through airline transport, from recreational to biz-jet—to operate safely and efficiently within an ever increasingly complex environment.

Student, recreational, private, and commercial pilots will develop abilities to recognize and avoid critical weather situations.

Pilots will learn to obtain weather reports and forecasts, through the FAA and other sources, then interpret and apply information to flight situations.

Pilots will understand the principles of forecasting, and applying forecasts and observations to the flight environment.

Pilots will understand weather collection and distribution, symbols and contractions, charts and forecasts, and how terrain affects weather.

Pilots will recognize cloud forms, conditions conducive to icing and other meteorological hazards, and the use of pilot weather reports.

The student pilot will have access to the knowledge of the airline transport pilot.

Technical meteorological concepts and terms are translated into language any pilot can easily understand. On the other hand, such subjects as *vorticity*, *microbursts*, and *upper level weather systems* will not be omitted because of complexity. Explanations of weather reports and forecast go beyond decoding and translating, to interpreting and applying information to actual flight situations. Discussions include applying weather information to VFR as well as IFR operations, and high-level as well as low-level flights.

A thorough understanding of the basics is essential: a sound foundation for the novice and a practical review for the experienced pilot. Judgment and application of judgment, plus a knowledge of the aviation weather system and its relation to air traffic control, are essential to a safe, efficient flight.

Weather reports, forecasts, and flight planning are interrelated; it might be necessary for the reader to complete the book to realize the most thorough understanding of the subject.

The book begins with a detailed description of surface weather reports including methods and criteria used by the weather observer. Failure to understand the observer's requirements often leads to pilot misunderstanding and unwarranted observer criticism. Limitations on observations are discussed with practical guidance on interpreting information.

Surface reports are related to hazards, such as thunderstorms, turbulence, icing, low ceilings and fog, precipitation, haze, smoke, and dust, as well as winds and low-level wind shear, and high density altitude. The automated weather observing system is discussed with its inherent advantages and limitations.

Most pilots are unaware of contributions through pilot weather reports, or the impact the reports can have on the system. Inaccurate or overestimated reports of turbulence and icing cause misleading advisories to be issued. Pilots making these reports gain unrealistic confidence in their ability to handle severe conditions. Pilots receiving unwarranted advisories, based on overestimated pilot reports, might conclude all advisories are pessimistic. When severe conditions develop, these pilots can be lead down the primrose path to disaster. PIREP criteria are discussed in detail, along with distribution and application.

The methods, criteria, and limitations of the forecasts are discussed. Numerous misunderstandings and misconceptions of forecast products and terminology, potentially catastrophic to the uninformed pilot, are explained. The book tells how the pilot can interpret and apply forecasts to specific flight situations, which will become increasingly important with direct user access terminals.

Approximately one dozen different forecasts are written for aviation; each has criteria, purpose, and limitations; often they overlap and might appear to be inconsistent. Analysis, however, most often reveals the forecasts are consistent within the scope of each product. Each forecast is analyzed and put into perspective. The pilot can then apply the array of forecasts available, with respect to regulations, aircraft performance, and pilot ability, to efficiently operate within the system and make sound go/no-go decisions.

Beyond written weather reports and forecasts, a multitude of charts is available. Each chart has a specific purpose, use, and limitations. All charts are discussed and analyzed with respect to their individual significance and application.

Three chapters are devoted to obtaining, updating, and using weather and aeronautical information. Discussions will help the pilot efficiently obtain weather and flight planning information which have become increasingly difficult with flight service station consolidation.

Navigation principles and techniques are not within the scope of this book. The final chapters are devoted to applying information to VFR and IFR flight planning situations. With direct user access terminals, pilots will not only obtain weather and NOTAMs, but file flight plans through a computer terminal. On the surface, this might seem a simple task, but it can be complicated and frustrating to the pilot and has the potential for trouble for the individual who fails to obtain or misinterprets information.

Text references are made to various cloud forms that frequently appear in weather reports with photographs to illustrate certain formations.

An excellent, detailed, color cloud chart, *The Cloud Chart*, is available through the National Weather Association, 4400 Stamp Road, Room 404, Temple Hills, MD 20748.

The following chapters, hopefully told with a little humor, explain how to use the weather system, translate, and interpret weather reports and forecasts, then apply them to a flight situation.

Incidents are not intended to disparage or malign any individual, group, or organization; the sole purpose is illustration.

Examples of weather reports and forecasts are real and taken off the weather circuit. None have been created.

References to FAR Part 91 *General Operating and Flight Rules*, due to a major reorganization and realignment, refer to regulations effective August 18, 1990.

Weather report phraseology used in the text is taken from FAA handbook 7110.10 *Flight Services*. This is the same phraseology pilots can expect in FSS radio communications and broadcasts.

1
Surface Observations
(SA)

ASK MOST PILOTS ABOUT CODED WEATHER REPORTS AND YOU'LL HEAR: "WHY do I have to read the weather? When I call flight service, they read and explain the reports." Pilots have been objecting to coded weather information since its inception in the early 1930s. But, with the Direct User Access Terminal System, (DUAT—pronounced doo-AT′) and commercially available weather systems, pilots will have to read and interpret weather on their own. Although the ability to read reports is essential, whether obtained from an FSS or other source, the skill and knowledge to interpret information is crucial. A pilot's knowledge of weather takes on greater significance with DUAT and Flight Service Station (FSS) consolidation.

Whether you are a beginner—even Steve Canyon started as a student pilot—or an old hand, examine the following reports taken on July 17, 1988, at Newark, NJ (EWR) and Philadelphia, PA (PHL). Translate and interpret the observations; you might make some notes. When you've finished the chapter see if your interpretation and understanding have changed.

```
EWR SP 2240 W0 X 0T + RW + 3545Q60/989/R04VR45 T + OVHD MOVG ESE FQT
     LTGICCCCG
EWR RS 2253 − X E15 OVC 3T + RW 102/75/70/0905/983/R5 T + B10 SE
     MOVG ESE FQT LTGICCCCG VSBY HIR W RB07 PK WND 3560/40
PHL RS 2250 W6 X 1TRW + F 102/77/74/3618G24/983/R27RVR30V60 + TB25
     ALQDS MOVG SE FQT LTGICCG RB38 PRESFR
PHL SP 2256 W5 X 3/4TRW + F 2921G28/989/R27RVR08V60 + WSHFT 55 T
     ALQDS MOVG SE FQT LTGICCG PRESRR
```

SURFACE OBSERVATIONS (SA)

Most weather reports are history by the time they are transmitted and available. In the teletype era, reports were often an hour-and-a-half old. Beginning in 1978 the Federal Aviation Administration (FAA) introduced a computer system known as Leased Service A (LSAS). With this and other computerized systems most reports are available within 20 minutes of observation.

The accuracy and validity of observations, and therefore their usefulness, depend on many factors: who is taking the observation, what is the extent of the observer's training and experience, and what type of equipment, if any, is available.

The National Weather Service certifies weather observers. However, the most accurate, valid, and detailed observations come from NWS, military, FSS, tower, and other observers, in that order because NWS and military observers are professionals located at major airports with the latest equipment. At FSS and tower locations weather observations are a secondary duty, and generally, equipment is not as sophisticated. As for the others, they are contract observers, retired air traffic controllers, local airport personnel, or even the fire department, often with little or no equipment, and the minimum of training and experience.

This is not to say that many of them don't provide quality observations, but in many cases they simply don't have the equipment, training, or experience. And the FAA and NWS have decided that Automated Weather Observing Systems (AWOS) will be the standard at major airport and Automated Flight Service Station (AFSS) locations. How will automation affect the quality of observations? More about AWOS later in this chapter.

Reports begin with a three letter location identifier (LCID—That's my contraction; the FAA doesn't have one). Most reports use three letters, but some consist of letters and numbers (S06 Mullan, ID). Official LCIDs are contained in FAA Handbook 7350.5 *Location Identifiers*, available for sale from the Superintendent of Documents. Pilots also have access to LCIDs through FSSs, DUATs, the *Airport/Facility Directory*—the green book—and the FAA's *Pilot's Guide to IVRS* (Interim Voice Response System). Appendix A, Contractions, contains LCIDs for most weather reporting locations.

Type of observation follows the station's identifier. Two basic types of reports are *record* and *special*.

SAs (record hourly airway surface observations) are taken each hour. Whenever a significant change occurs an SP (non-hourly special airway observation) is recorded. A complex criteria determines the requirement for specials. Generally they're required when the weather improves to, or deteriorates below, Visual Flight Rules (VFR) or approach and landing Instrument Flight Rules (IFR) minimums. Specials are also required for the beginning, ending, or change in intensity of thunderstorm activity. For severe weather, such as tornadoes, a single element urgent special (USP) can be issued.

XYZ USP 1527 TORNADO W MOVG E SPECIALIST HDG S

When special criteria are met at the normal time of observation the report is identified as RS (hourly record special airway observation). USP, RS, and SP reports alert all concerned to potentially significant changes. Specials are not available for all locations, however, these reports will normally carry the remark NO SPL. In such cases significant changes can occur without immediate notification.

2

Some locations take supplemental, non-scheduled observations. These are encoded SW (supplemental surface observations) and available only on an irregular basis.

Report type (SA, SP, SW, etc.) determines distribution priority and storage time. For example, USPs receive immediate distribution to all circuits, SAs are replaced hourly, and SWs stored for three hours unless replaced or updated. Carefully note SWs observation time, the report might be hours old.

Following observation of the last element, usually atmospheric pressure, the official time of observation is recorded (OAK SA "1956" . . .). Times are Coordinated Universal Time (UTC), referred to as ZULU or Z.

SKY COVER

Sky cover refers to clouds or obscuring phenomena as seen by an observer on the ground from horizon to horizon. Sky cover reported on SAs is the summation of layers based on specific criteria. Conditions aloft, as seen by a pilot, can differ substantially. The summation principle with terms like *obscuring phenomena* and *obscuration* are complex and often misunderstood.

Refer to TABLE 1-1 for sky cover definitions. Notice that even a report of clear (CLR) does not guarantee a cloud-free sky. In such cases, however, most observers will add a

Table 1-1. *Sky Cover.*

Symbol		Definition
CLR	Clear	Less than $1/10$ sky cover.
SCT	Scattered	$1/10$ to $5/10$ sky cover.
BKN	Broken	$6/10$ to $9/10$ sky cover.
OVC	Overcast	More than $9/10$ sky cover.
X	Sky Obscured	All of the sky hidden by a surface-based obscuring phenomena.

Note: BKN, OVC, and X represent a ceiling.

Symbol		Definition
-SCT	Thin Scattered	
-BKN	Thin Broken	At least $1/2$ of the layer is transparent.
-OVC	Thin Overcast	

Note: -BKN and -OVC do not constitute a ceiling.

Symbol		Definition
-X	Sky Partially Obscured	From $1/10$ to less than $10/10$ of the sky is hidden by a surface-based obscuring phenomena.

remark (FEW CU, few cumulus; or ST NW, stratus northwest). Variable sky cover describes a situation that varies during the period of observation, normally the 15-minute period preceding time of observation (15 SCT . . . /SCT V BKN, scattered layer variable to broken). Variability alerts pilots, briefers, and forecasters to rapidly changing conditions over the airport.

Sky cover heights on surface observations are always reported above ground level (AGL). Here, variability indicates a rapid fluctuation in ceiling height (M10V BKN . . . / CIG08V12, measured ceiling 1,000 variable broken . . . /ceiling variable between 800 and 1,200). A variable ceiling below 3,000 feet must be reported, above 3,000 only if considered operationally significant.

In FIG. 1-1 the observer sees $^3/_{10}$ cloud cover at 1,000 feet AGL and reports 1,000 scattered (10 SCT). Another $^3/_{10}$ cloud cover is measured at 1,800 feet AGL. According to the summation principle a total of $^6/_{10}$ ($^3/_{10}$ + $^3/_{10}$ = $^6/_{10}$) sky cover exists; a measured ceiling 1,800 broken (M18 BKN) is reported. The observer sees the remaining sky covered by cloud at 3,000 feet AGL, and reports 3,000 overcast (30 OVC). The observer is unable to determine the extent of higher layers and reports them as continuous.

This principle has led many a pilot to mistakenly question the accuracy of observations. Pilot reports (PIREPs) are usually the only means of determining the extent of upper layers and tops. A PIREP describing conditions in FIG. 1-1 might read: SCT 012/SCT 025/ SCT 035 (tops of SCT layers 1,200, 2,500, and 3,500 feet respectively). Given the summation principle the observation and pilot report are perfectly consistent.

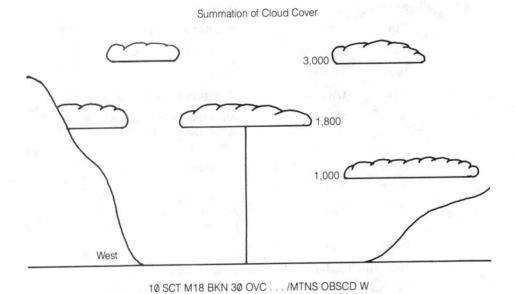

10 SCT M18 BKN 30 OVC . . . /MTNS OBSCD W

Fig. 1-1. *Cloud cover reported on SAs is the summarization of cloud layers as seen by an observer on the ground.*

Sky cover is always an estimate. As an FSS briefer for some 15 years, I have on occasion briefed doom and gloom only to find a bright, beautiful day. It would seem that certain tower observers use the following criteria: They consider the roof of the tower cab as opaque; therefore, one cloud is scattered, two is broken, and three is overcast with breaks! (So there's no misunderstanding, this was one attempt at humor.)

Notwithstanding the previous observation, care must be exercised climbing or descending VFR through a broken deck. Although it might be possible to safely negotiate the layer, several factors must be considered. Can appropriate distance from clouds as specified in Federal Aviation Regulation (FAR) 91.155 Basic VFR weather minimums be maintained? Is the weather improving or deteriorating? We don't want to get caught on top or between layers. Is the area congested with other VFR traffic or aircraft operating IFR? The criteria in FAR 91.155 are minimums; they do not necessarily equate to "safe." What alternates are available, if needed? Positive answers are required before an attempt. Any negative or uncertain responses would indicate a no-go decision.

How many times have you heard or said to yourself, "Well, I think I'll go take a look." There is no inherent danger in this practice as long as the pilot knows when to quit. So, the question becomes: When to turn around? When the thought, "I wonder if I should?" first occurs, that's the time to execute the 180. Ironically, most primary training sets the stage for an accident. Many instructors simulate the student flying into clouds, then require them to extricate themselves, when the better behavior is to turn around before entering IFR weather. Flying into clouds, or weather less than VFR, does not satisfy the requirement to recognize critical weather situations. Remember the all too common accident scenario, "Continued VFR. . . ."

CEILING

The lowest broken, overcast, or obscured layer, not thin or partial, is classified as a *ceiling*. When an observer can see through one-half or more of a layer it is reported as thin (−BKN, or −OVC). A thin layer does not constitute a ceiling because a pilot flying over the deck could see the ground. The pilot could penetrate the layer, assuming required horizontal visibility for that airspace could be maintained. In general, referring to FAR 91.155 Basic VFR weather minimums, this requires: one statute mile outside controlled airspace, three statute miles within controlled airspace, or five statute miles at or above 10,000 feet Mean Sea Level (MSL).

Ceilings are designated *estimated*, *measured*, or *indefinite*. Although, seemingly simple and self-explanatory, even a measured ceiling can be misleading. And, an indefinite ceiling is complex and often misunderstood. Like many specialties, aviation weather has its own language. For communication and understanding to take place, each party must use the same definitions. Take the pilot that called unicom and asked, "What's the ceiling?" After a pregnant pause the operator replied, "I think it's oak."

An estimated ceiling (E) is just that, a more or less educated guess by the observer. But, the fact remains it's just an estimate based on the observer's training and experience. Estimated ceilings must always be reviewed with caution, especially at night or close to minimums. In addition to an educated guess, pilot reports, ceiling balloons, surrounding terrain, or a calculation from temperature/dew point might be employed to determine an estimated ceiling.

Ceiling balloons are relatively accurate for low clouds below about 2,000 feet. Balloons, however, are affected by strong winds and precipitation. A balloon filled with helium to lift a known weight is released. The observer times the balloon until cloud penetration. The elapsed time is converted into height. At tower and FSS locations where observations are secondary this time-consuming procedure is rarely used.

A pilot report can be one of the most accurate means of determining the ceiling, assuming the pilot actually penetrates the clouds, or climbs or descends through a scattered or broken layer. Otherwise, it's just a pilot's guess. As pilots we should always pass cloud bases to the tower or FSS, especially when different from reported. But keep in mind, we reference cloud bases to a pressure altimeter set to read elevation MSL, and the observer reports clouds AGL. This explains some apparent inconsistencies between observer and pilot reported cloud bases.

Where available, surrounding terrain, buildings, or towers are usually quite accurate for determining cloud bases. But, they might not be representative of surrounding areas.

An estimate for the height of convective clouds can be determined from temperature/dew point. This procedure is based on surface heating of a parcel of air that rises and cools at the dry adiabatic lapse rate. When temperature reaches dew point, saturation occurs and clouds form at the Lifted Condensation Level (LCL). When the layer is produced by surface heating, apply the following formula: $T - Td \times 2.2 \times 100 =$ Cloud Base AGL. In this formula T = temperature F (Fahrenheit), Td = dew point F., and 2.2 and 100 are constants. For example, SA . . . 70/60 . . . temperature minus dew point $(70 - 60)$ equals 10 degrees; apply the formula, $10 \times 2.2 \times 100 = 2,200$. The approximate cloud bases are 2,200 AGL. As another example, use this observation for Denver, CO.

DEN SA 2350 90 SCT 150 SCT E250 BKN 45 075/91/44/1610/001

Applying the formula to the DEN SA, the cloud base works out to be approximately 10,000 AGL $(91 - 44 \times 2.2 \times 100 = 10,000)$. This is consistent with the observers report of 9,000 scattered. An article some years ago in a popular aviation magazine claimed this procedure could be used for any cloud layer. It's important to remember this procedure only applies to convective clouds produced by surface heating.

A measured ceiling (M) is the most accurate means of determining cloud height. Normally, either a Rotating Beam Ceilometer (RBC) or a ceiling light is used. The projector portion of the RBC shines a beam of light along the cloud base. When directly over the detector, a photoelectric cell activates. The observer reads cloud height directly off the indicator located in the tower, FSS, or weather office. A much less sophisticated system, the ceiling light, projects a vertical beam; using a clinometer—colloquially known as the coke bottle—the observer measures the angle from the ground to the point where the light reflects off a cloud along a predetermined base line. From a chart the observer converts angle into cloud height. (From personal experience I can say this is no fun in rain or snow.) Both methods, however, only measure cloud height at one point above the airport. This is why ceilometers are usually located at the approach end of the primary instrument runway.

A measured ceiling might not be representative of surrounding conditions, especially at night, or during low visibility, when the observer cannot see the whole sky. Refer to FIG. 1-1, if the observer were unable to see the scattered layer at 1,000 feet, a ceiling of 1,800 feet would be reported. Or, if the ceilometer went through a hole in the 1,800-foot layer, the observer might report a measured ceiling of 3,000 feet overcast. Such errors can, and do, occur because of limitations on equipment and the observer.

An indefinite ceiling (W), the least understood ceiling designator, is even defined incorrectly in some aviation texts. Technically an indefinite ceiling is the vertical visibility upward into a surface-based obscuring phenomena that completely conceals the sky: the distance at which a pilot can expect ground contact when looking straight down on descent, or the point at which the ground disappears on climb out.

So what's an obscuring phenomena? Most often caused by fog, it is anything that prevents the observer from seeing all or part of the sky. Snow, smoke, or even heavy rain can cause this condition (W∅ X . . . RW+ indefinite ceiling zero, sky obscured by heavy rain showers).

The accuracy of an indefinite ceiling depends on the observer and available equipment. Whether the value is determined by a ceilometer, pilot report, balloon, or just a guess by the observer it is reported as indefinite. In FIG. 1-2 the observer has either measured or estimated the vertical visibility as 200 feet. The sky is completely obscured. The observer, unable to determine cloud layers above, reports an indefinite ceiling 200, sky obscured (W2 X).

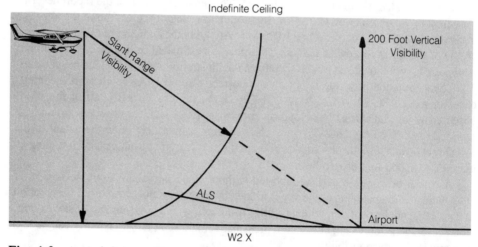

Indefinite Ceiling

Slant Range Visibility

200 Foot Vertical Visibility

ALS

Airport

W2 X

Fig. 1-2. *An indefinite ceiling represents the vertical visibility into a surface-based obscuring phenomena.*

Indefinite ceilings are most often associated with IFR conditions. Presume that a destination is reporting an indefinite ceiling 200 and that 200 feet is the decision height (DH) for the Instrument Landing System (ILS) approach. Assuming the observation is accurate, at DH the pilot should be able to look straight down and see the Approach Lighting System (ALS). However, he or she would not necessarily be able to see the runway due to increased slant range distance. This is illustrated in FIG. 1-2. In fact, slant range visibility could be less than vertical visibility! That's why approach lights are considered part of the ILS and minimums increase when they're out of service.

Would the conditions in the previous paragraph preclude a legal landing? Not necessarily, as long as the provisions of FAR 91.175 are met. A legal landing requires three conditions. The aircraft must remain in a position from which a normal descent to landing can be made. The flight visibility must not be less than that prescribed for the approach. And, the runway environment (approach lights, threshold, runway, etc.) remains distinctly visible. Any requirement not met or lost after DH requires an immediate missed approach.

How about VFR with an indefinite ceiling of 1,000 feet? Even though ceiling and surface visibility might technically meet legal minimums, flight visibility might be substantially less. Now consider the possibility that the observer might not have ceiling height-finding equipment, the reported ceiling might only be a guesstimate. Good operating practice dictates extreme caution operating close to minimums. If IFR, a legal alternate or two, or an escape route to where VFR conditions are known to exist, is a must!

Sky partially obscured ($-X$) is also easily misunderstood. A partial obscuration indicates from $1/10$ to less than $10/10$ of the sky is hidden by a surface-based obscuring phenomena. Precipitation, haze, smoke, and fog usually cause this condition. The observer, unable to evaluate the hidden portion of the sky, must consider it opaque when applying the summation principle.

In FIG. 1-3, half ($5/10$) of the sky is hidden. The remarks portion of the report describe the extent of the obscuration (. . . /F5). In the example, fog obscures $5/10$ of the sky. The observer can see $2/10$ cloud cover at 3,000 feet. Applying the summation principle, a total of $7/10$ of the sky is covered or hidden. Therefore, an estimated ceiling of 3,000 feet must be reported, even though, as can be seen from the illustration, only $2/10$ cloud cover exists.

The summation principle is not always correctly applied. A report from a contract observer read: ABC SA 1845 $-X$ 10 SCT E25 OVC . . . /F5. Because half of the sky is obscured by fog and at least $1/10$ cloud cover exists at 1,000 feet, the observer should have reported: $-X$ E10 BKN 25 OVC. . . . The observer cannot determine the extent of the 1,000-foot layer above the obscured portion of the sky. It might be quite a shock finding an unexpected 1,000-foot broken layer!

A partial obscuration may be reported without cloud layers, for example $-X$ . . . / HK3. Remarks indicate $3/10$ of the sky is hidden by haze and smoke. A partial obscuration in itself must not be confused with a ceiling. Although, with a large amount of sky hidden, cloud coverage amounts might not be representative, and slant range visibility can be less than reported surface visibility.

Normally, a pilot can expect ground contact while flying in areas with a reported partial obscuration. This is why they are not considered ceilings. However, the same principles apply to a partial obscuration as thin cloud layers. Penetrating a partial obscuration VFR requires the appropriate horizontal visibility be maintained for that airspace. A par-

Partial Obscuration

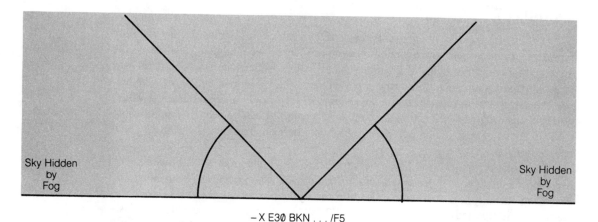

3,000 Feet

Sky Hidden
by
Fog

Sky Hidden
by
Fog

– X E30 BKN . . . /F5

Fig. 1-3. *A partial obscuration indicates the observer cannot evaluate the entire sky. When a large amount of the sky is obscured, cloud cover amounts might not be representative.*

tial obscuration with visibilities less than basic VFR can often be safely negotiated under the provisions of special VFR, discussed in Chapter 14.

After being briefed that his destination was reporting sky partially obscured, visibility two, in fog and haze (– X 2FH), the Beechcraft Baron pilot emphatically demanded to know the ceiling. He stated he must have this information to determine IFR minimums. There was no ceiling. IFR minimums, in this case, would be based on visibility alone. The pilot could expect to maintain ground contact throughout the approach, sighting the airport at about two miles.

At Redding, CA, the NWS observer made the following report:

RDD SP 1650 W30 X . . . KH

The reported vertical visibility is 3,000 feet, sky completely hidden by smoke and haze. A pilot flying in this area can only expect to maintain ground contact within about 3,000 feet of the surface. This situation could be extremely dangerous for the VFR pilot. Should the pilot climb above 3,000, he or she would be in IFR conditions without ground contact, and most probably without the natural horizon. Pilots attempting to operate in similar conditions have lost aircraft control with fatal results.

IFR pilots must also exercise caution operating close to minimums. The VOR-A approach to Ukiah, CA, has a Minimum Descent Altitude (MDA) of 3,400 feet (2,784 AGL). Ukiah was reporting 2Ø SCT E5Ø BKN. . . . Sure enough, the scattered layer was at the missed approach point. During the miss the aircraft broke into the clear and was able to land. Luck: never count on this happening.

VISIBILITY

Visibility is a measure of the transparency of the atmosphere. During the day visibility represents the distance at which predominant objects can be seen; at night, visibility is the distance that unfocused lights of moderate intensity are visible. One NWS observer was quite perplexed when the tower always reported increased visibility after sunset. The reason was the change in criteria for the observation. Pilots should note that daytime values do not necessarily represent the distance that other aircraft can be seen. At night, especially under an overcast, unlighted objects might not be seen at all, and there might be no natural horizon.

SAs report prevailing visibility in statute miles. That is, the greatest visibility equaled or exceeded throughout at least half the horizon circle, which need not be continuous. Prevailing visibility less than three miles that rapidly increases and decreases during the observation is reported variable (1V . . . /VSBY3/4V11/2, visibility one variable . . . /visibility variable between three-quarters and one and one-half). Variable visibility has the same implications as variable sky condition and ceiling—conditions rapidly changing at the airport.

Figure 1-4 illustrates a reported prevailing visibility of four miles. Because one sector has a visibility of only two, which is operationally significant, remarks contain VSBY N2 (visibility north two). Sectors might also exist with visibility greater than prevailing.

Prevailing Visibility

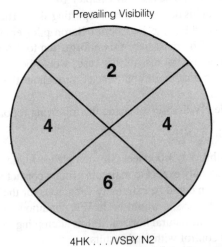

4HK . . . /VSBY N2

Fig. 1-4. *Prevailing visibility represents the greatest distance prominent objects can be seen throughout at least half the horizon circle, which need not be continuous.*

These values might or might not be reported in remarks. This accounts for some apparent inconsistencies. In FIG. 1-4 a pilot approaching the airport in the sector where the visibility is six miles may question the report. The observation remains consistent within the definition of prevailing visibility.

    LOL SA 1555 CLR 35 . . . /VSBY S 1/4

Could this be valid? Yes, indeed. A fog bank was south of the airport. A little while later, as the fog continued to move over the airport CLR 3/4F . . . /VSBY NE 35 was reported.

Conditions can be quite variable and change rapidly in areas affected by stratus and fog. The following SAs for Crescent City, CA, illustrate this point.

    CEC SA 1755 – X 3 SCT 3F . . . /F1 VSBY E 35 S – N 3/4
    CEC SP 1805 – X E3 BKN 3F . . . /F2 BKN V SCT VSBY N – E 35 S – NW 3/4
    CEC SP 1810 – X 3 – BKN 25 . . . /F1 VSBY S – NW 1

Conditions went from VFR to IFR and back in 15 minutes, which emphasizes the need for frequent weather updates. A VFR pilot should consider approaching or departing the airport to the east, where remarks indicate good visibility. VFR flights to this airport must plan for fuel to destination, a solid VFR alternate, and the required reserve. FARs don't require VFR alternates, but good judgment does.

At one Southern California airport, it appears local pilots estimate prevailing visibility in the following manner: "1/4 mile to the north, 1/4 mile to the east, 1/4 mile to the south and 1/4 mile to the west—great! Prevailing visibility is one mile, it's VFR." This, of course, is not only incorrect but extremely dangerous.

Pilots are required to be trained in estimating visibility while in flight because FARs specify visibility requirements in relation to flight visibility. To legally operate VFR where the visibility was reported as two in FIG. 1-4, a pilot must have flight visibility of three miles. If this cannot be done, the pilot would have to obtain an IFR or request a special VFR clearance, or depart the area. And, for landing IFR, visibility must not be less than that prescribed for the approach.

Reported surface visibility comes into play when a pilot plans to take off or land, or enter the traffic pattern VFR within a control zone. Surface visibility must be at least three miles. Or, if surface visibility is not reported, flight visibility must be at least three miles.

SAs report surface visibility, which does not necessarily represent conditions at altitude. Visibilities aloft are most often reduced by rain, snow, dust, smoke, and haze. And, with reduced visibilities, usually less than five miles, the apparent visibility looking toward the sun can be almost nil! Pilot reports are the only source of flight visibility.

NWS or FSS personnel take observations, at certain tower locations. These facilities are not usually collocated. Tower personnel report tower-level visibility when less than four miles. Because visibility can differ substantially over short distances, a complicated formula determines whether tower (TWR) or surface (SFC) visibility prevails.

The remarks portion of the report contains the other value (CLR 11/2F . . . /SFC VSBY 2; – X IF . . . /TWR VSBY 0). These remarks alert pilots to variable visibility over the airport. It is not unheard-of for the tower to report low visibility prevailing less than three or even one mile, thus preventing VFR or special VFR operations.

Two other visibilities might appear in remarks of SAs: *Runway Visibility* (RVV) and *Runway Visual Range* (RVR). RVV and RVR, located at the runway touchdown point, apply to instrument approach minimums found on IFR approach charts. They are surface measurements, not slant range. A report indicating landing minimums does not necessarily mean that visibility exists at the DH or MDA. RVV and RVR reflect the fact that visibility can vary substantially from the normal point of observation; that is the tower, FSS, or weather office, compared to the runway touchdown zone. RVV and RVR report a 10-minute average transmissometer value.

The transmissometer transmitter projects a beam of light toward the receiver. A photoelectric cell measures the amount of light reaching the receiver. This value is electronically converted into visibility and displayed at appropriate locations (tower, FSS, weather office, or a combination of locations).

RVV refers to visibility along a specific runway measured in miles and fractions (RVV30R11/4, Runway 30 Right visibility 1¹/₄).

RVR, also associated with a specific runway, reports the maximum distance high intensity runway lights can be seen, measured in hundreds of feet (RVR28L24V60+, Runway 28 Left visual range variable between 2,400 and more than 6,000 feet).

To appear in remarks, RVV must be less than two miles or prevailing visibility less than approach minimums, RVR 6,000 feet or less, or prevailing visibility one mile or less, and values must be continuously recorded. Because many locations have only instantaneous readouts, RVV or RVR values might not appear on the observation. This is because RVV and RVR values change relatively rapidly, instantaneous readouts are not considered significant for transmission, and may even be misleading.

ATMOSPHERIC PHENOMENA

Atmospheric phenomena—weather and obstructions to vision—follow prevailing visibility using standard aviation weather contractions contained in TABLE 1-2 and Appendix A. This can be the most significant portion of the report.

Weather

Because of its awesome potential, tornadic activity is always spelled out: TORNADO, WATERSPOUT, or FUNNEL CLOUD. Tornadoes are destructive, but thunderstorms have an even greater impact on aviation operations. Thunderstorms contain every aviation hazard, form in lines or clusters, and can even regenerate.

A thunderstorm (T) is reported when thunder is heard, or overhead lightning or hail (A) observed. Thunderstorm and associated weather observed away from the station appears in remarks (/CB NE, cumulonimbus northeast). A report of CBs implies thunderstorm, sometimes translated by briefers as "thunderstorms clouds. . . ." Convective activity reported at or near the station is a clue to possible low-level wind shear (LLWS), or microbursts. Convective LLWS and microbursts—which produce the most severe wind shear threat—are discussed in Chapter 9.

Table 1-2. *Weather and Obstructions to Vision.*

Weather and Precipitation		IPW	ICE PELLET SHOWERS
Funnel Cloud	FUNNEL CLOUD		
Waterspout	WATERSPOUT	S	SNOW
Tornado	TORNADO	SW	SNOW SHOWER
T+	SEVERE THUNDERSTORM	SP	SNOW PELLETS
		SG	SNOW GRAINS
T	THUNDERSTORM	IC	ICE CRYSTALS
Liquid		**Obstructions to Vision**	
R	RAIN	BD	BLOWING DUST
RW	RAIN SHOWER	BN	BLOWING SAND
L	DRIZZLE	BS	BLOWING SNOW
Freezing		D	DUST
ZR	FREEZING RAIN	F	FOG
ZL	FREEZING DRIZZLE	GF	GROUND FOG
Frozen		IF	ICE FOG
A	HAIL	H	HAZE
IP	ICE PELLETS	K	SMOKE

At the Ontario, CA, airport the FSS was responsible for weather observations. However, because of the FSS's poor observation point, the tower reported visibility. One night while working the mid shift I thought I heard thunder. I asked the tower if they heard thunder or saw lightning. "Oh yeah," he said, "I've been watching it for the last couple of hours." Well, so much for the system. The FAA has taken steps, however, to ensure tower controllers immediately report this type of activity.

When surface winds gust to 50 knots or more, or hail ³/₄-inch or greater accompany a thunderstorm, the storm is reported as severe (T+). Not a heavy thunderstorm, T+ has a specific definition with ominous implications.

Precipitation occurring at the station is assigned an intensity level: heavy (+), light (−), or with the absence of a symbol, moderate. Rather than an intensity, hail size appears in remarks (/HLSTO 1/2, hailstones 1/2 inch in diameter).

The weather phenomena TRW−, sometimes translated as a light thundershower, or worse, a light thunderstorm and rain showers, is neither. The correct translation: thunderstorm accompanied by light rain showers. There is no such thing as a light thunderstorm!

Drizzle (L), rain (R), or snow (S) indicate a stable air mass. Falling from stratiform clouds—stratus, altostratus, nimbostratus, or stratocumulus—precipitation is usually steady, can be widespread, and usually not heavy in intensity. Whereas, showery precipitation (rain showers (RW), snow showers (SW), etc.) fall from unstable air. Showers fall from cumuliform clouds—cumulus or cumulonimbus—usually brief and sporadic, and might be heavy in intensity.

Drizzle indicates a relatively shallow cloud layer. It usually takes a cloud thickness of 4,000 feet to produce precipitation. Drizzle restricts visibility to a greater degree than rain because it falls in stable air often accompanied by fog, haze, and smoke. *Snow grains* (SG), the solid equivalent of drizzle, are small, white, opaque grains of ice.

Snow can fall about 1,000 feet below the freezing level before melting. Snow can often begin with temperatures of 36° F; it's even possible to see snowflakes at temperatures around 50° F. This only occurs when the air is very dry. As snow falls into above-freezing air, it begins to melt. The water evaporates and cools the air. Evaporation cools the snow, which retards melting. Water vapor is added to the air, which increases dew point. Finally, the air cools and becomes saturated at 32° F.

Dry snow does not lead to the formation of aircraft structural ice. However, wet snow—snow that contains a great deal of liquid water—produces structural icing. WET SNOW can appear in remarks.

Snow pellets (SP)—small, white, opaque grains of ice—form when ice crystals fall through supercooled droplets and the surface temperature is at or slightly below freezing. Falling from cumuliform clouds, snow pellets are more prone to cause structural icing than snow grains.

Ice crystals (IC) might appear suspended, and fall from a cloud or clear air. They frequently occur in polar regions in stable air and only at very low temperatures. Ice crystals are not assigned an intensity.

Ice pellets (IP), formerly sleet, are grains of ice consisting of frozen raindrops, or largely melted and refrozen snowflakes. They fall as continuous or intermittent precipitation. Ice pellet showers (IPW) are pellets of snow encased in a thin layer of ice formed from the freezing of droplets intercepted by the pellets, or water resulting from the partial melting of the pellets. Ice pellets do not bring about the formation of structural ice, except when mixed with supercooled water. Frequently, ice pellets or ice pellet showers indicate areas of freezing rain above.

Freezing rain (ZR) and *freezing drizzle* (ZL) are caused by liquid precipitation falling from warmer air into air that is at or below freezing. Droplets freeze upon impact. Structural icing can be expected while flying through freezing precipitation. As stated in the U.S. Air Force manual, *Weather for Aircrews*: "Freezing precipitation is probably the most dangerous of all icing conditions. It can build hazardous amounts of ice in a few minutes and is extremely difficult to remove." Freezing rain can flow back along the aircraft, covering the static port with the resultant loss of accurate pitot-static instruments—airspeed, altimeter, and vertical velocity.

Aircraft without a heated pitot and alternate static source, especially in IFR conditions, would be in serious trouble. Another significant factor, especially for aircraft without ice protection equipment, is that accumulated ice could be carried all the way to the ground making landing extremely hazardous. It cannot be over emphasized that this hazard can affect VFR as well as IFR operations. Should this phenomena be encountered in aircraft without ice protection equipment virtually the only option, and certainly the safest, is to fly into warmer air and land. Pilots who fly into ice, with aircraft not certified for flight in icing conditions, must have the right stuff. Because, in every sense of the word, they become test pilots.

Forward visibility is reduced when flying through precipitation, but sideward and downward visibility tend to remain relatively unaffected. The more intense the precipitation, the greater the reduction in visibility. It is possible to have VFR surface visibilities reported with flight visibility less than VFR. Figure 1-5 illustrates how precipitation, especially when heavy, can dramatically reduce visibility and obscure terrain. These showers

Fig. 1-5. *Precipitation, especially when heavy, can dramatically reduce visibility and obscure terrain. These showers should be avoided.*

should be avoided. Flying through steady precipitation is generally smooth, showers tend to be turbulent. Avoiding showers will not only result in improved forward visibility, but a smoother flight.

Remarks of NWS, FSS, and military observations contain the time weather phenomena began or ended. For example, EWR RS 2253 . . . /T + B10 severe thunderstorm began 10 minutes after the hour (2210). More often these remarks refer to precipitation: SFO RS 2350 . . . /RB2252E02LB15LERB27RELB42 . . . rain began at 2252, ended at 02 (2302), drizzle began at 15, drizzle ended rain began. . . . Well, you get the idea. The purpose of these remarks is climatological, but they do alert pilots, briefers, and forecasters to weather, often significant, occurring at the station.

Obstructions to Vision

Obstructions to vision, caused by fog, haze, dust, and smoke, are reported with visibilities less than seven miles. When these phenomena exist with visibilities seven miles or greater, a remark might describe the condition (/H ALQDS, haze all quadrants). Briefers sometimes use the term *unrestricted* to describe visibilities of seven miles or greater. This sometimes causes confusion. A pilot told visibility unrestricted might respond, "What about the haze?" Thus, the phrase visibility unrestricted does not imply that smoke, haze, dust, or even fog are not present, just that visibility is seven miles or greater.

Fog (F), ground fog (GF), and ice fog (IF) describe the same condition, a cloud based on the ground. *Ground fog*, normally less than 20 feet deep, reduces visibility horizontally rather than obscuring the sky. Usually localized, formed by radiational cooling, ground fog tends to dissipate rapidly once clearing begins. *Ice fog* forms in cold weather at temperatures around −20° F from radiational cooling, and exhibits the same characteristic as radiation fog.

Radiation fog forms when air cools from contact with the ground and becomes saturated. This occurs at night and tends to be most dense around sunrise. Clear skies, light winds (less than five knots), high relative humidity, and stable air are favorable conditions for the formation of radiation fog. Low water vapor content in upper layers increases radiational cooling; dry air aloft enhances the formation of radiation fog. Overcast skies, strong winds, low relative humidity, and unstable air prevent or retard its formation.

Radiation fog tends to be patchy and shallow with lowest visibility around sunrise, usually burning off by mid morning. It tends to form in valleys after moisture has been added at the surface from passing storms. As high pressure—clear, stable conditions— build into an area, circumstances are right for the formation of radiation fog. This condition can become persistent in California's Central Valley during winter and early spring. After frontal passage a strong inversion locks moisture at lower levels and radiation fog forms. Zero-zero conditions over widespread areas can persist for days or even weeks, until the moisture evaporates, or another storm system moves through the area.

IFR pilots, normally, will have no difficulty operating in conditions caused by radiation fog, as long as they don't mind flying above zero-zero surface conditions. And, landing minimums might not prevail until late morning or afternoon, if at all, in California's Central Valley. The VFR pilot will be delayed until the condition dissipates. In the Central

Valley, many pilots routinely move their aircraft to mountain airports above the fog layer during winter months.

Advection fog forms when moist air moves over colder ground or water. The air cooled from below becomes saturated. Advection fog can form under an overcast. This is a persistent condition along the Pacific coast during the summer months. The prevailing onshore flow moves the layer into coastal sections and valleys. It is usually deepest and farthest inland at sunrise and retreats toward the ocean during the day. Figure 1-6 illustrates the effectiveness of satellite imagery for determining the extent of the layer. It is especially useful in areas without weather reporting service. Winds of five to 15 knots tend to cause low ceilings rather than fog.

Fig. 1-6. *Visual satellite imagery, available at many FSSs, reveals the extent of stratus layers.*

VFR pilots planning flights into or out of coastal areas should plan arrivals and departures during afternoon hours. If this is not possible, moving the aircraft to an airport a few miles inland will often allow a morning departure.

Upslope fog forms as air is forced upward, expands, and cools at a relatively constant rate. Moist air must be forced upslope, which requires a wind of five to 15 knots. This condition occurs during winter and spring in the Midwest where terrain rises steadily from the Gulf of Mexico to the Rockies. It can be widespread and will persist as long as favorable conditions continue. During upslope fog conditions the VFR pilot is pretty much out of luck. The IFR pilot might not be much better off. He or she might encounter IFR landing minimums, but the condition often exists over areas the size of several states. A legal IFR alternate might be beyond the range of the aircraft.

Rain-induced fog, also known as *frontal fog*, occurs when warm rain falls through cooler air, evaporates, and condenses forming fog; it can be dense and will persist as long as the rain continues. Winds must generally be light. This condition is usually associated with stationary, warm, or shallow cold fronts. A potential for clear icing exists in areas of rain-induced fog.

Steam fog develops as cold air moves over warm water. Evaporation from the water takes place and saturation occurs. Low-level turbulence develops as the warm water heats lower levels creating a shallow layer of instability. Also known as evaporation fog, steam fog occurs in cold climates over lakes, such as the Great Lakes, in the autumn.

Haze (H) is caused by the suspension of extremely small, dry particles invisible to the eye, but sufficiently numerous to reduce visibility. Haze, combined with *smoke* (K), often describes conditions in metropolitan areas—sometimes translated as hack and kough. Figure 1-7 was taken over Atlanta, GA. Large anticyclones—high pressure cells—can dominate the Southeast United States trapping haze and pollutants, especially in industrial areas. Above the haze layer, visibilities are unrestricted and temperatures cool, resulting in a much more comfortable flight.

Strong inversions over cities or industrial areas can trap haze and smoke, reducing visibility to less than one mile. Landmarks are all but invisible. Dense haze often appears solid, like a cloud layer, in the distance; this occurs with high relative humidity. When the sun strikes the layer, light waves scatter, causing the layer to appear white. This accounts for apparent inconsistencies in surface observations. SAs might report clear or partially obscured skies with visibilities three to five miles in haze and smoke. A pilot looking into the sun often has no forward visibility or natural horizon. Pilots caught in such situations, technically VFR, have become spatially disoriented and lost control of the aircraft.

Haze and smoke are usually restricted to an area below 5,000 feet, although they can extend to above 10,000 feet. During the devastating September 1987 forest fires in California, smoke tops were reported as high as 19,000 feet, with visibilities aloft zero. The gray areas of the Central and Northern California interior, and southern Oregon, in FIG. 1-8, a visual satellite image, show dense smoke caused by the fires.

Inversion-induced wind shear turbulence develops along the boundary between cool air trapped near the surface and warm air aloft. The turbulence tends to be strongest in valleys during morning hours. Moderate or greater turbulence might be encountered penetrating the layer. After an initial outside air temperature rise during the climb through the

Fig. 1-7. *Large anticyclones—high pressure cells—can dominate the Southeast United States trapping haze and pollutants, especially in industrial areas, as shown by this photograph of Atlanta, GA. Above the haze layer, visibilities are unrestricted and temperatures decrease, which result in a much more comfortable flight.*

haze, the air on top will be clear and cool. It is possible to have several haze or smoke layers trapped in inversions aloft. In the Los Angeles Basin, a haze boundary often develops with a Santa Ana—a warm, dry foehn wind—condition. Warm, dry desert air overruns haze trapped in cooler, moist marine air. Moderate or greater wind shear turbulence can be expected penetrating the transition zone. Takeoff and landing can be hazardous with the boundary in the vicinity of the runway, often marked by a distinct transition between clear and hazy air. PIREPs are usually the only source for haze layer tops.

Dust (D) and *blowing dust* (BD), a combination of fine dust or sand particles suspended in the air, can be raised to above 16,000 feet by the wind. Visibilities, surface and aloft, can be at or near zero. Because of its fine particles, dust can remain suspended for several days after the wind subsides.

1615 03SE87 28A-1   01711 22984 WA2

Fig. 1-8. *Gray areas of the Central and Northern California interior, and southern Oregon reveal dense smoke caused by forest fires. The smoke caused widespread IFR conditions from the surface to well above 10,000 feet.*

Blowing sand (BN), made up of particles larger than dust, usually remains within a few hundred feet of the surface. It can also reduce visibility to near zero. But, when the wind subsides particles fall back to the surface and visibility improves rapidly. A pilot approaching Lovelock, NV, skeptical of a reported visibility of two miles in blowing sand, reported his flight visibility was 20 miles. Upon landing, however, he concurred, stating the tops of the blowing sand were at 200 feet AGL.

Blowing snow (BS) produces the same characteristics as blowing sand when strong winds blow over freshly fallen snow. Visibility can be near zero close to the surface, with rapid clearing after the wind subsides.

Every year, pilots become lost, even lose control of aircraft, flying in reduced visibilities. Often conditions can be improved by climbing to a higher altitude. Once above the layer, slant range visibility is usually greater with a distinct horizon preventing disorientation. The seemingly obvious assumption, the closer to the ground the better to see it, usually isn't true.

ATMOSPHERIC DATA

Our working definition of *atmospheric data* will be sea level pressure, temperature, dew point, and altimeter setting. Full reports contain these elements, in a numeric series, following atmospheric phenomena. Not all aviation weather reporting locations, however, observe all elements.

Sea Level Pressure

NWS, FSS, military, and certain contract observations report *sea level pressure* in millibars. This three-number code follows visibility and obstructions to vision (. . .1TRW+ "102"/77/74 . . .). Used to prepare surface analysis charts, sea level pressure must never be substituted for the altimeter setting in millibars. Sea level pressure is not reported by Limited Aviation Weather Reporting Stations (LAWRS) (towers and most contract observers), and will only appear on hourly reports.

The code contains the last three digits of the sea level pressure to the nearest 10th of a millibar, decimal point omitted. Because average pressure is 1013.2 millibars, prefix the code with a 9 or 10, whichever brings it closest to 1000.0. The sea level pressure code group in the previous paragraph is 102. Prefix the group with a 10, which decodes a sea level pressure as 1010.2 millibars.

Temperature and Dew Point

Temperature and *dew point*, reported in degrees Fahrenheit except Canada, Mexico, and most of the rest of the world, which use Celsius (C), are important beyond their comfort value. High and low temperatures effect aircraft operation and performance.

Temperature and dew point follow sea level pressure or atmospheric phenomena (. . . 1TRW+ 102/"77"/"74"/ . . . ; or (. . . 1TRW+ "77"/"74"/ . . .). Certain locations only report temperature, while others contain neither. When reported, temperature always precedes dew point. And, dew point can never be higher than temperature. A reported dew point greater than temperature usually results from equipment malfunction, or transposition of numbers upon transmission. Some observers have yet to learn this fact and will report dew point higher than temperature, rather than as missing (/M/). Decoding the example, the temperature is 77° and dew point 74.

High temperatures at high altitude airports produce high *density altitude*. Atmospheric pressure and humidity are also factors, however, temperature and elevation are paramount. Surface temperature forecasts are not normally available, but maximum temperatures usually occur during mid- or late afternoon. Arrival and departure times must be planned based on aircraft performance.

I have flown Cessna 150s out of Bryce Canyon, UT (Elev. 7,586), and Grand Canyon, AZ (Elev. 6,606), and a Cessna 210 out of Mammoth Lakes, CA (Elev. 7,128). There is no additional hazard in such operations as long as we calculate, and do not attempt to exceed, aircraft performance. Multiengine pilots must consider that airport density altitude might be above the inoperative engine ceiling.

After calculating that the aircraft has sufficient performance for conditions, it's a good idea to determine an abort point on the runway. If the aircraft is not airborne and climbing, this point should allow the pilot to come to a safe stop on the remainder of the runway. Remember, aircraft performance data are based on brand new airframe and engine, and perfect pilot technique.

Low temperatures cannot be ignored. Snow, snow melt, freezing rain, and frost produce structural ice that can be difficult to remove from a parked aircraft. Even a thin layer of frost can severely affect performance, and must be removed before takeoff, according to regulations. Some years ago four of us flew a Cessna 172 into the South Lake Tahoe Airport in November. After our stay, about three quarters of an inch of ice had formed on the airplane. Being naive at the time about such conditions, I assumed it would blow off during the takeoff roll.

An experienced tower controller, however, suggested we clean the ice. It had to be scraped off with a plastic scraper! Later I calculated we had between 300 and 400 pounds of ice on the airplane. I had no experience with this condition at the time. I shutter to think what would have happened during a takeoff in a low performance airplane, 300 pounds over gross, at a high-altitude airport, with three-quarters of an inch of ice on the airfoils. This is a perfect example of where the test almost came before the lesson.

The solution to this problem is to hangar the aircraft, arrange for a deicing service, or plan the departure later in the day when the sun has melted the ice. During taxi, avoid areas of slush. Slush thrown into wheel wells, wheel pants, and control surfaces can freeze, resulting in locked controls and frozen landing gear. With a descent through an icing layer, and surface temperatures close to or below freezing, a pilot must be prepared for an approach and landing with airframe icing, possibly to an ice or snow covered runway.

If snow, ice or slush are on the runway, aircraft control might be difficult, especially in high winds, and braking action reduced, resulting in a longer than normal ground roll. Without windscreen deice—that's deice, not defrost—a pilot could be faced (pardon the pun) with zero forward visibility during the landing. FAR 91.103 requires the pilot to consider, ". . . runway lengths at airports of intended use . . ." Pilots operating in this environment must consider these factors when selecting destination and alternate airports, or even the advisability of making the flight.

Daytime heating causes rising air currents that produce *thermal turbulence*. Thermal turbulence usually occurs within 7,000 feet of the surface in stable or conditionally unstable air. This means that vertical movement requires an initiating force, in this case surface heating. In stable or extremely dry air, skies remain clear. Should air parcels reach the lifted condensation level, saturation occurs, and *stratocumulus*, or *fair weather cumulus*, clouds will form. These clouds are most often scattered, and rarely become overcast. Should the air be conditionally unstable—a parcel of air that becomes unstable on the condition it is lifted to the *level of free convection* (LFC)—*cumuliform* clouds form, which can develop into air mass thunderstorms.

Although thermal turbulence rarely becomes severe, it can be extremely uncomfortable and annoying. Because thermal turbulence is caused by surface heating, it can usually be avoided by flying before mid-morning or waiting until late afternoon. Otherwise, the only remedy is to climb above the turbulent layer, which might be marked by clouds. A word of caution to the VFR pilot: If you elect to fly above the clouds be careful not to get caught on top. Should the air mass be conditionally unstable, clouds can build at an alarming rate and close up even faster.

Flying a new Cessna 150 from Kansas to California I found myself flying between Winslow, AZ, and Needles, CA, during the afternoon. Skies were clear, and winds aloft light and variable. I had to climb to 12,500 to get smooth, cool air. Descending into Needles the turbulence was continuous light to moderate below about 11,000 feet, surface winds were calm.

On another occasion, I was flying one afternoon between Oklahoma City and Amarillo in air that was conditionally unstable. As is my habit, I prefer to fly above the clouds in clear, smooth, cool air. The cumulus appeared to top out at about 9,000 feet. So, I thought I'd climb to a cruising altitude of 10,500. Something was strange. I was in what appeared to be level flight, but only indicating 60 knots in my Cessna 150. A scan of the instrument panel revealed the problem. I was not in level flight, but in a climb attitude above a sloping cloud deck! Topping the clouds was impossible, and I was forced to descend and bounce the rest of the way to Amarillo at 4,500 feet.

When air is cooled to its dew point, moisture is added to raise the dew point, or both, fog can form. Temperature and dew point within 5° F is an indicator for the possible development of fog. FSS briefers normally provide temperature/dew point under these conditions. FAA aviation weather broadcasts use this criteria. The formation of fog, as noted above, requires more than a close temperature/dew point spread.

Wind

Crucial for determining crosswind component, especially in areas with large magnetic variation, *wind direction* reported on SAs is always true north, and given as the direction from which the wind is blowing. Wind direction, to the nearest 10°, is the first two digits of the wind group (. . .116/85/48/"2712"/ . . . , wind 270°). Should direction fluctuate by 60° or more, variability appears in remarks (/WND 24V30, wind direction variable between 240 and 300). Variable wind direction can make takeoff and landing difficult, even at relatively slow speeds. Wind speed, reported in knots, is the second pair of digits in the wind group. In the example, wind speed is 12 knots.

Gusts (G) refer to rapid fluctuations in speed that vary by 10 knots or more. Therefore, the report . . .18G24 reflects an average speed of 18 knots with fluctuations between 14 and 24 knots. Gustiness is a measure of turbulence. The greater the difference between sustained speed and gusts, the greater the turbulence and possibility of low-level wind shear. When a sudden increase of at least 15 knots, sustained at 20 knots or more for at least one minute occurs, a *squall* (Q) is reported (3545Q60). Usually associated with thunderstorm activity, squall implies severe low-level wind shear as well as severe turbulence.

Wind direction, speed, and character (gusts or squall) must be considered when determining crosswind component, or the advisability of landing at a particular airport. And, as well as gustiness, surface winds in excess of 20 knots indicate moderate or greater mechanical turbulence, especially over rough terrain. Favorable conditions for turbulence exist just before, during, and after storm passage, especially when winds blow perpendicular to mountain ridges. For example, consider the following report for Mammoth Lakes, CA (MMH) that occurred just after storm system passage with winds perpendicular to the rugged California Sierra Nevada Mountains.

MMH SA 1545 50 SCT E120 BKN 50 46/ – 3/2345G90/002

The MMH runway is 09-27 and magnetic variation is 15° east; runway headings are magnetic and SA winds true; to convert wind direction from true to magnetic, subtract easterly variation (east is least). Therefore, the MMH wind is blowing from 215° magnetic (230 − 015 = 215). At an angle of 55° to the runway (270 − 215 = 55), this results in a 35-knot crosswind component for the sustained speed, and 70 knots for the gusts.

Obviously, this airport would not be suitable for landing. For one thing, the highway patrol closed the roads and no one could pick you up after the, umm, arrival. Most aircraft manuals specify maximum demonstrated crosswind component. Every year pilots attempt to test these values—some pilots even succeed. Each pilot should know his or her limitations, and that of their aircraft. As a flight instructor I always give my students specific crosswind limitations, always with an alternate should they be exceeded.

Wind shift describes a change in direction of 45° or more that takes place in fewer than 15 minutes (WSHFT 55, wind shift occurred at 55 minutes past the hour). A wind shift of relative light winds might only indicate a local change; in coastal areas the shift often signals the advance or retreat of stratus or fog. In the Midwest the shift might precede the formation or dissipation of upslope fog. Wind shift is usually a good indicator of frontal passage. In Southern California a shift often indicates the advance or retreat of a Santa Ana condition.

Peak wind appears in NWS, FSS, and military remarks when speed exceeds 25 to 30 knots. The direction, speed, and time of occurrence is reported (PK WND 3560/40), peak wind from 350° at 60 knots occurred at 40 minutes past the hour). Peak wind might substantially exceed the value in the body of the observation.

Should either the *wind vane* (direction) or *anamometer* (speed) be out of service or unreliable, the wind group is reported as estimated (E2515, wind estimated 250 at 15). We have no way of knowing whether direction, speed, or both, are the reason for the report.

Altimeter Setting

The last three digits of the altimeter setting follow the wind group. The normal range of altimeter settings varies from 28.00 inches to 31.00 inches of mercury; most altimeters are calibrated within this range. An extremely cold high pressure area developed over Alaska in 1989 causing the altimeter setting to rise well above 31.00 inches. Because these values were not in the range of most altimeters, special emergency rules were enacted.

Decode an altimeter setting with the first digit an 8 or 9 by inserting a 2: . . . /899 decodes 28.99. When the first digit is a 0 or 1 prefix a 3: . . . /045 decodes 30.45.

Remarks

Remarks use standard aviation weather contractions, and follow the altimeter setting, separated by a slant. Contractions are contained in Appendix A. Remarks can be the most important part of the report. NWS, FSS, and military observations might contain numerical codes describing meteorological and climatological conditions (/1001 211 45). These code groups describe weather, cloud type, pressure tendency and change, and maximum/minimum temperatures.

Remarks amplify information already reported, describe conditions observed but not occurring at the station, or contain information considered operationally significant. Routine remarks, amplifying information, have already been discussed. Again, NWS, FSS, and military observers, because of their training and experience, tend to do a better job. Although they can get carried away.

The following observation was taken at March AFB, CA. RIV SA 1955 . . . /CREPUS-CULAR RAYS SW. The *Glossary of Meteorology* defines crepuscular rays as, "Literally, 'twilight rays'; alternating lighter and darker bands (rays and shadows) that appear to diverge in fan-like array from the sun's position at about twilight." Towering cumulus produce this effect, especially with haze in the lower atmosphere. This would seem a rather complicated way of saying: HAZY TCU SW (hazy with towering cumulus southwest).

This observation came from an NWS observer at Denver, CO: DEN SA 2359 . . . / DSIPTG GUSTNADO N, dissipating gustnado north—a glorified dust devil. Well, *gustnado* is a local term used to describe a funnel cloud that develops along the gust front of a thunderstorm, not a tornado that would warrant a single element special report.

Remarks can be ambiguous, as this report taken by an FSS illustrates: DEF SA 1755 – X E40 OVC . . . /F9 TOPS 015. This observation would seem to indicate a 4,000-foot ceiling with tops at 1,500 feet, which is impossible. Could the observer have meant 400 overcast? Upon checking, 9/10 of the sky was obscured by fog and the observer could see cloud cover at an estimated 4,000 feet. The remarks should have read: /F9 TOPS OBSCN 015, tops of the obscuration 1,500 feet.

The only way to clarify a report is check with the observer. For individuals using DUAT this will be all but impossible. An FSS will usually be able to check through its telecommunications system. But, don't even ask unless some very serious—meaning emergency—operational requirement exists.

Figure 1-1 contains an excellent example of an operationally significant remark. The observer has reported: /MTNS OBSCD W, mountains obscured west. If an overcast ceiling of 1,500 feet exists, VFR flight below the clouds could be conducted. However, due to mountain obscurement, VFR flight into or out of the valley might not be possible. Pilots accustomed to flying over flatlands need to exercise extra caution evaluating conditions in mountainous areas. Studying terrain is as important as checking the weather.

A sky condition example for Ukiah, CA, was presented earlier and a scattered cloud layer existed at the missed approach point. If the observation had carried the remark / MTNS OBSCD E – W (mountains obscured east through west) a pilot reviewing the approach and terrain could deduce that the scattered layer existed at the missed approach point.

This example also illustrates how observers indicate phenomena coverage. The observer starts at true north and works clockwise. If the remark read /MTNS OBSCD E S – N, it would be translated as mountains obscured east and south through north. It's important to understand this convention to correctly relate weather in relation to the station.

I was over Palmdale on a flight to Van Nuys, CA, in a Cessna 150 that was not equipped for IFR. Coastal stratus obscured the mountains with Van Nuys reporting E30 OVC. Because of my experience and familiarity with the area, I knew where there was often a hole. On this occasion the hole was there and I proceeded. Of course, I had plenty of fuel to return to the desert. Another pilot attempting to depart the L.A. Basin, under similar conditions, was not so fortunate; he wound his way out through the mountains and finally into a blind canyon and the Cessna 182 came to rest on a 45° slope. Fortunately the only casualty was the airplane—it was totaled.

The following paragraphs describe cloud types significant to aviation routinely carried in remarks of observations.

ACCAS (*Altocumulus Castellanus*), a mid-level cloud, indicates moisture and vertical movement. ACCAS might indicate thunderstorm development. Showers falling from these clouds can evaporate before reaching the surface as illustrated in FIG. 1-9. This phenomena appears in remarks as VIRGA. Evaporative cooling turbulence develops in the vicinity of *virga*: precipitation evaporates and cools the air, causing downdrafts. A pilot penetrating these areas will encounter wind shear turbulence, which can be severe. Turbulence can be avoided by circumnavigation of these areas. At times, ice crystals or snowflakes can fall from cirrus clouds. As they fall into dry air they *sublimate*—change directly from a solid to a gas. These dangling white streamers are known as *fall streaks*.

ACSL (*Standing Lenticular Altocumulus*), SCSL (*Standing Lenticular Stratocumulus*), and CCSL (*Standing Lenticular Cirrocumulus*) indicate *mountain wave* activity. Lenticular clouds appear smooth and remain stationary to the observer; they might develop as horizontal bands produced by long ridges as in FIG. 1-10, or circular and stacked from isolated peaks as in FIG. 1-11. Although these clouds imply turbulence, turbulence will not always be found.

I encountered a mountain wave in California's Owens Valley while flying a Cessna 150. With cruise power and attitude the airplane rode the wave, at the rate of 500 feet per minute, from 8,500 feet to 13,500 feet, and back down again. The ride was absolutely smooth!

Notwithstanding the previous example, the November 1977 *Approach* magazine reported: "A Navy T-39 trainer was flying a low-level, high-speed navigational training route in mountainous terrain when it encountered severe turbulence. Gust acceleration

Fig. 1-9. *Altocumulus Castellanus, especially with virga—rain that evaporates before reaching the surface—indicates moisture and vertical movement at midlevels. Turbulence and possible microbursts should be expected in the vicinity of virga.*

Fig. 1-10. *Altocumulus Standing Lenticular usually develop as horizontal bands produced by long ridges.*

Fig. 1-11. *Altocumulus Standing Lenticular become circular or stacked from winds off isolated mountain peaks.*

loads were so high that aircraft design limits were exceeded, resulting in separation of the tail. . . ." All aboard were killed. The article went on to say, "Mountain waves should never be taken lightly. In addition to the T-39 crash, mountain waves were identified in the crash of a C-118 and in extensive damage to a B-52. . . . While this type of turbulence is obviously critical to traditional low fliers like helicopters, all aircraft are susceptible."

Rotor, bell-shaped, clouds that often appear as tubular lines of cumulus or fractocumulus clouds parallel to the ridge line underneath the lenticulars always imply severe or greater turbulence. One such situation occurred at Reno, NV, where surface winds were reported gusting to 73 knots. The pilot of a corporate jet reportedly abandoned the approach when all the bottles in the cabin's liquor cabinet broke. (A new definition for severe turbulence?)

Mountain waves develop when strong winds, usually 40 knots or greater at crest level, blow perpendicular to a mountain range. Speed usually increases with altitude in stable air. Mountain waves can cause sustained updrafts and downdrafts occasionally reaching 3,000 feet per minute. Effects of the wave might reach from the ground to 35,000 feet, and extend hundreds of miles downstream. Altimeter errors might exceed 1,000 feet. And, waves occasionally occur in clear air. Figure 1-12, a visual satellite image, clearly shows the presence of wave clouds in northern Nevada and Utah. It illustrates the extent of wave activity. Chances are also good that wave conditions exist in the clear air over the northern Sierra Nevada Mountains and central Nevada.

To avoid the worst conditions, most authorities recommend the pilot remain at least 5,000 feet above mountain crests. In the west, most light aircraft simply don't have that performance. This leaves three options: select a course with lower terrain, wait it out, or take a chance on getting your fillings knocked loose and maybe losing the airplane. Passenger comfort and safety should be the priority consideration.

CBMAM (*Cumulonimbus Mamma*—previously called *mammatus*), from the Latin word meaning udder or breast, result from severe updrafts and downdrafts. They are characterized by lobes that protrude from the bottom of the cloud as illustrated in FIG. 1-13. They indicate probable severe or greater turbulence, and often appear just before or at the beginning of a squall. Avoid these areas.

Associated with convective activity, three additional cloud types can appear in SA remarks. A *shelf cloud*, layered and resembling shelves, can appear under a thunderstorm. A *wall cloud*, usually on the southwest edge of the thunderstorm, has a lowered base, and indicates the storm might be severe. A *roll cloud* appears as a detached, dense, horizontal cloud at the lower front part of the main cloud. All three indicate thunderstorms and a potential for severe weather.

BINOVC (breaks in the overcast) or the synonym HIR CLDS VSB (higher clouds visible) mean from 95 percent to less than 100 percent of the sky is covered. Such a report should never imply VFR flight through a layer is probable or even possible. However, it might be the first indication of a layer beginning to dissipate.

PRESFR (pressure falling rapidly) and PRESRR (pressure rising rapidly) signify the approach or passage of a frontal system. Pressure rising rapidly accompanied by a wind shift might be reported as FROPA (frontal passage) or APRNT FROPA (apparent frontal

1915 31MY87 38A-1   01682 23174 WA2

Fig. 1-12. *Visual satellite imagery clearly shows the presence of wave clouds in northern Nevada and Utah.*

Fig. 1-13. *Cumulonimbus Mamma are produced by the strong updrafts and downdrafts associated with a thunderstorm.*

passage). And, PRJMP (pressure jump) can indicate the approach of a prefrontal squall line.

Freezing level data—RADAT—appears in remarks on 00Z and 12Z SAs associated with radiosonde (upper air) observations. These locations can be found in the back of the appropriate *Airport/Facility Directory*. The data consists of the freezing level in hundreds of feet MSL, and relative humidity at that level. For example, . . . /RADAT 32078; the first two digits represent relative humidity (32 percent) at the freezing level of 7,800 MSL. High relative humidity indicates moisture and the possibility of icing at and above the freezing level.

Multiple freezing levels can occur. Figure 1-14 illustrates three crossings. Note first surface temperature, in the example 42° F. The surface is above freezing. The first crossing occurs at 8,100 MSL (081), the second 10,500 MSL (105), and the third 12,400 MSL (124). The highest relative humidity, 96 percent, was measured at the middle (M) crossing (L represents lowest and H highest). In this example, air temperature that is above freezing occurs from the surface to 8,100 feet, and again between 10,500 and 12,400 feet. This could be significant, should an altitude to shed ice be required.

Two crossings can occur with surface temperature below freezing. For example, MFR . . . 30/ . . . /RADAT 78H035097; temperatures are below freezing from the surface to 3,500 feet MSL, with a layer above freezing from 3,500 to 9,700 feet. Relative humidity of 78 percent occurred at 9,700 feet the high (H) crossing.

Other RADAT messages indicate the sounding was missed (MISG), due to equipment trouble or other factors, or delayed (DLAD). If the entire sounding is below 0° C, (RADAT) ZERO will be reported.

A word of caution. Lack of significant remarks does not infer the absence of hazardous weather. Omission of phenomena like lightning, cumulonimbus clouds, and other significant phenomena, occurs, usually due to inadequate observer training.

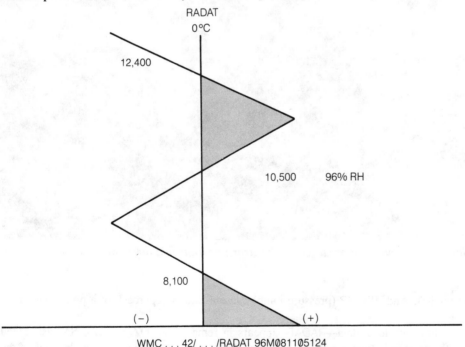

WMC . . . 42/ . . . /RADAT 96M081105124

Fig. 1-14. *Observed freezing level data appears in remarks of 0000Z and 1200Z SAs associated with radiosonde observations.*

AUTOMATED WEATHER OBSERVING SYSTEM (AWOS)

Approximately 1,600 FAA, NWS, and Department of Defense (DOD), automated weather observing locations will be operational by the mid 1990s. Most pilots will be dealing with AWOS, to one degree or another, on a continuous basis. AWOS, and the National Weather Service equivalent *Automated Surface Observing System* (ASOS), has the potential to provide an extra degree of safety, or to lure the unsuspecting pilot to disaster.

Attempts at automated weather observations have existed for more than 25 years. Today's science strives to reach the accuracy and reliability, and reduce some of the limitations, of the human observer. Surface observations have been decreasing on a regular basis over the last decade, with others part-timed. According to the FAA, AWOS has the requirement "To provide accurate, 24-hour airport weather information for pilot and air traffic control system personnel at over 1,000 airports with instrument approaches but without adequate weather observation capability." Private installations, purchased by local airport authorities, will also be available.

The new technology, however, has its faultfinders. FSS weather briefers and NWS forecasters are among the critics. Briefers are dubious about the quality and extent of, and forecasts based on, these observations.

Norman Schuyler, pilot and former NWS meteorologist, stated in the November 1988 *Private Pilot*: "The Federal Aviation Administration is still determined to complete the Automatic Weather Observing System (AWOS) program, a program that no one has a good word for."

Automated surface observations began with the *Automatic Meteorological Observing Station* (AMOS). Unfortunately, the system was only capable of reporting temperature, dew point, wind direction and speed, and pressure. Occasionally, human observers manually entered data to provide a complete report.

The *Automatic Observing Station* (AUTOB), a refinement of AMOS, added sky condition, visibility, and precipitation reporting. AUTOB, however, is limited to cloud amount and height measurements of 6,000 feet AGL, and three cloud layers. Visibility values are reported in whole miles, to a maximum of seven.

AWOS, operationally classified into four levels, consists of AWOS-A, which reports altimeter setting only; AWOS-1 (the equivalent of AMOS) reporting temperature, dew point, wind, and altimeter setting; AWOS-2 adds visibility information; and AWOS-3 reports sky conditions and ceiling along with the other elements.

Normally installed near the touchdown zone of the primary instrument runway, observations updated minute-by-minute are broadcast by synthesized voice over selected frequencies. Eventually, approximately 110 hourly and special observations will automatically be transmitted over the FAA's telecommunications network.

Formatted into standard reports, AWOS observations contain time of observation, sky condition, visibility, temperature, dew point, wind direction and speed, and altimeter setting. Some will report precipitation and density altitude. Although AWOS is designed to be self-contained, human observers will be able to edit and supplement data.

A laser ceilometer CHI (cloud height indicator) determines AWOS sky condition.

Similar to the rotating beam ceilometer, cloud elements reflect the laser. Heights will range from the surface to a maximum of 5,000 to 12,000 feet depending on the system. Observed heights will be reported to the nearest hundred feet from the surface to 5,000 feet, nearest 500 feet to 10,000 feet, and nearest 1,000 above 10,000 feet. Normally, two cloud layers will be reported, lowest and highest. Higher layers might be added, based on satellite and other data. AWOS has an advantage because all heights are measured, rather than estimates from a human observer.

Obscurations will be estimated based on visibility, temperature, and the computer cloud algorithm, which is a computer program for solving problems in a logical order. During evaluations, AWOS reported more obscurations than the human observer. AWOS does not have the capability to report a partial obscuration. Excessive reporting of obscurations has the potential of crying wolf.

A 30-minute history of cloud elements passing over the sensor determine sky cover (SCT, BKN, OVC), based on the computer algorithm. As noted in the September, 1988, *ASOS Progress Report*, "Yes this means that the algorithm assumes that the clouds are in motion above the CHI. That may not always be the case. . . . This automated approach to sky condition reporting has been tested by the NWS and the Air Force . . . with very favorable results." AWOS tests indicated that, at times due to the algorithm, up to two-tenths coverage might not be reported. AWOS, however, has the almost instantaneous ability to determine and report changing conditions.

AWOS determines visibility from a backscatter device or transmissometer. Figure 1-15 shows the backscatter device in the center of the picture, with the CHI to the left. Values are reported from one-quarter to a maximum of five to 10 miles, with variability added as needed. This value might be considerably different from prevailing visibility. Proponents of AWOS point out that automated observations will be more consistent, objective, standardized, continuous, and representative. This will certainly be true for IFR operations because the sensors are normally located at the approach end of the instrument runway.

Unfortunately, AWOS, at least initially, only measures sky condition and visibility at one point on the airport. It might not be representative of surrounding conditions. Should a single cloud element remain stationary over the sensor, the system would report a ceiling, when in fact the layer might be scattered. Conversely, should the beam pass through a small hole in an overcast layer, the system could report clear. Meteorologists responsible for forecasts based on AWOS are understandably concerned.

AWOS does not have the capability to observe the entire celestial dome—the sky viewed to the horizon in all directions. Because of these limitations the VFR pilot must view observations, especially close to minimums, with even more skepticism than those from a human observer. Proposals have been made to increase and disperse the number of sensors to help alleviate some drawbacks.

Present weather will include rain, snow, freezing rain, and drizzle. Obstructions to vision, such as fog and haze, will also be reported based on the computer algorithms. Additionally, AWOS will be able to accept lightning data, and report the presence of thunderstorms in the vicinity of the airport.

Fig. 1-15. *AWOS determines visibility from a backscatter device, center, and a laser cloud height sensor, left.*

Remarks normally will not appear on AWOS observations. The FAA views remarks as irrelevant and not necessary to aviation operations. This would seem to be confirmed by the NWS's test at Topeka, KS. The study evaluated remarks added to ASOS reports by control tower personnel. The NWS concluded that this augmentation was unreliable, often not appropriate, and inconsistent; that remarks have value only if the observer is also a user. And, of course, that augmentation was expensive. These conclusions, to say the least, are controversial.

Many question the validity of a test conducted in the middle of Kansas at a VFR non-federal control tower.

Ironically, the FAA's own *VFR Pilot Exam-O-Gram* Number 46 states: "A common misconception is that the regularly reported data alone, in the main body of the reports, reflects the overall weather situation at the reporting station. Frequently, remarks are added at the end of the report to cover unusual aspects of the weather, and often contain information which is as important as that found in the main body."

Reports of cloud type, such as altocumulus castellanus, standing lenticular altocumulus, rotor clouds, and cumulonimbus will not appear, nor will other weather phenomena, such as virga and weather not occurring at the station. A great number of pilots, briefers, and forecasters often view remarks as the most significant part of the report. With AWOS, pilot reports will take on an even greater significance.

During the FAA's evaluation commenters favored the AWOS by about two to one. "Pilots indicated foremost that 'availability' and 'currency' were the most favorable characteristic. . . . AWOS performance increased considerably during degraded weather conditions." The FAA concluded: "The demonstration program made evident that AWOS can consistently provide accurate real-time weather information directly to pilots." Planned enhancements include RVR and Low-Level Wind Shear Alerting Systems (LLWAS).

AWOS performs best in less than VFR conditions; a primary function of the equipment is to provide ceiling, visibility, and altimeter setting for IFR operations but VFR flights will also benefit. For example, a pilot might cancel a flight rather than "taking a look" with IFR or marginal VFR reported. Accurate temperature, wind, and altimeter settings will increase flight safety. For example, consider the Mammoth Lakes report:

    MMH SA 1545 50 SCT E120 BKN 50 46/ – 3/2345G90/002

The AWOS-1 broadcast from the Mammoth Airport would alert pilots that wind conditions were unsuitable. The pilot could then divert before encountering severe conditions, rather than possibly arriving without enough fuel for a suitable alternate, despite best efforts to follow regulations.

AWOS installation and commissioning began in September, 1989. Upon commissioning, AWOS-3 will become the official source of weather observations. AWOS will appear at major airports as well as uncontrolled fields; Oklahoma City's Will Rogers World Airport, home for the FAA's Mike Monroney Aeronautical Center, is scheduled for AWOS in 1990. Actual commissioning dates will be published as a Notice to Airmen (NOTAM). Availability of the service, frequencies, and telephone numbers are advertised in the *Airport/Facility Directory*.

The advantages of AWOS are undeniable. Observations will be available for many more locations, on a continuous basis. This will allow commercial operations into airports previously inaccessible due to lack of weather data. Airports with part-time observations will be usable for IFR operations 24 hours a day. Blind reliance on AWOS, however, has the potential for disaster. Remarks indicating thunderstorms or mountain waves, normally, will not appear. A VFR pilot planning to land at an AWOS airport reporting clear would have quite a shock finding an overcast with breaks. With weather reported close to minimums (VFR or IFR), extra caution must be exercised, terrain considered, and suitable alternates available. The observation that "Weather reports might not be accurate, but they are official," should be considered sage advice.

Ready or not, on an ever increasing basis, pilots can expect to hear:

"Automated weather observation; Ukiah Airport; Two zero five six zulu; Clear below one two thousand; Visibility one zero; Temperature six two; Dew point four eight; Winds one three zero at one two; Altimeter two niner niner five."

Or read UKI SA 2056 AWOS 120 CLR 10 62/48/1312/995.

Weather observations are only as useful as a pilot's understanding. This requires a knowledge of the methods of the observer, and knowledge of the limitations due to equipment, training, experience, and time of day. Today's pilot must not only be able to read and translate reports, but interpret their meaning and significance, then apply them to a flight situation (VFR or IFR), capability of the aircraft, terrain, and alternates that might be required.

Sample surface observations were presented at the beginning of the chapter with a request to translate and interpret the meaning. A strong cold front was moving through the northeast and things were happening at Newark and Philadelphia.

EWR SP 2240 W0 X 0T + RW + 3545Q60/989/R04VR45 T + OVHD MOVG ESE FQT
    LTGICCCCG
EWR RS 2253 − X E15 OVC 3T + RW 102/75/70/0905/983/R5 T + B10 SE
    MOVG ESE FQT LTGICCCCG VSBY HIR W RB07 PK WND 3560/40

The EWR SP 2240 reports an indefinite ceiling zero sky obscured, visibility zero in heavy rain showers and a severe thunderstorm. Rain has reduced both vertical and horizontal prevailing visibility to zero. The wind group reports peak gusts in squalls to 60 knots, which meets criteria for a severe thunderstorm. Remarks indicate Runway 04 visual range is 4,500 feet, above landing minimums. A severe thunderstorm is overhead moving east southeast with frequent lightning in cloud, cloud to cloud, and cloud to ground. Severe low-level wind shear with microbursts are a distinct possibility. Nobody has any business flying in this.

EWR has technically improved to VFR at 2253, although the severe thunderstorm that began 10 minutes before the last hour is still reported to the southeast. Moderate rain showers obscure $5/10$ of the sky. Quite probably the base of the clouds has not changed significantly since the previous special, but because the heavy rain showers have moved through, the observer can see the cloud base. The ceiling report should be considered with a little skepticism.

Be alert for the development of fog; temperature and dew point are within 5°, wind almost calm. Rain can suddenly cool the air and increase moisture near the surface, making fog likely. The report indicates that conditions are improving from the west: T + MOVG ESE VSBY HIR W.

```
PHL RS 2250 W6 X 1TRW + F 102/77/74/3618G24/983/R27RVR30V60 + TB25
    ALQDS MOVG SE FQT LTGICCG RB38 PRESFR
PHL SP 2256 W5 X 3/4TRW + F 2921G28/989/R27RVR08V60 + WSHFT 55 T
    ALQDS MOVG SE FQT LTGICCG PRESRR
```

Philadelphia's 2250 record special reports an indefinite ceiling six hundred, sky obscured, visibility one, heavy rain showers, fog, and a thunderstorm. Apparently well above IFR landing minimums. But, note the RVR. Runway 27R's visibility is variable between 3,000—close to minimums—and more than 6,000 feet. With a thunderstorm in progress in all quadrants, frequent lightning, and pressure falling rapidly, conditions will continue unsettled, with a distinct possibility of surface wind shifts, LLWS, and microbursts. Temperature/dew point spread is 3°, rain is adding moisture and cooling the air, and even with strong gusty winds, fog has formed. Pilots attempting an approach must be alert for severe wind shear and gusty crosswinds, and be prepared to go around at any point on the approach if severe shear is encountered, as well as a possible missed approach.

A special was issued only six minutes after the record observation; conditions can change rapidly. Ceiling and visibility have deteriorated, along with the variability in the RVR. However, a wind shift occurred at 2255 and the pressure is rising rapidly. WSHFT and PRESRR are indicators of frontal passage and improving weather.

I flew a Cessna 182 from Springfield, IL, to Oklahoma City under conditions similar to those described in the previous SA examples; VFR conditions, with scattered thunderstorms, existed to St. Louis. Rather than file IFR, without thunderstorm detection equipment, I prefer VFR to see what I'm getting into. We arrived in St. Louis just prior to the front. At the FSS, cell after cell was reported along the airway to Oklahoma City; this was no-go VFR or IFR. Several hours later, after the front passed, conditions improved rapidly and the trip was completed.

A final caution and a theme that will be repeated: Never rely on a single piece of information. The preceding reports were taken and analyzed out of context. Observations have their place. But, to be used effectively, surface reports, especially AWOS, must be viewed within the overall picture that includes weather advisories, synopses, PIREPs, and forecasts.

The weather condition W0 X 0F is sometimes translated in the vernacular: WOKS'-off.

2
Pilot Reports
(UA, PIREPs)

EVER COMPLAIN ABOUT FORECASTS; THINK THEY WERE PREPARED IN A sterile environment; conclude that pilots have no influence on their preparation? If we wish to participate, pilots can and do influence forecasts. According to the National Weather Service, PIREPs are the most important ingredient for AIRMETs, SIGMETs, Center Weather Advisories (CWA), and winds and temperatures aloft forecast amendments. In addition to the influence on forecasts, certain phenomena such as cloud layers and tops, icing, and turbulence can only be observed by the pilot. Add the fact that over the last decade the observational network has dwindled due to FSS and NWS consolidation, and military base closures—and with AWOS untested on a large scale—the need for accurate pilot reports cannot be overstated.

Satellites, plus upper air and radar reports supplement surface observations; satellites only observe cloud tops; upper air observations are infrequent and widely spaced; radar only provides storm information. An urgent need exists for information on weather conditions at flight altitudes, along routes between weather reporting stations—especially in mountainous areas—and at airports without weather reporting service. In many cases the pilot is, the best, and only source of actual weather conditions.

The FAA, recognizing the importance of PIREPs, has directed air traffic controllers and flight service specialists to actively solicit PIREPs, especially during marginal or IFR conditions, and periods of hazardous weather. Pilots operating IFR must by regulation ". . . report . . . any unforecast weather conditions encountered. . . ." These reports are not only of value to other pilots, but to controllers, briefers, and forecasters alike.

PILOT REPORTS (UA, PIREPs)

PIREPs can be provided to any air traffic facility (center, tower, FSS). However, to ensure widest distribution it's best to report directly to flight service, preferably Flight Watch—En route Flight Advisory Service (EFAS). More information about Flight Watch is in Chapter 12, Updating Meteorological and Aeronautical Information.

PIREPs are transmitted under the location identifier for the surface report (SA) nearest the occurrence using the file type UA (SAC UA, Sacramento pilot report). Reports can be appended, however, to major hub locations to ensure greatest prominence and widest distribution. Unfortunately, this FAA handbook requirement is not always followed. The following PIREP illustrates a serious problem:

```
HHR UUA /OV MQO/ . . . /TB SVR/ RM 2 N SBP
```

This report of severe turbulence occurred two miles north of the San Luis Obispo, CA, airport (SBP). However, the person who transmitted the report—which could be NWS or FSS—appended it to the Hawthorne, CA, (HHR) file. A pilot or briefer would only by accident see this report during a briefing to SBP. Some systems display PIREPs along with the associated SA, others don't. Pilots using DUAT, or other commercial systems, must consult the vendor to see how their system handles these messages.

PIREP FORMAT

PIREPs are entered using the standard format illustrated in FIG. 2-1. There is no need to memorize the form because FSS/NWS specialists encode the report. However, an understanding of the format illustrates information needed, and will assist in decoding and interpreting reports. Standard contractions contained in Appendix A are used.

Report Type: UUA or UA

An *urgent pilot report* (UUA) represents a hazard, or potential hazard, to flight operations. The message type UUA receives special handling and immediate distribution. Urgent PIREPs contain information on tornadoes, severe or extreme turbulence, severe icing, hail, low-level wind shear, or any other phenomena considered hazardous. Others, designated UA, receive routine distribution.

Location: /OV

The location where the phenomena was observed is reported in relation to one or more radio navigational aids (NAVAID). For example: a fix (/OV LAX or /OV LAX 060010, Los Angeles VOR or the Los Angeles 060 radial at 10 nautical miles (nm)), or between fixes (SEA – BTG, Seattle VOR and the Battleground VOR; SLC 245080 – JNC 210040, Salt Lake City 245 radial at 80 nm and the Grand Junction 210 radial at 40 nm). Normally, if a PIREP contains conditions at an airport or specific geographical location such as a mountain pass, the code for that airport or location will appear in remarks.

```
DEN UUA /OV DEN 301021 . . . /TP MAN/RM OG 1V5 WND 50 – 80G100 + BLOWING
    3/4 GRAVEL
```

PIREP FORM

Pilot Weather Report

3-Letter SA Identifier

→ ≡ *Space Symbol*

1. **UA →** _____ **UUA►** _____

_____ ___ ___ →

Routine Report   Urgent Report

2. **/OV →** | Location:

3. **/TM →** | Time:

4. **/FL** | Altitude/Flight Level:

5. **/TP →** | Aircraft Type:

Items 1 through 5 are mandatory for all PIREPs

6. **/SK →** | Sky Cover:

7. **/WX →** | Flight Visibility and Weather:

8. **/TA →** | Temperature *(Celsius)*:

9. **/WV →** | Wind:

10. **/TB →** | Turbulence:

11. **/IC →** | Icing:

12. **/RM →** | Remarks:

FAA FORM 7110-2 (1-85) Supersedes Previous Edition

Fig. 2-1. *FSS and NWS specialists encode PIREPs using the PIREP form. Pilots need not memorize the form, but it does indicate information needed.*

This report contains conditions observed on the Denver 301 radial at 21 nm. The *remarks* (/RM) indicate the report refers to conditions on the ground (OG) at Boulder Municipal Airport (1V5). It seems the wind is gusting to more than 100 knots and blowing ³/₄-inch gravel around. This information would certainly indicate a no-go decision, and illustrates the importance of such reports.

Decoding reports can be difficult without a copy of FAA Handbook 7350.5 *Location Identifiers*. Major identifiers can be found in Appendix A, Contractions, and DUATs has a decode command; often a current Sectional or World Aeronautical Chart (WAC) will suffice. If necessary, a pilot can always call an FSS.

Time: /TM

Time when the phenomena was observed, referenced to *Coordinated Universal Time* (UTC).

Altitude/Flight Level: /FL

The altitude, in hundreds of feet MSL, that the phenomena was encountered.

Type Aircraft: /TP

Type aircraft is self-explanatory; standard contractions are used. Although, not specifically intended to decode aircraft types, Appendix A, Aircraft Types-Encode, with a little practice, can be used to decode UA /TPs. From time to time, this element will contain /TP PUP (pickup truck), /TP CAR, /TP FBO (airport Fixed Base Operator), or as reported on the Denver PIREP /TP MAN.

Sky Cover: /SK

Sky cover describes the amount of clouds (CLR, SCT, BKN, or OVC), bases and tops, in hundreds of feet MSL. Remember sky cover is always an estimate, based on the observer's—in this case, the pilot's—training and experience. If more than one layer is reported, the layers will be separated by a slant (055 SCT 070/105 BKN 130, bases of a scattered layer 5,500, tops 7,000 feet; bases of a higher broken layer 10,500, tops 13,000 feet).

It's important to remember that PIREP bases and tops are always MSL. This accounts for some perceived surface observation errors. The observation in FIG. 1-1 reported: 10 SCT M18 BKN 30 OVC . . . . If field elevation is 2,500 feet, a pilot flying in the area might report 035 SCT/043 SCT/055 SCT. Because of the summation principle used by the observer and the fact that field elevation is 2,500 feet, the surface observation and PIREP are perfectly consistent.

Weather: /WX

Weather encountered and flight visibility are reported in this element. Flight visibility should be reported to the nearest whole statute mile (sm) (FV01, FV05). Unrestricted visibility will be encoded FV99. FV99 has potential ambiguity. Does it mean visibility 99 miles or greater, or seven miles or greater? Pilots should report specific values to 100 miles to eliminate any possible misunderstanding. Weather, when reported, uses standard contractions and appears following the visibility.

Air Temperature in Celsius: /TA

Self-explanatory.

Wind: /WV

Wind direction and speed is encoded using three digits to indicate direction and three digits to indicate speed (/WV 360020, observed wind 360° at 20 knots). In spite of the FAA's *Flight Service* handbook, direction should be reported in relation to true north, which is consistent with other reports and forecasts. Speed is in knots.

Turbulence: /TB

The intensity and altitude (when different from /FL) of turbulence appears in this element. *Clear Air Turbulence* (CAT) and CHOP should be added when appropriate. (Both terms will be defined shortly.) When turbulence has been forecast, but reports indicate smooth /TB NEG is entered. Therefore, /TB NEG is interpreted as smooth, rather than turbulence that bounces the aircraft down.

Icing: /IC

The intensity, type (clear, rime, or mixed) and altitude, when different from /FL, is entered in this element.

Remarks: /RM

This element reports low-level wind shear, convective activity, dust storms and sandstorms, surface conditions at airports, or other information to expand or clarify the report.

Remarks of some PIREPs have read: /RM SMOKE OVER NWS BUILDING DRIFTING EAST—SOMEONE THINKING; /RM VFR NOT RECOMMENDED—THREE AIRCRAFT COULD NOT MAINTAIN VFR DUE TO ICING IN CLOUDS. Something odd; oh well, I guess it is difficult to maintain VFR in the clouds when you're icing up. Or, /RM HAD TO CLIMB TO FL200 TO REMAIN VFR—NOW LEAVING FREQ TO CONTACT ZOA. Because this pilot is already 2,000 feet into the Positive Control Area, leaving the frequency to contact ZOA (Oakland Center) seems like a "right good" idea.

Cloud bases and tops, temperatures, and even winds can be measured. Flight visibility and weather are direct observations. Intensities of turbulence and icing, however, are some of the most misunderstood quantities in aviation. That's because they're subjective, usually based on the pilot's training and experience. (We talked about training and experience in the introduction.) Take for example the rather shaky voice that called flight service to report moderate to severe turbulence. The specialist asked the novice pilot if he, ". . . actually lost control of the aircraft." The pilot replied, "Well, no." The specialist then asked, "Would it be okay if we called it light to moderate turbulence?" The pilot agreed.

TURBULENCE

Classifications for the intensity of turbulence can be found in the *Airman's Information Manual* and *Aviation Weather Services*; however, I prefer the following.

Light

A turbulent condition during which your coffee is sloshed around, but doesn't spill, unless the cup's too full. Unsecured objects remain at rest; passengers in the back seat are rocked to sleep.

Moderate

A turbulent condition during which even half-filled cups of coffee spill. Unsecured objects move about; passengers in the back seat are awakened by a definite strain against their seat belts.

Severe

A turbulent condition during which the coffee cup you left on the instrument panel whizzes by the passengers in the back seat. The aircraft might be momentarily out of control, but you don't let on. Anyone not using their seat belt is peeling themselves off the cabin ceiling.

Extreme

Usually associated with rotor clouds in a strong mountain wave or a severe thunderstorm, extreme turbulence is a rarely encountered condition where the aircraft might be impossible to control. The turbulence can cause structural damage. Your passengers are becoming concerned by the beads of sweat on your brow, and your white knuckles, and new frequency and new transponder code you have just selected—121.5 and 7700.

The following reports illustrate mountain wave activity.

RNO UUA /OV FMG 330025/TM 2345/FL105/TP BE35/TB SVR/RM TMPRY LOST
CONTROL . . . PILOT CUT ARM IN TURBC . . . RTNG TO RNO.

A SIGMET was in effect for severe turbulence, Reno surface winds were out of the west gusting to 27 knots, and winds across the Sierra Nevada mountains were gusting to near 50 knots. The pilot had the clues, but elected to go. From the PIREP it would appear he or she regretted the decision.

Another pilot caught in a mountain wave reported:

RNO UUA /OV FMG 270012 . . . /TP C404 /TB EXTREME 130 – 110 MDT – SVR
110 – 090 /RM EXPERIENCING STRUCTURAL DAMAGE.

The airlines are not immune to mountain waves:

DEN UUA /OV DEN 313047/TM 0158/FL350/TP L101/TB SVR/RM SVR MTN WAVE
PLUS AND MINUS 6000 FPM.

This Lockheed Tristar (L101) at 35,000 feet over the Rockies experienced severe turbulence and 6,000 feet per minute updrafts and downdrafts. This illustrates the severity of mountain waves and illustrates that they can extend to the stratosphere.

Turbulence encountered in clear air not associated with cumuliform clouds, usually above 15,000 feet and associated with wind shear should be reported as clear air turbulence (CAT). Slight, rapid, and somewhat rhythmic bumpiness without appreciable changes in altitude or attitude defines CHOP.

In addition to intensity, duration of turbulence should be reported.

Briefly. Turbulence encountered for an extremely short period, usually only one or two jolts (/TB LGT /RM 2 MDT JOLTS could be reported /TB LGT BRFLY MDT).

Occasional. Less than 1/3 of the time.

Intermittent. Between 1/3 and 2/3 of the time.

Continuous. More than 2/3 of the time.

Chapter 1 discusses how to use an SA to determine likely areas for turbulence. Recent and accurate PIREPs can verify or refute its presence. If reports or forecasts indicate turbulence, a pilot can minimize the hazard when encountered. Turbulence imposes gust loads that appear to be almost instantaneous. Gust loads increase with the speed of the aircraft and gust velocity.

If light or moderate turbulence is encountered or expected, avoid flight in the caution range—the yellow arc on the airspeed indicator. If severe turbulence is encountered or expected, reduce to *maneuvering speed*. Maneuvering speed is not printed on the airspeed indicator, although it's usually placarded in the vicinity of the instrument. Because gust load factor decreases as wing loading increases, maneuvering speed increases with the aircraft's gross weight. Therefore, it's usually necessary to determine maneuvering speed based on gross weight.

In moderate or greater turbulence fly attitude rather than altitude. Disengage the autopilot altitude hold, if in use. The aircraft should already be slowed to turbulent air penetration speed. Don't chase airspeed or altitude. It's like riding a horse, go with it rather than fighting it. The object's to avoid imposing additional abrupt maneuvering loads. For the most part, ignore altitude unless terrain clearance becomes a problem; VFR, try to avoid IFR cardinal altitudes (4,000, 5,000, 6,000, etc.), or opposite direction VFR altitudes; IFR, inform air traffic control (ATC) of the problem and any altitude deviations required. ATC increases vertical separation during severe conditions.

ICING

As with turbulence, there is a tendency to overestimate icing intensity, especially with new or low-time pilots. A recently rated instrument pilot, after experiencing his second encounter with icing in a Cessna 172, reported severe icing. The encounter lasted about 30 minutes, he was unable to maintain altitude and forced to descend. This description, however, is only of moderate intensity. Icing intensity has been classified for reporting purposes in AIM. Perhaps personal definitions are more descriptive.

Trace

Ice becomes perceptible and the rate of accumulation is slightly greater than the rate of sublimation. It is not hazardous even though ice protection equipment is not utilized, unless encountered for more than one hour; your spouse admires how pretty it looks on the wing; ATC has just instructed you to climb. You advise them icing is probable and request descent. The controller calmly replies that in that case "you can declare an emergency or land." Shortly, you're handed off to the next controller. You inquire about a lower altitude and the controller responds, "Is that Terry up there?" (A friend at L.A. Center.) A lower altitude was approved in about 15 minutes.

Light

The rate of accumulation can create a problem if the flight continues for more than one hour. Occasional use of ice protection equipment removes or prevents accumulation. Ice should not present a problem if the protection equipment is used. Your student hasn't noticed the ice yet; your pilot friend in the back seat is hoping he has enough life insurance; you're negotiating with ATC for a lower altitude, which they can approve in 15 miles. This will only take about eight minutes, but each minute seems like 10.

Moderate

The rate of accumulation, even for short periods, becomes potentially hazardous and the use of ice protection equipment or flight course diversion becomes necessary. On his second encounter with ice, a friend and his passengers, in an aircraft without ice protection equipment, survived moderate icing only because the terrain was lower than the freezing level.

Severe

The rate of accumulation is such that ice protection equipment fails to reduce or control the hazard. Immediate diversion is necessary. This is a situation where the person in the left seat very rapidly ceases being the pilot and becomes a passenger; the wing is an ice cube. Certain pilots will report icing intensity as heavy. This is a misnomer because all ice is heavy.

The type of icing has also been classified for reporting purposes.

Rime Ice

Rime ice is milky, opaque, and granular, normally formed when small supercooled water droplets instantaneously freeze upon impact with the aircraft. It is most frequently encountered in stratiform clouds at temperatures between 0° C and −20° C.

Clear Ice

Clear ice is glossy and formed when large supercooled water droplets flow over the aircraft's surface after impact, and freeze into a smooth sheet of solid ice. It is most frequently encountered in cumuliform clouds or freezing precipitation. Brief, but severe accumulations occur at temperatures between 0° C and −10° C, with reduced intensities at lower temperatures, and in cumulonimbus clouds down to −25° C.

Rime Ice and Clear Ice (Mixed Icing)

Mixed ice is a hard, rough, irregular, whitish conglomerate formed when supercooled water droplets vary in size or are mixed with snow, ice pellets, or small hail. Deposits become blunt with rough bulges building out against the airflow.

The term *ice protection equipment* in the icing intensity definitions refers to aircraft and equipment certified for flight in known icing conditions. Although many aircraft have limited ice protection equipment (pitot heat, prop anti-ice, alternate static source, etc.), it should never be construed as allowable for flight in icing; their purpose is for emergency use only, should icing be inadvertently encountered.

Icing potential exists anytime visible moisture exists—clouds or precipitation—at temperatures of 0° C or less. This contradicts the notion that icing can only occur in clouds. Chapter 1 discusses how freezing rain can be the most serious icing hazard, and the icing potential of wet snow. Both phenomena can affect the VFR pilot. The greatest icing potential occurs between the freezing level and −10° C to −15° C, or within a layer approximately 5,000 and 7,500 feet deep. Icing has been encountered in convective clouds at altitudes of 30,000 to 40,000 feet in temperatures less than −40° C.

If the weather briefing indicates even a remote possibility of encountering ice, the pilot should accomplish several tasks. Ensure the pitot heat works with a very light touch during preflight. Check ice protection equipment for proper operation. Remember that a heated pitot is an anti-icing device, to be turned on before encountering ice; deicing equipment usually requires ice buildup before activation; improper operation can actually increase ice buildup and prevent its removal! Check alternate air or carburetor heat for an alternate source of air if the air filter ices over.

The object with ice is to minimize exposure. With temperatures 0° C or less, avoid flying in clouds or precipitation. Should ice be encountered, immediately notify ATC and initiate a plan of action. The first consideration might be to climb to colder air, or above the layer based upon PIREPs and the weather briefing. Ice will slowly *sublimate*—change from a solid directly into a gas—when on top. Or, descend to warmer air based upon the actual freezing level on climb out. This requires a careful check of *minimum en route altitudes* (MEA). Finally, if you have to, turn around because presumably, you came from an ice-free area. The point is, do something!

A non-turbocharged, non-deice Baron departed Reno, NV, for Southern California. Moderate icing and severe turbulence were forecast. The pilot elected to fly a direct course along the crest of the Sierra Nevada mountains, the route where the most intense icing and turbulence could be expected. The aircraft iced up resulting in a fatal accident.

PILOT REPORTS (UA, PIREPs)

The pilot had no way out because the MEA was the aircraft service ceiling. The terrain was well above the freezing level and the pilot failed to reverse course at the first sign of ice. What other options were available? The pilot could have crossed the mountains near Sacramento, minimizing exposure to ice and over the Sierras, it was all downhill. He could have flown toward Las Vegas where the weather was considerably better, or simply waited for better weather conditions.

When the aircraft became ice covered, the pilot had no option but to ride the airplane to the crash site.

A Bonanza pilot departed the San Francisco Bay area on a flight to Los Angeles. Icing above 7,000 feet was forecast and reported. The pilot elected to fly at 11,000 feet. His last words were, "I've iced up and stalled." The crash occurred in the San Joaquin Valley where the elevation was near sea level. Minimum altitudes in the vicinity of the crash were well below the freezing level. The pilot simply did nothing until he lost control of the aircraft. In both instances, an ominous PIREP describing icing intensity might read: /IC FATAL.

If a descent through an icing layer is required, remember the objective is to minimize exposure. Under such circumstances, negotiate with ATC to obtain a continuous descent. Avoid, if possible, level flight in clouds. ATC is usually very responsive to such requests.

A word of caution. A popular notion in some aviation publications is that a pilot's mere mention of ice will receive emergency-like handling. Icing might be an emergency, but remember the controller's job is to separate aircraft within a finite amount of airspace. ATC might have to assign a higher altitude, but ATC cannot, and should not, be expected to fly the aircraft, or assume the responsibility of pilot in command.

No one has any business flying in these conditions:

```
FAT UUA /OV FAT 090030 . . . /FL160-240 /TP F18/IC SVR CLR
BFL UUA /OV PMD 330040 . . . /FL100 /TP C402/IC SVR RIME/RM PUP 1
    INCH CANT SEE THRU WINDSHIELD
```

PIREPs are the pilot's only source of reported induction system icing: iced over air intake systems and carburetor ice. Both result in loss of engine power, and left unchecked, complete power failure. The solution is to use the alternate air source on fuel injected engines, or carburetor heat on normally aspirated—carbureted—engines.

Induction system icing takes place anytime structural icing occurs. Symptoms are a gradual loss of power. On a flight from Van Nuys, CA, to San Francisco in a Cessna 172 we encountered light icing after an ATC request to climb. I periodically applied carburetor heat. Something unusual occurred. With carburetor heat on, the engine ran fine: off, the engine faultered. On the ramp at San Francisco we parked next to a Navion that had also flown from L.A., but at a higher altitude and encountered more ice. Sure enough, in the Navion's air filter was a large chunk of ice. I realized that the carburetor heat in the 172 was apparently functioning as an alternate air source. I'm sure this seems ridiculously obvious; it didn't at the time, which illustrates the hazards of learning by experience.

In addition to air intake icing, normally aspirated engines can develop ice in the carburetor throat. Known as *carburetor icing*, ice can form with outside air temperatures as high as 90° F. As air is accelerated through the carburetor, and fuel evaporates, temperatures can be lowered as much as 60° F. Whether ice will develop depends on the velocity of the fuel/air mixture, outside air temperature, humidity, and carburetor system. Conditions most favorable for carburetor ice are outside temperatures between 0° F and 60° F, high relative humidity, and low-power settings.

Carburetor ice is detected in aircraft with fixed pitch propellers by a loss of rpm, in aircraft with constant speed propellers by a loss of manifold pressure. At the first indication of carburetor ice, power loss or engine roughness, apply full carburetor heat. Be prepared; this will result in additional power loss and engine roughness. Leave it on until the engine smooths out, which might take several minutes. Avoid using partial heat unless the aircraft is equipped with a carburetor air temperature gauge. At times it might be necessary to leave heat on for an extended period. A flight from Page, AZ, to Las Vegas, NV required continuous use of heat due to carburetor icing in a Cessna 150. Don't forget to relean the mixture.

Carbureted engines are more susceptible to icing during reduced-power operation. Some aircraft and engine manufacturers recommend the use of carburetor heat during all power reductions, others only when ice is suspected. Pilot's should follow the aircraft manufacturer's recommendations. If full power is required, such as a go-around, full carburetor heat and full power might cause early detonation or engine damage. It will certainly prevent the engine from developing full power, which might be critical in low-power aircraft at high-density altitudes. Again, know and follow the manufacturer's recommendations.

Pay Attention

I had remained over night in Amarillo, TX, because of a line of thunderstorms that approached from the west. The Cessna 150 was parked into the wind when torrential rains moved through the area. The next morning was clear, with abundant surface moisture, temperature in the 60s, and nearly 100 percent relative humidity.

My first clue of trouble was the increased throttle setting required to obtain idle rpm. Engine runup also took more throttle than usual. I suspected carburetor ice and a water saturated air filter because of the conditions. I had 13,000 feet of runway.

Full throttle only gave me about 2,200 rpm. The increased ground run to rotation speed—about 7,000 feet—should have been another clue. I was off the ground and with no runway remaining and 200 feet of altitude the engine started losing rpm. I applied carburetor heat and the engine was running very rough producing about 1,700 rpm.

There was a tremendous psychological urge to reduce the heat and get that rpm back. I was preparing to crash straight ahead but the engine was still producing power and I decided to make a 180° turn and land on a taxiway. Then I informed a suprised tower controller of what happened; remember, a pilot's first job is to fly the airplane.

After running the engine for 20 minutes, and one aborted takeoff later, I launched into the air. The engine again performed normally above the shallow, moist layer. It was a perfect example of having the clues and disregarding them. I was extremely fortunate.

PILOT REPORTS (UA, PIREPs)

REMARKS

Remarks amplify information or describe conditions not already reported:

SAC UUA /OV SAC/TM 1753/FL30/TP C172/TB MDT – SVR/RM LTGCG

The pilot observed lightning cloud to ground.

BFL UA /OV WJF – BFL/TM 1845/FL500AGL/TP UH60/SK 050 OVC/TB LGT
OCNL MDT/RM THRU TSP PASS UNDER CLDS. OK FOR HELIO NOT SO HOT
FOR FIXED WING

SNA UA /OV SNA – GMN/TM 2218/FL125/TP PA28/TA 00/WV 330015 – 020
/TB MDT/RM LIKE AN E TICKET AT DISNEYLAND

An E ticket was for the big rides.

DEN UA /OV DEN 240060/TM 1715/FL350 – 390/TP H/DC8/TB MDT CAT
/RM MDT CAT AT 373 SMTH BLO 367 [ZDV]

This report was filed by Denver Center's Weather Service Unit (CWSU) [ZDV]. It amplifies the turbulence portion indicating that moderate CAT was encountered at 37,300 and it was smooth below 36,700.

Remarks also describe *low-level wind shear*, which is shear that occurs within 2,000 feet of the surface. Because of its significance, pilot reports on wind shear are extremely important. Wind shear PIREPs include location, altitude, and airspeed changes.

RNO UA/ OV RNO . . . /TP DC9 /RM LLWS 001 – SFC +30 TO 40 KTS

The pilot experienced a 30- to 40-knot increase in airspeed between 100 feet and the surface.

STS UUA/ . . . /FL 030 – 020/TP C500/TM DURGD RY02 LLWS RESULTING IN 80
KTS CHG AIRSPEED.

RDD UA/ . . . /FL010/TP PA31/RM LLWS ± 20 – 25KT 010 – SFC DRGD UNABLE
TO LND RY16.

Interesting remarks abound:

/RM STRONGEST TURBC I HAVE EXPERIENCE IN 15 YEARS reported by a King Air
pilot.

/RM 2 PASSENGERS INJURED . . . HAD TO TURN BACK reported by a Navy P3 pilot.

/RM IFR NOT RECOMMENDED DUE TO STRONG HEAD WINDS AND 2000 FT PER
MIN UP AND DOWN DRAFTS WILL NEVER DO IT AGAIN reported by a Cessna
182 pilot.

/RM SOME REAL GOOD JOLTS PUT KNOT ON HEAD aircraft type missing.

/RM ONE LARGE JOLT, STEW FELL DOWN (SHE IS OK) LOTS OF DRINKS
SPILLED reported by a Fairchild 27 pilot.

/RM UNA TO CONTROL HELICOPTER. RETURNED. NURSES KISSED THE GROUND.

/RM WIND O/G at FCH **(Fresno Chandler Airport)** IS 300 – 330 DEGREES AT 40 KTS AND ALL THE C150'S AND C152'S ARE INTMTLY FLYING ON THEIR CHAINS.

/RM SVR LLWS AFTER 3 APCHS UNABLE TO LAND reported by a Lear Jet.

/RM LOTS OF BAD TURBC. THIS ISN'T THE SMARTEST THING I'VE EVER DONE. HUGHES COPTER.

/RM ROUGHER THAN A COBB is the good old standby.

/OV AVX . . . /TP FBO/SK CLR/WX CLR/TB NONE/RM LET'S GO FLY . . . AVX is Catalina Island's Airport in the Sky. If you're in the L.A. area, try to get out there and order a Buffalo Burger at the restaurant.

LAX UA /OV SXC 213186/TM 1911/FL070/TP VYGR/SK BKN 040/TB LGT /RM VOYAGER 1 is an actual report filed by a Voyager pilot on the record-setting around-the-world flight.

A strong Santa Ana wind in Southern California was responsible for the conditions described in the following SA and PIREPs at Ontario, CA (ONT).

```
ONT SA 1450 CLR 50 46/01/0234G45/990/WIND 330V040
ONT UUA /OV ONT/TM 1425 /FL050/TP B727/TB MDT OCNL SVR
ONT UUA /OV ONT/TM 1445/FL050/TP B727/TB MDT OCNL SVR 050 – SFC
     /RM CRCLG FAP LNDG ONT
ONT UUA /OV ONT/TM 1450/FL020/TP B727/RM UNABLE TO LAND DUE TO
     X – WINDS
```

PIREPs from air carriers, the military, and corporate aircraft tend to be more accurate because of the pilot's training and experience. Few student pilots fly DC-10s or F-14s. New and low-time pilots (inexperienced) tend to overestimate intensities of turbulence and icing, then they think they've experienced severe conditions and might not heed reports or forecasts. This is not to say PIREPs from pilots of Cessna 150s or Piper Tomahawks are never accurate, and should be ignored because turbulence and icing are transitory and difficult to forecast.

Pilots must evaluate PIREPs within the context of surface reports, forecasts, and other PIREPs. A single report of severe turbulence from a Beech Sundowner under clear skies and light winds should be viewed with skepticism. On the other hand, a report of severe turbulence from a Cessna 172 with conditions favorable for a mountain wave, and advisories in effect, should be taken very seriously. PIREPs that are not objective are worse than useless. Not only do they give false impression to other pilots, but forecasters must take them as fact and issue advisories, which undermine forecast credibility.

Every time we fly we become observers, but reports must be timely. Some pilots have a tendency to wait until the latter portion or end of a flight to provide a report. A pilot on a flight from Seattle to Los Angeles contacted Oakland Flight Watch and reported conditions departing Seattle two and a half hours earlier. A somewhat over zealous briefer instructed the student to make a pilot report at the conclusion of his flight. The student calling the FSS the following day meekly apologized for failing to provide the report, then proceeded to recount in detail the conditions encountered. I'll bet he doesn't forget on his next flight. Get into the habit of routinely providing timely reports because reports confirming the forecast are as important as those for unforecast weather.

The next time someone complains about the lack of weather information or forecast accuracy, ask if they routinely provide objective pilot reports. And, the next time you fly and just don't get around to making a report remember this: BFL UA /OV BFL /TM 1450 / FLUNK /TP ALL /RM WISH I HAD A TOP REPORT FROM BFL TO ONT.

FSS and NWS specialists sometimes tend to editorialize on PIREPs, usually around the time of championship sporting events. Although, unauthorized and unprofessional, pilots can expect to see these reports, usually humorous, from time to time.

Other comments contain social or political messages like the following example from December 20, 1989, appended to the Salinas, CA, (SNS) SA at Ft. Ord, CA, (OAR) as the United States was removing Panamanian dictator Manuel Noriega: SNS UA /OV OAR/ TM 0200/TP NUMEROUS C130 C141/RM MERRY CHRISTMAS MANNY.

3
Forecasts

SIR WILLIAM NAPIER SHAW'S *MANUAL OF METEOROLOGY* PUBLISHED IN THE
late '20s, nicely sums it up: "Every theory of the course of events in nature is necessarily based on some process of simplification of the phenomena and is to some extent
therefore a fairy tale."

Aviation weather forecasts began with the Wright brothers' request for surface winds
at Kitty Hawk, NC, in 1903. In the early 1920s aviation forecast centers were established
at Washington, D.C., Chicago, and San Francisco. Establishment of lighted airways in the
mid '20s encouraged the Weather Bureau to begin night forecasting. Several airlines had
established their own forecasting systems by the mid 1930s. Because meteorologists
could, and sometimes were held responsible for weather-related accidents, forecasts
tended to be pessimistic.

Forecasts were limited by lack of observational data and the complexity of the atmosphere. Meteorologists were plagued with unexpected thunderstorms, the transient nature
of icing and turbulence, and the unanticipated development of fog.

Advances were made in the late '30s and '40s with upper air observations and facsimile transmission of weather charts. By the late 1950s weather radar was added to the
observational arsenal. Today, satellites and computers help produce forecasts. However,
due to the lack of observational data and the complexity of the atmosphere, computer programs can only generate approximations.

Observational data comes from surface, upper air, and radar reports, satellite imagery, and PIREPs and their influence on forecasts. Figure 3-1, the National Aviation
Weather System chart, illustrates how PIREPs fit into the overall picture.

National Aviation Weather System

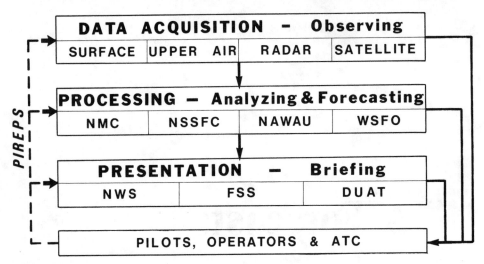

Fig. 3-1. *The National Aviation Weather System consists of many governmental offices and agencies and is dependent on the pilot's active participation.*

Data processing—analyzing and forecasting—is accomplished at the National Meteorological Center (NMC), in Washington, D.C., the National Severe Storms Forecast Center (NSSFC) and the National Aviation Weather Advisory Unit (NAWAU), both at Kansas City, MO, and local Weather Service Forecast Offices (WSFO). Meteorologists from the satellite section at the NWS Kansas City office discuss the day's weather, in FIG. 3-2, using a satellite loop that provides a moving picture of weather systems.

Meteorologists develop a forecast based on an equation:

Existing Weather + Weather Trend = Expected Weather

Trend can be the rate of change in the weather. *Advection*—the movement of an atmospheric property from one location to another—and *development* create the weather trend. Fronts and upslope fog are examples of an atmospheric property moving from one location to another, producing weather. Development is the growth of air mass thunderstorms, increase in afternoon thermal turbulence, or the dissipation of radiation fog.

ACCURACY

Are aviation forecasts accurate? The FAA admits that needs, ". . . cannot be met by an immediate application of existing technology. The need for accurate short-term forecasts exists in every phase of flight operations and is critical to an efficient, smoothly operating air traffic control system." To this end the FAA and National Weather Service

Fig. 3-2. *Meteorologists from the satellite section of the NWS's Kansas City office discuss the day's weather patterns using a satellite loop that provides a moving picture of weather systems.*

established an En Route Flight Advisory Service, including the implementation of high altitude Flight Watch, and Center Weather Service Units at Air Route Traffic Control Centers (ARTCC).

Forecast accuracy begins—or maybe begins to deteriorate—with observational data. The limited number of observations hinders forecast accuracy. The observational network has dwindled and AWOS, with its own limitations, has yet to be fully implemented. Upper air observations, radar, and satellites help, but extensive areas remain outside the observational network. Fully half of the forecast is based on existing weather.

Available data is computer processed and analyzed. Computer equations represent the atmosphere at points approximately 125 miles apart, depending on the computer model, and at various heights. Large-scale *synoptic* weather systems are detected, but smaller scale *mesoscale* weather systems, such as individual thunderstorms, might not be detected. Additionally, because of computer model limitations, factors such as the interaction of water, ice, and local terrain cannot be adequately taken into account. These are major limitations to the second factor in the weather equation, weather trend.

The National Weather Service monitors forecasts, but other than amendment criteria, no specific factors exist to determine forecast accuracy. And, of course, who defines accuracy? C. Donald Ahrens wrote in *Meteorology Today* (St. Paul: West Publishing Co.,

1985), "At present, there is no clear-cut answer to the question of determining forecast accuracy." Few pilots and FSS briefers are aware of forecast limitations or amendment criteria. Many have developed their own perceptions that are erroneous, more often than not, due to misconceptions and misunderstandings.

SPECIFICITY

Each forecast is written for a specific purpose in accordance with specific criteria. *Area Forecasts* cover entire states, *TWEB Route Forecasts* cover routes 50 miles wide, and *Terminal Forecasts* relate conditions within five miles of an airport. Differences are to be expected due to scale, interpretation of the weather situation, issuance times, and starting conditions. For example, localized areas of fog predicted in TWEB Route or Terminal Forecasts might not appear in the Area Forecast. Or, the Area Forecast might contain a prediction for thunderstorms that might not appear in individual Terminal Forecasts when the forecaster does not expect the phenomena to occur at that airport. Forecasters might legitimately differ in interpretation. The Area Forecast might predict frontal passage at one time and the Terminal Forecast at another time. Forecasts are issued at different times. Therefore, information available to the forecaster, on which to base the forecast, will differ.

A thorough understanding of format, limitations, and amendment criteria are required to adequately apply a forecast, especially using a self-briefing media. The FAA and NWS have said: "There probably is no better investment in personal safety, for the pilot as well as the safety of others, than the effort he spends to increase his knowledge of basic weather principles and to learn to interpret and use the products of the weather service." Then there's the legal requirement. Each pilot in command is required by regulations to become familiar with all available information concerning a flight. This includes: "For a flight under IFR or a flight not in the vicinity of an airport, weather reports and forecasts. . . ." Even student pilots must receive instruction in the ". . . use of aeronautical weather reports and forecasts . . ." before venturing solo cross-country.

From TABLE 3-1, Limitations on Aviation Weather Forecasts, the following conclusions are apparent. Forecasts for good weather are more likely to be correct than forecasts for poor weather; this should be no surprise, good weather occurs more often than poor weather. Forecasts are most accurate during the first few hours of the period. Accuracy deteriorates below 80 percent beyond four hours when less than VFR conditions are forecast. Accurate forecasts of specific values beyond three hours is not yet possible. Forecast issuance and valid times, and amendment criteria are based on the above limitations. Forecasts are most reliable for distinct weather systems (fast moving cold fronts, squall lines, or strong high pressure areas). Synoptic scale systems are detected within the forecast models.

Phenomena such as the time freezing rain will begin, severe or extreme turbulence, severe icing, the movement of tornadoes, ceilings of 100 feet or zero before they exist, the onset of thunderstorms that have not yet formed, and low-level wind shear, are difficult to predict with accuracy. These phenomena are often caused by mesoscale systems, or are

Table 3-1. *Limitations on Aviation Weather Forecasts.*

1. Forecasts 12 hours and beyond for good weather (ceiling 3,000 feet or more; visibility three miles or greater) are more likely to be correct than forecasts for poor weather (ceiling below 1,000 feet; visibility below one mile).
2. Poor weather forecast to occur within three to four hours has a better than 80 percent probability of occurrence.
3. Forecasts for poor weather within the first few hours of the period are most reliable with distinct weather system.
4. Errors occur with attempts to forecast a specific time poor weather will occur. Errors are less frequent forecasting poor weather within a time frame.
5. Surface visibility is more difficult to forecast than ceiling.

Forecasters can predict with 75 percent accuracy:
1. Within two hours, the passage of fast moving cold fronts or squall lines up to 10 hours in advance.
2. Within five hours, the passage of warm fronts or slow moving cold fronts up to 12 hours in advance.
3. Within one to two hours, the onset of thunderstorms, with radar available.
4. Within five hours, the time rain or snow will begin.

Forecasters cannot predict with an accuracy that satisfies operational requirements:
1. The time freezing rain will begin.
2. The location and occurrence of severe or extreme turbulence, or severe icing.
3. The location of the initial occurrence of a tornado or low-level wind shear.
4. Ceilings of 100 feet or zero before they exist.
5. The onset of a thunderstorm that has not yet formed.

transitory and remain undetected within the normal observational system. Computer models are of limited use. The most hazardous weather is the most difficult to forecast.

Outlook forecasts for good weather are more likely to be correct than forecasts for poor weather. Errors in timing are more prevalent than errors of occurrence. One forecaster put it this way, "We're never wrong, our timing's just off sometimes." Or, forecasts are 100 percent correct—90 percent in the summer and 10 percent in the winter!

Unwarranted pessimism is a major forecast complaint. In a 1981 National Aeronautics and Space Administration (NASA) study pilots complained of cancelling flights based on forecasts when the weather turned out to be VFR. One pilot took off in spite of the forecast and completed his flight. The report did say, however, "in this latter case . . . the forecast was substantially correct and the pilot was fortunate enough to find breaks in the overcast . . . at his destination."

EXPECTATIONS

Pilots also complain about pessimistic forecasts and unforecast weather. Pilots, often, have an over expectation of forecasts. Each situation is different, with many variables, and local factors. The limitations in TABLE 3-1 remain and forecasts are going to be missed. Errors fall into two categories: timing and the Mae West (Big Bust). The 1965 edition of *Aviation Weather* said it best: "The weather-wise pilot looks upon a forecast as professional advise rather than as the absolute truth."

It's essential to remember these concepts during forecasted weather discussions. Forecast issuance times, purpose, conditional terms, amendment criteria, and Federal Aviation Regulations reflect the limitations on aviation forecasts. Meteorologists sometimes produce a strategic forecast.

The National Weather Service's modernization/restructuring is underway in the 1990s. Approximately 250 Weather Service Forecast Offices will be reduced to 115 Weather Forecast Offices. A new computer system known as the Advanced Weather Interactive Processing System (AWIPS) will come on line. AWOS and next generation weather radar (NEXRAD) observations should expand the observational network.

The next generation weather satellite (GOESNEXT) is scheduled to be launched in the early 1990s. These satellites located at approximately 80° and 135° west longitude will provide enhanced pictures and other improvements. The *wind profiler*, a doppler radar system, will replace radiosonde observations at the turn of the century for upper air wind data. These technological advances promise to improve the accuracy and reliability of weather forecasts. But, for now, pilots will have to deal with today's system and its limitations.

From the FAA publication *The Weather Decision*: "At the weather briefing keep in mind that: Meteorologists tend to be optimists." Say again, please. . . .

4
Advisories

DURING THE LATTER PART OF THE '50s THE WEATHER BUREAU ISSUED warnings of potentially hazardous or severe aviation weather in the form of *flash advisories*. These were subsequently divided into AIRMETs (WA) and SIGMETs (WS). AIRMETs and SIGMETs alerted pilots that significant, previously unforecast, weather had developed. Twenty-one Weather Bureau offices routinely issued advisories but by 1970 the number of Flight Advisory Weather Service offices was reduced to nine. And, although ". . . the In-Flight Weather Advisory program is intended to provide advance notice of potentially hazardous weather developments to en route aircraft . . .," according to the Weather Service Operations Manual, advisories were issued even when conditions were contained in the *Area Forecast* (FA). During this period there were AIRMETs by the number, SIGMETs by the score. It was not uncommon to have four or more AIRMETs continuously in effect, and to this end the *Continuous AIRMET* (WAC) was developed. Weather advisories issued by adjacent offices were not always consistent and often overlapped. This lead to confusion for briefers and pilots alike.

The Area Forecast was changed in 1978 to include a *hazards* or *flight precautions* section to reduce the number of advisories. The FA was still issued by local NWS offices. Responsibility for issuing AIRMETs and SIGMETs for the 48 contiguous states was centralized in 1982 in Kansas City at the National Aviation Weather Advisory Unit.

SIGMETs were issued for convective activity until a DC-9 crashed in a severe thunderstorm near Atlanta in 1977. From this accident the *Convective SIGMET* (WST) evolved. The National Aviation Weather Advisory Unit (NAWAU) in Kansas City has WST responsibility. Specifically assigned meteorologists issue these advisories.

Center Weather Service Units (CWSU) were established at Air Route Air Traffic Control Centers (ARTCC) in 1980. The CWSU purpose is to assist controllers and flow control personnel, and alert pilots of hazardous weather through a Center Weather Advisory (CWA). As is often the case with government bureaucracy, the cart came before the horse. There were no instructions for ATC personnel when CWAs first appeared. Distribution went all the way from immediate broadcast to the trash can. The FAA took months to decide that the CWA had the weight of a SIGMET and apply identical distribution and broadcast procedures.

Public forecasts, Alert Weather Watches (AWW) and Severe Weather Watch Bulletins (WW), are also produced. The Severe Local Storms office (SELS) in Kansas City issues AWWs and WWs for severe thunderstorms and tornadoes.

AIRMETs, SIGMETs, Convective SIGMETs, Center Weather Advisories, and Alert Weather Watches and Bulletins, plus flight precautions in the FA are issued when phenomena reach specified criteria, and, like urgent PIREPs (UUA), receive priority handling and distribution. They are considered automatic amendments to other forecast products, even though other forecasts will be amended to ensure all concerned receive the change.

With the number of advisories, it would seem impossible to fly into an area of hazardous weather without warning. But, this is not necessarily the case. An advisory cannot be issued for each thunderstorm, instance of turbulence or icing, mountain obscuration, or IFR condition. Severe weather can develop before an advisory is written and distributed. The absence of an advisory is no guarantee that hazardous weather does not exist or will not develop.

AIRMETS AND SIGMETS

AIRMETs and SIGMETs are identified by forecast area, alphabetic, and product designators. The FA forecast area (MIA—Miami, BOS—Boston, SFO—San Francisco, etc.) specifies within which FA the advisory applies. (FA areas are depicted in Appendix D, Geographical Area Designators.) Next appears the alphabetic designator for the phenomena being described (ALPHA through NOVEMBER for WSs and OSCAR through ZULU for WAs).

The product designator (1, 2, 3, etc.) indicates the number of successive times the advisory has been issued. For example, a cold front causing severe turbulence might begin as San Francisco SFO ALPHA 1, as the front moves into the Rocky Mountains become Salt Lake City SLC ALPHA 2, and into the Plains Chicago CHI ALPHA 3. To assure continuity and alert pilots, briefers, and controllers that ALPHA 3 is the first CHI issuance, a referencing remark will be appended to the message (FOR PREVIOUS ISSUANCE SEE SLC ALPHA 2). Updates often contain changes; they must be reviewed for affected area, altitudes, and times. Therefore, it's important to note both phenomena and product designators.

```
SFOJ WS 152130
SIGMET JULIET 3 VALID UNTIL 160130
CA
FROM FOT TO 50NW RNO TO 50NE BFL TO SBA TO 40W SBA TO 30W SFO
```

TO FOT
OCNL SVR TURBC BLO 100 XCP BLO 150 VCNTY SIERRAS. STG UDDFS
VCNTY MTNS AND LLWS POTENTIAL BLO 20 AGL. CONDS CONTG BYD 0130Z.

In the above example the FA designator is San Francisco ("SFO"J). The alphabetic phenomena designator is J (SFO"J"). The issuance date-time group follows the product designator (WS). This SIGMET was issued on the 15th day of the month at 2130Z (152130). SIGMET JULIET is spelled out on the following line along with the product designator (3). WSs are valid for four hours as indicated by the VALID UNTIL time, the 16th day of the month at 0130Z (160130).

San Francisco SIGMET JULIET 3 affects all or part of California (CA). Specific geographical areas are described using VORs on the In-flight Advisory Plotting Chart, Appendix C, starting with the most northern and continuing clockwise.

(Appendix C also contains a list of location identifiers to decode chart locations. Names of some VORs not collocated with the airport of the same name have been changed since the chart was developed. For example, the name of the Santa Barbara (SBA) VOR has been changed to San Marcos (RZS), however, the In-flight Advisory Plotting Chart identifier remains SBA. The phenomena will usually lie well within the delineated area.)

Figure 4-1 shows SIGMET JULIET 3 laid out—the gray area—on an In-flight Advisory Plotting Chart. The inset in FIG. 4-1 is a portion of the Geographical Area Designators map contained in Appendix D. The gray area again shows the area covered by the SIGMET. The advisory affects a small portion of Northern California and most of Central California. Plotting might be required to determine the extent of the advisory and it is extremely helpful to visualize affected areas. Occasional severe turbulence is expected below 10,000 feet MSL, except below 15,000 feet MSL in the vicinity of the Sierra Nevada mountains. Strong updrafts and downdrafts in the vicinity of the mountains and low-level wind shear are anticipated. Conditions are expected to continue beyond the end of the advisory period (0130Z). This means SIGMET JULIET 4 should be issued prior to 0130Z. However, if something like transmission trouble delays the updated advisory, pilots should consider the advisory still in effect, unless a cancellation message is received.

AIRMETs and SIGMETs often cover large areas due to the widely scattered and transitory nature of the phenomena they report. Therefore, the term *occasional* (OCNL) frequently appears. Occasional means a better than 50/50 chance of occurrence during less than half of the forecast period. Additionally, phenomena might move through, or only affect certain geographical features within, the advisory area. In the example, strong updrafts and downdrafts are only expected in the vicinity of the mountains. Failure to completely read and understand an advisory has lead many a pilot and briefer to unjustified criticism of the reports.

SFOQ WA 152255
AIRMET QUEBEC 1 VALID UNTIL 160440
CA
FROM GUP TO ROW TO ELP TO 60S TUS TO SAN TO LAX TO EED TO GUP
MDT RIME ICIC 50 – 150. CONDS CONTG BYD 0440Z.

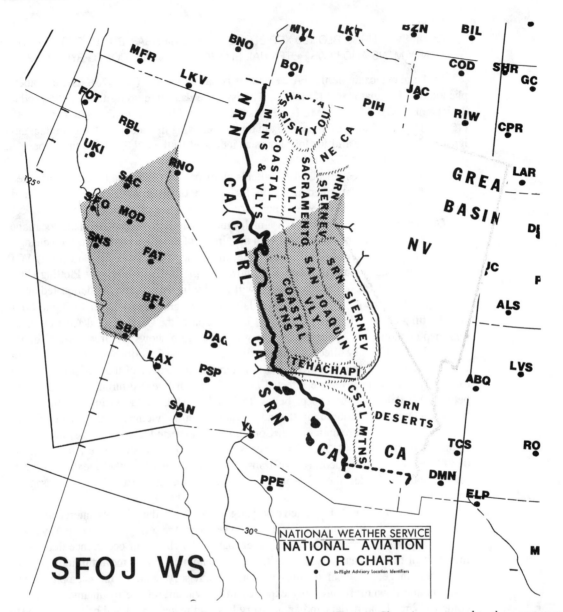

Fig. 4-1. *SIGMET JULIET 3 laid out on an In-flight Advisory Plotting Chart is compared to the same area on the Geographical Area Designators map. Weather advisories do not necessarily pertain to all of the delineated area. Pilots must compare the delineated area with terrain and the text of the advisory to properly apply a weather summary.*

```
SLCQ WA 152255
AIRMET QUEBEC 1 VALID UNTIL 160440
AZ NM
FROM GUP TO ROW TO ELP TO 60S TUS TO SAN TO LAX TO EED TO GUP
MDT RIME ICIC 50 – 150. CONDS CONTG BYD 0440Z.
```

The above examples illustrate a situation where phenomena covers more than one FA area. In this case, two AIRMETs, San Francisco ("SFO"Q) and Salt Lake City ("SLC"Q), forecast moderate rime icing in clouds between 5,000 and 15,000 feet MSL. The phonetic alphabet is the alphabetic designator (Q is Quebec). The phenomena covers portions of California, Arizona, and New Mexico. WAs are valid for six hours.

AIRMETs are only issued when the Area Forecast does not report the phenomena in HAZARDS. Additionally, the condition must be widespread. That is, occurring or forecast over an area of at least 3,000 square miles, which is approximately three times the size of Rhode Island. Localized occurrences do not warrant the issuance of an advisory.

AIRMETs are issued when the following phenomena occur or are expected to develop:

1. Moderate icing.
2. Moderate turbulence.
3. Sustained wind of 30 knots or more at the surface.
4. Ceilings less than 1,000 feet and/or visibility less than three miles affecting more than 50 percent of the area at any time.
5. Extensive mountain obscurement.

A SIGMET will be issued even when the phenomena is contained in the FA; it must be widespread to warrant an advisory. Local severe turbulence and icing will only appear in the body of the FA. SIGMETs are issued when the following phenomena occur or are expected to develop:

1. Severe icing.
2. Severe or greater non-convective turbulence.
3. Moderate or greater Clear Air Turbulence (CAT). A SIGMET reports CAT as *non-convective turbulence* occurring at or above 15,000 feet, but it usually refers to turbulence above 25,000 feet. Because of the difficulty to forecast this phenomena, the term *moderate or greater* (MOGR) indicates a threat of CAT. SIGMETs contain *severe* or *extreme* only with actual reports.
4. Widespread dust storms, sandstorms, or volcanic ash reducing visibility below three miles over an area covering at least 3,000 square miles.

Weather Service Forecast Offices in Alaska and Hawaii that are responsible for FAs also issue SIGMETs for these conditions. Additionally, these WSFOs issue SIGMETs for tornadoes, hail greater than 3/4 inch in diameter, and embedded thunderstorms or lines of thunderstorms.

CONVECTIVE SIGMETS

Convective SIGMETs provide detailed, specific forecasts for thunderstorm related phenomena. NAWAU's WST unit makes extensive use of radar data to analyze thunderstorm systems. Meteorologists compare radar data with satellite imagery, lightning information, and other conventional sources to determine the need for a SIGMET. WSTs are issued when the following phenomena occur or are expected to develop:

1. Tornadoes.
2. Hail greater than or equal to 3/4-inch diameter.
3. Isolated severe thunderstorms. A severe thunderstorm produces hail with at least 3/4-inch diameter, or surface winds of 50 knots.
4. Embedded thunderstorms. An embedded thunderstorm occurs within non-convective precipitation.
5. A line of thunderstorms.
6. Thunderstorms, of VIP level four (very strong) or greater, affecting 40 percent or more of an area of at least 3,000 square miles. (TABLE 9-1 contains a description of Radar Precipitation Intensity VIP Levels.)

When the conditions described in one through five occur, a WST might be issued regardless of the size of the affected area.

The 48 contiguous states are divided into three areas for Convective SIGMET issuance: West (MKCW WST), Central (MKCC WST), and East (MKCE WST). These areas are shown on the In-flight Advisory Plotting Chart, Appendix C. Issued hourly, beginning with Number 1 at 0000Z, WSTs contain a forecast for up to two hours and an outlook from two to six hours.

```
MKCC WST 191155
CONVECTIVE SIGMET 20C
VALID UNTIL 1355Z
TX
FROM 30W LBB – 70SW SPS – ABI – 90WSW SJT – 30W LBB
DVLPG AREA SVR TSTMS MOVG FROM 2330. TOPS ABV 450.
HAIL TO 2 IN . . . WIND GUSTS TO 50 KT PSBL.

OUTLOOK VALID UNTIL 1755Z
FROM ARG – MEM – TXK – 100WSW SJT – LBB – SPS – ARG
TSTMS CONT TO DVLP ALG DRYLN OVR WRN TX AS PVA AND CD AIR ALOFT
MOVE EWD OVR THE AREA. UPR LVL WINDS RMN STRG AND DIFFLUENT
WHILE AMS RMNS MDLY UNSTBL WITH LIFTED INDEX OF MINUS 6.
```

This central (MKC"C") WST was issued on the 19th day of the month at 1155Z (191155). It is the 20th central issuance for this ZULU day (CONVECTIVE SIGMET "20"C). It affects portions of Texas, valid for two hours (VALID UNTIL 1355Z).

Specific areas are described using the VORs on the In-flight Advisory Plotting Chart.

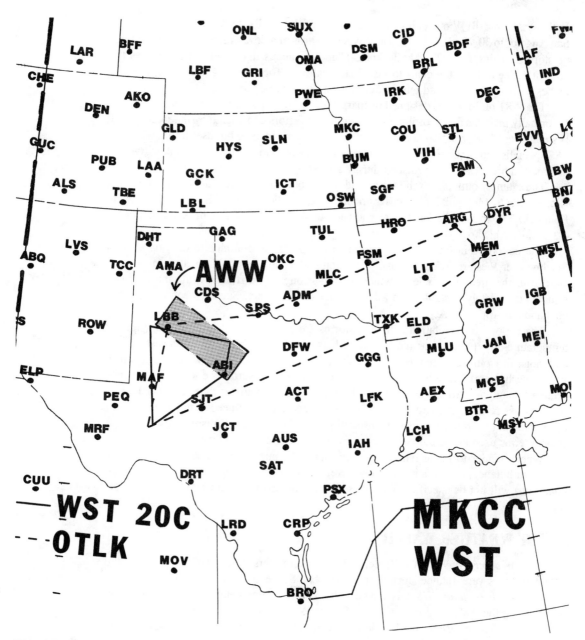

Fig. 4-2. *Convective SIGMETs and Alert Weather Watches are issued and valid for different times and serve different purposes, therefore aerial coverage might not coincide.*

In this case from 30 W of Lubbock, to 70 SW of Wichita Falls, to Abilene, to 90 WSW of San Angelo, to 30 W of Lubbock. The advisory warns of a developing area of severe thunderstorms moving from 230° at 30 knots. The continuous line in FIG. 4-2 encloses this area; it's nice to have the chart to visualize locations. Tops above 45,000 feet, hail two inches in diameter and wind gust to 50 knots are possible.

The WST outlook was designed primarily for preflight planning and aircraft dispatch. It normally includes a meteorological discussion of factors considered by the forecaster. It is supplemental information not required for weather avoidance, but useful to CWSU and FSS specialists for analysis and background information. Normally the outlook will not be included in broadcasts nor provided during a briefing.

The example outlook is valid for an additional four hours, covers an area from Walnut Ridge, AR, to Memphis, TN, to Texarkana, AR, to 100 WSW of San Angelo, TX, to Lubbock, TX, to Wichita Falls, TX, and back to Walnut Ridge. The broken line in FIG. 4-2 encloses this area.

The outlook translates: Thunderstorms are expected to continue to develop along a dry line over Western Texas as positive vorticity advection and cold air aloft move eastward over the area. Upper level winds remain strong and diffluent while the air mass remains moderately unstable with a lifted index of minus six. Standard contractions are contained in Appendix A.

The outlook interpretation is thunderstorms are going to develop along a dry line or temperature-dew point front; the boundary between dry air from the Southwest deserts and moist air from the Gulf of Mexico. Positive Vorticity Advection (upward moving air; a lifting mechanism) and cold air (instability) aloft move eastward. The upper level winds remain strong and diffluent (a divergent flow activates/perpetuates thunderstorms) while the air mass remains moderately unstable. The three elements needed for thunderstorm development are present: moisture, instability, and a lifting mechanism. Most meteorological terms used in the outlook discussion are contained in the Glossary.

When thunderstorms or related phenomena are the purpose of an advisory, severe or greater turbulence, severe icing and low-level wind shear are implied. Therefore, these conditions will not be specifically addressed in the advisory nor during a weather briefing.

ALERT WEATHER WATCH

Alert Weather Watches (AWW) alert forecasters, briefers, pilots, and the public to the potential for severe thunderstorms or tornadoes. Subsequent to the AWW, a *Severe Weather Watch Bulletin* (WW) is issued. The WW contains details on the phenomena described in the AWW. An example of a Severe Weather Watch Bulletin is contained in Appendix E. These unscheduled bulletins are primarily a public forecast, whereas the WST is a combination observation and aviation forecast.

Although SELS (FIG. 4-3) and NAWAU meteorologists coordinate their products, criteria and time frames differ. Therefore, aerial coverage might not coincide. The issuance of an AWW might precede or coincide with a WST. The following AWW was issued just prior to the WST in the previous example. (Refer to the shaded area in FIG. 4-2.)

Fig. 4-3. *Forecasters at the Severe Local Storms section of the Kansas City NWS office prepare Alert Weather Watches and Bulletins.*

```
MKC AWW 191147
WW 99 SEVERE TSTM TX 191215Z – 191800Z
AXIS . . 70 STATUTE MILES EITHER SIDE OF LINE . .
20N LBB/LUBBOCK TX/ – 50NE ABI/ABILENE TX/
HAIL SURFACE AND ALOFT . . 2 INCHES. WIND GUSTS . . 60 KNOTS.
MAX TOPS TO 550. MEAN WIND VECTOR 22035.
```

The WST describes a developing area of interest to aviation. Expect later WSTs to cover the area toward the northeast, into the AWW, and along the area described in the WST outlook.

CENTER WEATHER ADVISORIES

CWAs, unscheduled in-flight advisories, are issued when conditions are expected to significantly affect IFR operations and help pilots avoid hazardous weather. The advisories update or expand AIRMETs, SIGMETs, or the FA, and might be issued when conditions meet advisory criteria. In such cases, the CWSU will coordinate with NAWAU forecasters for the issuance of the appropriate advisory. CWAs are also issued when local hazardous conditions develop that do not warrant other advisories. Because they often report localized phenomena, the area might be described using locations other than those on the Geographical Area Designators map, or VORs on the In-flight Advisory Plotting Chart.

The CWA numbering system is somewhat complex, but facilitates computer processing and distribution. Each CWA will have a phenomenon number (1 through 6). A separate phenomenon number will be assigned each distinct condition (turbulence, icing, thunderstorms, etc.).

ZDV1 CWA 01 132050 – 132250
CAUTION FOR MDT – SVR TURBC/MTN WAVE ACTVTY PSBL ALL FLGT LVLS OVER AND NEAR MTNS IN WY AND CO. STRONG CLD FNT MOVG THRU AREA THIS AFTN AND EVE WITH PSBL SFC WND GUSTS TO 60KT. HIGH WND WARNINGS ARE IN EFFECT FOR FNT RANGE AREA BEGINNING 14/0000Z. THIS ADVRY SUPPLEMENTS SIGMET NOVEMBER 2.

This Denver Center CWA describes phenomenon Number 1 (ZDV"1"). It is the first issuance for this phenomenon (ZDV1 CWA "01"), valid from the 13th day of the month at 2050Z until 2250Z. If the advisory requires updating at 2250Z, it will become ZDV1 CWA 02. The CWA advises caution for moderate to severe turbulence associated with mountain wave activity for all flight levels over and near the mountains of Wyoming and Colorado. Additionally, a strong cold front moving through the area during the afternoon and evening might bring surface winds with gusts to 60 knots. High wind warnings are in effect for the Front Range area beginning on the 14th at 0000Z. This advisory supplements SIGMET NOVEMBER 2.

This example illustrates many uses of the CWA. The advisory expands on SIGMET NOVEMBER 2 by indicating phenomena is due to mountain wave activity and mechanical turbulence. The CWA also mentions high wind warnings for the Front Range. The Front Range, normally a local geographical reference, refers to the mountains just west of Denver, from Fort Collins to about 40 miles southwest of Denver.

ZHU1 CWA 01 061355 – 061455
FM A BPT to 40SE LFT LN . . S 150 MI INTO GULF . . . AREA SCT LVL 3 – 5 TSTMS MOVG N 15 KTS. NMRS TOPS ABV 450.

The Houston Center CWSU has issued this advisory for an area of scattered VIP level 3 to 5 (see TABLE 9-1) thunderstorms moving north at 15 knots, with numerous tops to above 45,000 feet MSL. The area extends along a line from Beaumont, TX, to 40 miles southeast of Lafayette, LA, south 150 miles into the Gulf of Mexico. These locations are not on the In-flight Advisory Plotting Chart. The condition has not yet met the criteria for a WST.

CWSUs also issue *Meteorological Impact Statements* (MIS). Strictly an in-house product, the MIS alerts controllers of weather that might affect the flow of IFR traffic. The MIS describes conditions already contained in other advisories and forecasts. From time to time overzealous FSS briefers might refer to an MIS or tower controllers record it on the Automatic Terminal Information Service (ATIS).

DISSEMINATION

Advisories are routinely provided during FSS standard briefings and offered during abbreviated briefings. (Weather briefings are discussed in Chapter 11, Obtaining Meteorological and Aeronautical Information.) DUAT users must check with the vendor to determine how the respective system handles these products; certain advisories are not available on certain systems.

When advisories pertain to an area within 150 miles of a Flight Service Station, or NAVAID controlled by the FSS, the advisory will be broadcast over VOR voice channels that do not carry ATIS or Transcribed Weather Broadcasts (TWEB). WAs, WSs, and CWAs are broadcast at 30-minute intervals, a quarter past and a quarter to the hour; WSTs and AWWs are broadcast at 15-minute intervals, each quarter hour. Additionally, during routine FSS radio contacts, advisories within 150 miles will be offered when they affect the pilot's route. It's important to note advisory series and number to ensure receipt of the latest information.

Normal FSS broadcasts have been discontinued in areas where Hazardous In-flight Weather Advisory Service (HIWAS) has been commissioned. Advisories and urgent PIREPs are broadcast continuously over selected VORs. At present HIWAS is available in the Atlanta, Houston, Jacksonville, and Miami ARTCC areas. The expansion of HIWAS has slowed and the continued growth of this service is in doubt. Unfortunately, other than asking an FSS or control facility, the only government source specifically referring to HIWAS is the *Airport/Facility Directory*. And, rather than listing HIWAS facilities, the green book simply shows HIWAS within the NAVAID data. Jeppesen lists HIWAS on charts next to the NAVAID providing the service.

When a WS, WST, or CWA affects an area within 150 miles of an ARTCC sector's jurisdiction an alert is broadcast once on all frequencies. Approach controls and towers also broadcast an alert, but it might be limited to phenomena within 50 miles of the terminal. When the advisory affects operations within the terminal area an alert message will be placed on the ATIS. Overzealous controllers have been known to place SIGMET alerts for conditions hundreds of miles away on the ATIS.

The existence of an advisory, or lack thereof, does not relieve the pilot from using good judgment and applying personal limitations. Like all pilots, I have parked a Cessna 150 and "flown" a Boeing 727: When you have time to spare, go by air; more time yet, take a jet. When you don't have the equipment or qualifications to handle the weather, don't go. This doesn't mean cancel every time an advisory is issued, merely take a close look at all available information.

Prior to a flight from Las Vegas, NV, to Van Nuys, CA, I was told by the briefer: "Well, you aren't going today." My jaws locked up and I replied: "Oh yes, I am." I hadn't looked at the weather; my statement was a gut reaction to this individual's horrible technique. Advisories for turbulence, mountain obscurement, and rain showers were in effect. As is often the case in this part of the country, a direct flight was out. A course over lower terrain, VFR, is frequently possible. My decision was based on my experience, knowledge of terrain, a thorough review of all available weather reports and forecasts, and always having an out should the weather ahead become impassable.

The absence of an advisory does not guarantee the absence of hazardous weather. An unfortunate pilot learned this lesson the hard way. The synopsis described a moist unstable air mass. Thunderstorms were not forecast for the time of flight, but were expected to develop; thunderstorms, however, were already being reported along the route. The pilot without storm detection equipment, encountered extreme turbulence inadvertently entering a cell. The pilot, with three passengers, filed an IFR flight plan based on the fact that there were no advisories.

About a half-hour into the flight, according to the pilot's statement to the FAA and National Transportation Safety Board (NTSB) from the accident report, ". . . we noticed a heavy layer of clouds at and below our altitude and some 20 miles ahead. . . . The layer in front of us seemed to be light cumulus with a heavier layer behind it (not ominous looking)." After the encounter, the pilot could not understand why he was, ". . . never given a precaution or advisory regarding that system." He went on to say that the accident "would not have happened if (the) pilot had been aware of weather conditions. . . ." There were no advisories in effect because, at the time of the briefing, none were warranted. The pilot had the clues—moist unstable air and thunderstorms already reported—but put his complete trust in a forecast that included no flight precautions or advisories.

The preceding examples illustrate two "go" decisions. One resulted in a routine flight, the other almost fatal. The intent is not to brag about personal skills, or criticize another individual, merely to show the process—based on available information, a knowledge of weather products, and limitations—that led to the decisions.

All too often, briefers hear pilots flying aircraft without storm detection equipment say, "Thunderstorms, ah, well, I'd better go IFR." Not for me, thanks. I want to be clear of clouds where I can see and avoid convective activity. Pilots who fly aircraft without storm detection equipment in clouds when conditions are conducive to thunderstorms will one of these days find themselves on the inside of a cell wishing they were out.

If we wish to be accorded, and exercise, the privileges of pilot in command we have to understand the system and its limitations. We must evaluate all available information—as required by FARs—and make a flight decision based on our knowledge and limitations, and that of our aircraft and its equipment.

A popular aviation saying goes: "Aviation in itself is not inherently dangerous. But to an even greater degree than the sea, it is terribly unforgiving of any carelessness, incapacity or neglect."

5
Area Forecasts
(FA)

PILOTS, BRIEFERS, AND METEOROLOGISTS SHARE MISCONCEPTIONS AND misinterpret the purpose and scope of the *Area Forecast*. A forecast for the desert portion of a fuel proficiency air race predicted scattered thunderstorms and rain showers, with wind gusts to 35 knots (SCT TRW G35). Pilots criticized the forecast, complaining they didn't encounter any gusts; by avoiding the thunderstorms they remained clear of the winds. The thunderstorms were there, and you can bet gusty winds could be found in the vicinity of the cells. The forecast was perfectly correct.

Others criticize an FA for being too lengthy and—ironically, in the next breath—not containing enough detail. A West Coast FSS manager was quoted (April 1986 *Pacific Flyer*, Lance Stalker) as saying, "Before, you had people that were familiar with the local conditions and put that into their forecasting." That's still true. Local NWS offices issue TWEB route and *Terminal Forecasts* (FT). The Area Forecast is not now, nor has it ever been intended to cover every single condition.

The Area Forecast predicts conditions over an area the size of several states. Due to limitations on size, computer storage, and communications equipment the forecast cannot be divided into smaller segments, nor provide the detail available in TWEB route or FTs. Widely varying conditions over relatively large areas must be included, therefore small scale events are often described using conditional terms (OCCASIONAL, CHANCE, ISO-LATED). The FA provides a forecast for the en route portion of a flight and destination weather for locations without Terminal Forecasts. This contradicts a widely held notion that without an FT there is no destination forecast. Conditions are forecast from the surface to 70 millibars (approximately 63,000 feet).

AREA FORECASTS (FA)

FAs in the 1960s were issued every six hours, valid for 12 hours, with a 12-hour outlook. This was time consuming for the forecaster and, therefore, expensive. FAs in the 1970s were issued twice a day, valid for 18 hours with an additional 12-hour categorical outlook (IFR, MVFR, or VFR). Today they are issued three times a day, valid for 12 hours, with a six-hour outlook. The increased number of issuances and reduced valid times directly reflect forecast limitations.

Area Forecasts for the 48 contiguous states were reduced to six in 1982. Rather than being issued by local offices, responsibility was transferred to the National Aviation Weather Advisory Unit (NAWAU) in Kansas City. Appendix D, Geographical Area Designators, depicts FA coverage areas. Alaska local NWS offices in Anchorage (ANC), Fairbank (FAI) and Juneau (JNU) issue FAs three times a day; the Honolulu (HNL) WSFO issues FAs four times a day. Alaskan and Hawaiian FA areas are depicted in Appendix D and use the same format as "FAs" in the contiguous states. Examples are contained in Appendix E, Selected Sample Aviation Weather Products.

TABLE 5-1 contains FA issuance times. Note that UTC or ZULU issuance times within the 48 contiguous states change twice a year with daylight savings. Because the SFO and SLC FAs are issued together, and the Mountain Time Zone is one hour ahead of Pacific, the SLC FA becomes available one hour earlier local, in that time zone. Forecasts become valid on the hour following issuance: issued 1040, valid 1100.

The Area Forecast is divided into five sections: HAZARDS, SYNOPSIS, ICING AND FREEZING LEVEL, TURBULENCE AND LOW-LEVEL WIND SHEAR, and SIGNIFICANT CLOUDS AND WEATHER. Each section contains issuance and valid times, and might be individually amended.

Table 5-1. *Area Forecast Issuance Times.*

SFO & SLC UTC	CHI & DFW UTC	BOS & MIA UTC	LOCAL /SLC FA
1040/1140	0940/1040	0840/0940	4:40 a.m./5:40 a.m.
1940/2040	1840/1940	1740/1840	12:40 p.m./1:40 p.m.
0240/0340	0140/0240	0040/0140	8:40 p.m./9:40 p.m.

ANC & FAI UTC	LOCAL*	JNU UTC	LOCAL*	HNL UTC	LOCAL**
1440	5:40 a.m.	1340	4:40 a.m.	1540	5:40 a.m.
2240	1:40 p.m.	2240	1:40 p.m.	2140	11:40 a.m.
0640	9:40 p.m.	0640	9:40 p.m.	0340	5:40 p.m.
				0940	11:40 p.m.

* Alaskan Standard Time
** Hawaiian Standard Time

HAZARDS

HAZARDS, or *flight precautions* (FLT PRCTNS), alert briefers and pilots to AIRMET or SIGMET conditions. The hazard is identified and general location by state provided (FLT PRCTNS . . . IFR . . . WA OR CA). The hazard, however, might not cover the entire state. Specific conditions and locations are described in the body of the forecast. According to the National Weather Service, the user must ascertain where in the area the flight precautions pertain. The pilot is the only person who can decide if a particular hazard is pertinent to his or her proposed flight.

Flight precautions for thunderstorms only appear when coverage is expected to be at least scattered (affect 25 percent to 54 percent of an area), or require the issuance of a Convective SIGMET. Therefore, a forecast for isolated or widely scattered thunderstorms will, normally, only appear in SIGNIFICANT CLOUDS AND WEATHER.

Generally, phenomena must be widespread for inclusion in HAZARDS—cover an area of at least 3,000 square miles. Phenomena not meeting this criteria (local moderate icing, local IFR, etc.) will only appear in the body of the forecast. A lack of HAZARDS does not necessarily mean the absence of adverse weather.

Defining "local" is difficult. According to Dick Williams, NAWAU forecaster, in the FAA's June 1988 *Air Traffic Bulletin*, "FAs written on the scale of whole states do not endeavor to describe every single occurrence of IFR, icing, or turbulence. The forecaster, wishing to indicate that there may be isolated observations, pilot reports, or hazardous weather, may use the term 'local.' No hard and fast rule exists for determining when 'local' becomes widespread. The forecaster relies on observations, pilot reports, satellite imagery, and his or her own judgment in determining the extent of weather features."

Federal Aviation Regulations recognize the fact that every occurrence of adverse weather cannot be forecast. FAR Part 61.93 requires that even student pilots receive instruction in "the recognition of critical weather situations (and) estimating visibility while in flight. . . ." In other words, the excuse, "They didn't tell me," is just that, an excuse, not a reason.

```
SFOH FA 141140
HAZARDS VALID UNTIL 150000
WA OR CA AND CSTL WTRS
FLT PRCTNS . . . IFR . . . WA OR CA
```

This HAZARDS section of the San Francisco FA (SFOH FA) was issued on the 14th day of the month at 1140Z (141140), valid at 1200Z. HAZARDS are valid until the 15th day of the month at 0000Z (150000), totalling 12 hours. This FA covers the states of Washington, Oregon, California, and their coastal waters (WA OR CA AND CSTL WTRS). Because land and water significantly affects the behavior of air masses, the NWS has decided to treat coastal waters as a separate paragraph (CSTL WTRS) in the SIGNIFICANT CLOUDS AND WEATHER section. Coastal waters extend 100 miles offshore.

In the example, flight precautions exist for ceilings below 1,000 feet and/or visibilities less than three miles during all or part of the period, for all or parts of Washington, Oregon, and California. The SIGNIFICANT CLOUDS AND WEATHER section provides details on the hazard.

From AC 00-6 *Aviation Weather*, "A thunderstorm packs just about every weather hazard known to aviation into one vicious bundle." The following statement appears on every FA to eliminate redundancy and serve as a friendly "we told you so:"

TSTMS IMPLY PSBL SVR OR GTR TURBC SVR ICG AND LLWS.

Thunderstorms imply possible severe or greater turbulence, severe icing, and low-level wind shear—I hope this isn't news to anyone. A report or forecast of thunderstorms implies these and other hazards associated with thunderstorms: hail, lightning, gusty winds, and altimeter errors; therefore, the body of the FA will not contain specific precautions, nor will briefers normally include this statement. The fact that thunderstorms are reported or forecast infers all hazards associated with a thunderstorm.

NON MSL HGTS NOTED BY AGL OR CIG.

This statement simply means all heights are mean sea level, MSL, unless noted as above ground level, AGL (AGL 30 SCT – BKN), or ceiling, CIG (CIGS 15 – 30 OVC). This distinction can be significant, especially in mountainous areas. Forecasts for mountainous states will normally reference cloud bases to MSL, while forecasts for flat terrain will normally reference bases to AGL. This differentiation must be considered when comparing the FA with SAs.

One evening, several FSS specialists brought the "East of the Cascades" portion of the SFO FA to my attention. They contended the observations and the forecast had nothing in common. However, after converting the SAs to MSL altitudes, the observations and forecast were perfectly consistent. This example emphasizes the point that to apply a forecast, a pilot or briefer must have a thorough knowledge of terrain.

THIS FA ISSUANCE INCORPORATES THE FOLLOWING AIRMETS STILL IN EFFECT . . . OSCAR 3.

With a new FA issuance, AIRMETs still in effect—in this case OSCAR 3—will be incorporated in HAZARDS with details in the body of the forecast. This, in effect, cancels the AIRMET, and terminates FSS broadcast requirements.

SYNOPSIS

The SYNOPSIS describes the location and movement of pressure systems and fronts, and weather patterns, usually as a brief, generalized statement. The following example is quite detailed.

COLD UPR SYS OFF WA CST AT 19Z INVOF 48N 127W MOVG EWD AT ABT 10 –
15 KTS. PVA INDUCED/ENHANCED CNVTV CLDS WERE ROTG ONSHR FROM NRN
CA THRU SWRN WA. AMS THIS RGN APPRS QUITE MOIST AND UNSTBL AND
WL SPRD ACRS NRN HLF OF FCST AREA THRU THE PD.

A cold upper level low pressure system is off the Washington coast at 11 a.m. PST about 100 miles west of Seattle moving east at about 10 to 15 knots. Positive Vorticity Advection is inducing and enhancing convective clouds that were rotating onshore from

Northern California through southwestern Washington. The air mass in this region appears quite moist and unstable and will spread across the northern half of the forecast area through the period.

I prefer a detailed synopsis because my training and experience allows extra insight regarding the weather situation. This is especially important if the weather improves or deteriorates more rapidly than forecasted. This synopsis would normally be summarized during FSS briefings and on broadcasts: "An upper level low off the Pacific Northwest is bringing moist unstable air over Washington, Oregon, and Northern California. Translating and summarizing in this manner is a prime function of FSS weather briefers. Pilots using DUAT will have to decode, translate, and interpret the synopsis on their own.

From this example, a conclusion might be that on a flight from Northern California to Washington the best weather lies to the east, ahead of the system. The example also contradicts a widely held misconception that fronts are the only weather producing systems.

A synopsis describes the cause of the weather, therefore language and detail will depend on the situation. The synopsis will vary from the lengthy detail in the previous example to HI PRES OVR THE ERN GLFALSK WL MOV OVR THE PNHDL AND WKN (High pressure over the eastern Gulf of Alaska will move over the panhandle and weaken).

Synopsis importance cannot be overemphasized. For example, the significance of a forecast for IFR conditions will depend on whether IFR is due to a coastal marine layer, upslope fog covering several states, a frontal system, or a tropical storm. Here's another example:

```
CHIS FA 300940
SYNOPSIS VALID UNTIL 310400
AT 10Z CDFNT FROM LS SWWD THRU NWRN IA INTO NWRN KS THEN WWD THRU
CO. HI PRES OVR OH VLY AND MT. THE CDFNT WL CONT EWD AND BY 00Z
WL EXTEND FROM LWR MI SWWD INTO SRN KS AS HI PRES BLDS OVR DKTS.
MRNG FOG/ST OVR ERN GRTLKS WL IPV BY 16Z. AFTN/EVE TSTMS MOST
ACTV ALG FNT FROM IL NEWD THRU MI . . . . WILLIAMS . . .
```

This Chicago FA SYNOPSIS (CHIS FA) was issued on the 30th day of the month at 0940Z (300945), valid until the 31st at 0400Z. The synopsis covers the entire 18-hour forecast period. At 1000Z a cold front extended from Lake Superior southwestward through northwestern Iowa into northwestern Kansas then westward through Colorado. High pressure dominates the Ohio Valley and Montana. The cold front will continue eastward and by 0000Z will extend from Lower Michigan southwestward into southern Kansas as high pressure builds over the Dakotas. The morning fog and stratus over the eastern Great Lakes will improve by 1600Z. Afternoon and evening thunderstorms will be most active along the front from Illinois northeastward through Michigan. This forecast was prepared by Williams.

The CHIS synopsis has been plotted in FIG. 5-1. Notice the ease of visualizing conditions. A VFR flight from La Crosse, WI (LSE), to Denver, CO (DEN), might be well advised to delay until after frontal passage. An IFR flight might be planned direct Minneapolis, MN (MSP), to penetrate the front at a right angle and minimize exposure to its weather.

WEATHER LOG

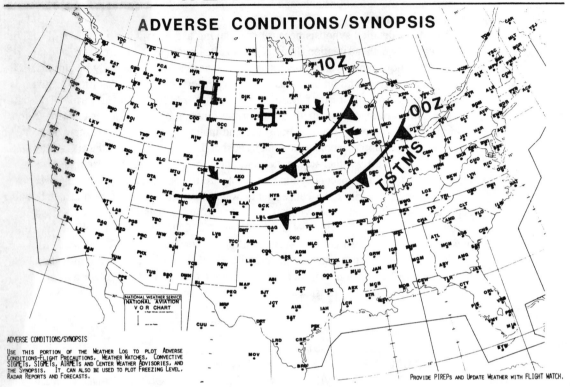

ADVERSE CONDITIONS/SYNOPSIS

USE THIS PORTION OF THE WEATHER LOG TO PLOT ADVERSE
CONDITIONS—FLIGHT PRECAUTIONS, WEATHER WATCHES, CONVECTIVE
SIGMETS, SIGMETS, AIRMETS AND CENTER WEATHER ADVISORIES, AND
THE SYNOPSIS. IT CAN ALSO BE USED TO PLOT FREEZING LEVEL,
RADAR REPORTS AND FORECASTS.

PROVIDE PIREPS AND UPDATE WEATHER WITH FLIGHT WATCH.

Fig. 5-1. *The location of fronts and weather systems, and their expected movement can be visualized by plotting the synopsis.*

ICING AND TURBULENCE

Because hazards often affect more than one FA area, and to provide an overview, flight precautions are issued using the common set of VORs on the In-flight Advisory Plotting Chart, Appendix C, starting with the most northern and continuing clockwise. This is the same procedure used with AIRMETs and SIGMETs.

Forecast phenomena usually lies well within the delineated area. The phenomena might move through the area during the forecast period. Therefore, the condition might affect only a portion of the area at any particular time. Details appear in the text of the FA. For example, an icing advisory might cross several FA boundaries. Specific altitudes might vary due to different temperatures, humidity, and frontal locations. When a phenomenon is peculiar to a specific mountain range, coastal area, river basin, or valley, the geographical area might be included: SNAKE RIVER VALLEY, TEXAS WEST OF THE PECOS. Appendix D contains Geographical Area Designators used in the Area Forecast.

Conditional terms describe widely varying conditions over large areas. (See TABLE 5-2, Conditional Terms Used on the Area Forecast.) They're self-explanatory, with the

Table 5-2. *Conditional Terms Used on the Area Forecast.*

Term	Contraction	Definition
Occasional/ Occasionally	OCNL/ OCNLY	Greater than a 50 percent chance of occurrence/occuring for less than 1/2 of the forecast period.
Chance	CHC	30 percent to 50 percent probability.
Slight Chance	SLGT CHC	10 percent to 20 percent probability.
The following terms refer to the aerial coverage of thunderstorms or precipitation.		
Isolated	ISOLD	Single cells (No percentage).
Widely Scattered	WDLY SCT	Less than 25 percent of area affected.
Scattered	SCT	25 percent to 54 percent of area affected.
Numerous	NMRS	More than 54 percent of area affected.

exception of *occasional* (OCNL). Occasional describes a better than 50/50 chance of occurrence during less than half of the forecast period. OCNL often describes turbulence, icing, mountain obscurement, and IFR conditions, and reflects the transitory nature of these phenomena. A pilot might or might not encounter the condition flying through a forecast area of "OCNL," but he or she has been warned. Look at it this way: If you do run into it, they're right, if you don't, they're still right! We'll discuss how to interpret and apply conditional terms throughout this chapter.

ICING AND FREEZING LEVEL

ICING AND FREEZING LEVEL describes the location, intensity, and type (rime, clear, or mixed) of non-thunderstorm icing. *Layers*, where significant icing can be expected, are expressed as specific values or ranges with bases, most often the freezing level (FRZLVL), and tops. This section includes forecasts for light or local moderate icing. Because these intensities do not meet AIRMET criteria, icing will not appear in HAZ-ARDS. Trace or the absence of icing is indicated by the statement NO SGFNT ICING EXPCD. A separate report paragraph contains forecast freezing levels. Terms such as *sloping* or *lowering* describe varying levels.

Icing is difficult to forecast. Forecasters must determine which areas contain enough moisture to form clouds, which cloud areas will most likely contain supercooled droplets during the forecast period (12 to 18 hours), and location of the freezing level. Needless to say, this is not an easy task.

Most aircraft that are certified for flight into known icing are capable of climbing through icing layers and flying well above potential icing areas, therefore icing PIREPs are not plentiful and PIREPs are the only means of validating the forecast. One reason for the lack of icing PIREPs might be a pilot's fear of receiving a violation, or, by reporting ice, the report might ground aircraft that could handle the conditions. In reality, unless an inspector is in the aircraft or emergency ATC assistance is provided, violations are rare. (I would hope these individuals would be as concerned about their fellow pilots and passengers—and our insurance rates.) Two fatal icing accidents are reviewed in Chapter 2. If these pilots had received hard evidence from a PIREP, or confessed their fate at the first indication of ice, two airplanes and five people might still be around.

A definition for known icing cannot be found in FAR Part 1 *Definitions and Abbreviations*, or in the *Pilot/Controller Glossary*. We've discussed the difficulty of forecasting and the transitory nature of icing. Would a report of light icing above 8,500 feet, with cloud bases 8,000 and cloud tops 9,000 prevent flight for aircraft not certified for flight in known icing? What if the terrain was at 7,800 feet and cloud tops 15,000 feet? Do we really want a hard answer?

The decision as to whether the flight can be made safely rests solely with the pilot in command, where it will stay until we prove we're not worthy of the responsibility. Approximately 80 to 100 icing accidents occur each year, about half from structural icing, the others involve induction system and ground icing. Most are preventable.

The following illustrates the decision-making process with flight precautions in effect for occasional moderate icing. The aircraft was a turbocharged Mooney on an IFR flight from Bakersfield, CA, to Hayward, CA. The synopsis indicates a moist, but stable air mass. Cloud bases along the route were reported around 5,000 feet and tops 9,000 to 11,000 feet and the freezing level at 7,000 feet. Except for the coastal mountains, terrain along the route was close to sea level. The flight was planned at 12,000 feet because tops were relatively low and the aircraft had the performance to quickly climb through the potential icing layer. Trace to light icing was encountered and on top the ice sublimated quickly. Buildups were above 12,000 feet, which prompted deviations to avoid the clouds.

Icing and turbulence were avoided by circumnavigating the buildups. The airplane had the performance to quickly climb on top and if that had not been possible the pilot had the option to return because cloud bases were more than 4,000 feet above terrain and well below the freezing level. The decision as to whether the flight can be safely conducted rests solely with the pilot, based on his or her training and experience, and the capability of the aircraft.

The ICING AND FREEZING LEVEL section looks like this:

```
SFOI FA 091140
ICG AND FRZLEVEL VALID UNTIL 100000
WA OR CA
FROM YQL TO GGW TO BFF TO ALS TO 120W SFO TO 120W FOT TO 120W TOU
TO YQL
OCNL MDT RIME/MXD ICGICIP FRZLVL TO 140 WA AND 160 OR/CA. CONDS
CONTG BYD 00Z. SEE SLC FA FOR DETAILS THAT AREA.
FRZLVEL . . WA W OF CASCDS . . 045 LWRG BY 00Z TO 035.
          WA CASCDS EWD . . AT/NEAR SFC WITH MULT FRZLVLS TO 30 – 35.
          OR W OF CASCDS . . 55 NORTH TO 65 SOUTH. AFT 18Z 50 NORTH
                    TO 75 SOUTH.
```

OR CASCDS EWD . . AT/NEAR SFC WITH MULT FRZLVLS TO 40 – 50.
CA . . AT/NEAR SFC SIERRAS AND NE PTN TIL 18Z. ELSE NEAR
    70 NORTH SLPG TO 90 SOUTH. AFT 18Z 70 NORTH SLPG TO
    90 CNTRL AND 100 SOUTH.

This section is valid for 12 hours (1200Z through 0000Z). The flight precaution area extends from Lethbridge, Alberta (YQL), to Glasgow, MT (GGW), to Alamosa, CO (ALS), to 120 nm west of San Francisco, CA (SFO), to 120 nm west of Fortuna, CA (FOT), to 120 nm west of Tatoosh, WA (TOU), and back to YQL. This area includes the coastal waters.

Occasional moderate rime or mixed icing in clouds and precipitation is forecast from the freezing level to 14,000 feet MSL over Washington, and 16,000 feet MSL over Oregon and California. Conditions are expected to continue beyond the end of the forecast period (0000Z). The pilot is referred to the Salt Lake City FA for details on icing conditions within that FA area because intensities, types, and altitudes might differ significantly.

Next appears the freezing level paragraph (FRZLVL). Notice how the areas are defined using Geographical Area Designators in Appendix D. West of the Cascades in Washington, the freezing level is expected to lower from 4,500 feet MSL to 3,500 feet MSL by 0000Z. East of the Cascades, the freezing level is at or near the surface with multiple freezing levels between the surface and 3,000 to 3,500 feet MSL. Multiple freezing levels are caused by overrunning warm air, such as a warm front; freezing rain occurs in this area. Similar conditions are expected in Oregon, but at different freezing levels and times.

The freezing level in California is forecast at or near the surface in the Sierra Nevada mountains and northeast portion of the state until 1800Z. Elsewhere the freezing level is expected near 7,000 feet MSL in the north, sloping to 9,000 feet MSL in the south. After 1800Z the freezing level is forecast to remain 7,000 in the north, and rise in the central and southern portions to 9,000 to 10,000 feet.

The forecaster has described an icing layer 6,000 to 10,000 feet deep, that slopes upward 2,000 feet from north to south. The type of ice forecast, mixed, and depth of the anticipated icing layer indicate an unstable air mass. IFR pilots with aircraft certified for flight in icing conditions should have little trouble in these areas, assuming performance will allow them to climb out of the icing layer. The pilot must be prepared to contend with freezing rain east of the Cascades, and icing to the surface in parts of California. IFR pilots of aircraft without ice protection equipment should consider this forecast a very strong no-go indicator, especially east of the Cascades and the mountains of California. The VFR pilot flying in Washington or Oregon east of the Cascades will be just as susceptible to icing as an IFR pilot because of multiple freezing levels and possible freezing rain.

Pilots planning flights under the freezing level should not expect to receive this precaution during an FSS preflight briefing, because icing will not affect their proposed flight. Some briefers fail to understand and consider this, and issue the precaution even though it is not a factor. This practice undermines the credibility of both the forecast and the briefing. A pilot planning a flight and briefed for low altitudes should keep this point in mind if instructed by ATC, to climb to a higher altitude; the pilot might well consider the advisability of accepting the clearance without additional information on icing and freezing level.

TURBULENCE AND LOW-LEVEL WIND SHEAR

TURBULENCE AND LOW-LEVEL WIND SHEAR describe the location, intensity, and height of non-thunderstorm related turbulence. Localized moderate turbulence that does not require the issuance of an AIRMET appears in this section (LGT LCL MDT). Remember that local moderate turbulence will not be included in HAZARDS. Light or no turbulence is indicated by NO SGFNT TURBC EXPCTD.

Turbulence forecasts are based on wind flow, winds aloft, evaluation of terrain, and PIREPs. Generally, moderate intensity is forecast when the winds reach 25 to 30 knots or severe intensity when winds exceed 40 knots. High-level turbulence is difficult to forecast. The term moderate or greater (MOGR) might be used in a forecast for Clear Air Turbulence (CAT). Severe or extreme only appears when CAT is reported. Both cases will normally require the issuance of a SIGMET.

```
CHIS FA 201040
SYNOPSIS VALID UNTIL 210500
COLD FNT ALG LN MOT – LBF – ABQ AT 11Z WL MOVE TO A DLH – DSM – ALI LN BY
23Z AND DISIPT BY 210500Z.
CHIT FA 201040
TURBC VALID UNTIL 202300
FROM ISN TO MQT TO COU TO ACT TO SJN TO FMN TO DEN TO ISN
OCNL MDT TURBC BLO 150 WI 100 ML OF COLD FNT.
```

The preceding CHI FA synopsis and turbulence sections have been plotted in FIG. 5-2. A cold front is expected to produce occasional moderate turbulence. The turbulence forecast must cover the 12-hour forecast period 1100Z through 2300Z. However, the hazard will move through the flight precaution area with the front, as shown by the shaded area. This illustrates how a hazard can move through the delineated area, only affecting specific portions at anytime during the forecast period. Unfortunately, some briefers fail to understand and consider this, and issue the precaution whether or not it applies, undermining the credibility of both forecast and briefing.

Frontal turbulence is caused by surface temperature differences exceeding 8° F within 50 miles of the front, and usually occurs below 15,000 feet MSL. Since temperature is the determining factor, frontal speed or type of front is not involved in the extent of frontal turbulence. Turbulence such as mechanical or wind shear may also accompany a front. Rapid changes in wind direction and speed below 3,000 feet AGL within 200 miles of an advancing front can produce low-level wind shear.

The probability of moderate turbulence is better than 50 percent within the shaded area of FIG. 5-2. However, turbulence is expected to occur for less than half of the forecast period. A pilot could expect a greater probability in the vicinity of the frontal zone, with its approach, and shortly after passage. This is not inconsistent, but reflects the dynamic character of weather.

Several flight procedures can avoid or minimize frontal turbulence. Fly above the affected area or remain on the ground until frontal passage to avoid turbulence. Turbulence can be minimized by penetrating the front at a right angle, thus reducing exposure, as in the example in FIG. 5-1.

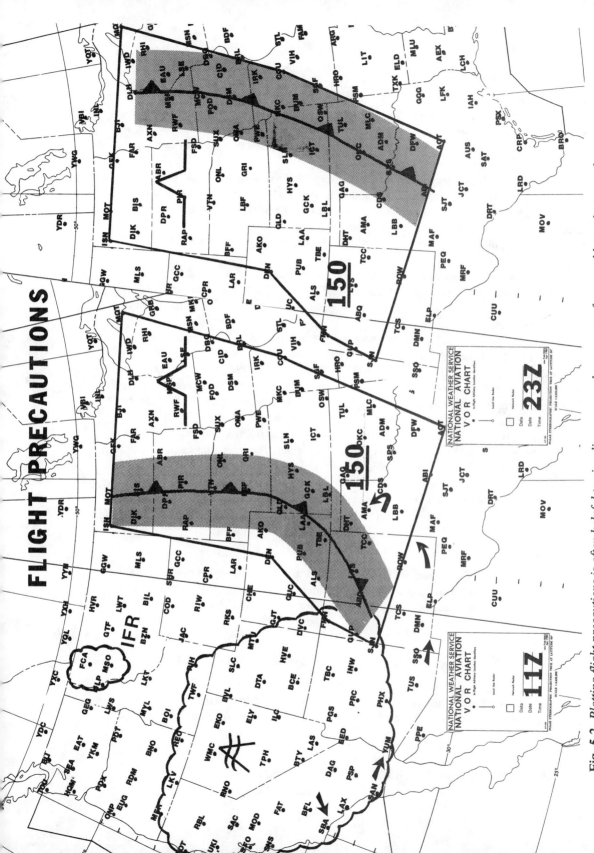

FLIGHT PRECAUTIONS

Fig. 5-2. Plotting flight precautions is often helpful to visualize areas and movement of expected hazardous weather.

Thus far we've discussed thermal, evaporative cooling, mechanical, mountain wave, inversion, and frontal turbulence. When turbulence is moderate or greater, and widespread, it will be carried in the HAZARDS section of the FA. We also know that the delineated area in the turbulence section is usually larger than the affected area, and must consider phenomena moving through the area during the forecast period. This explains a widely held misinterpretation.

Turbulence will not necessarily occur at every location within a flight precaution area, during the entire forecast period. The example in FIG. 5-2 perfectly illustrates this point. Forecasts for mechanical turbulence often cover wide areas. However, the greatest intensity will occur in the vicinity of mountains, leaving valleys and coastal areas relatively smooth. Often the forecaster reflects this by stating OCNL MDT TURBC VCNTY MTNS.

Understanding the causes of turbulence and the forecast helps a pilot determine the most likely turbulent areas and plan accordingly. This includes reducing to turbulent air penetration speed, securing objects, and briefing passengers before entering the areas of probable turbulence.

Non-thunderstorm low-level wind shear will be included in a separate paragraph. It will state LLWS potential, location, and cause: LLWS POTENTIAL OVER MOST OF NEW ENGLAND AFTER 03Z DUE TO STG NWLY FLOW BHND CSTL LOW PRES SYS. There is a potential for LLWS over most of New England after 0300Z due to a strong northwesterly flow behind the low pressure system over the coast. Non-thunderstorm LLWS can be caused by fronts, low-level jet streams, terrain, valley effect, sea breezes, lee side effect, inversions, or Santa Ana and similar foehn-like winds. The occurrence, exact location, and intensity of turbulence, and LLWS is difficult to predict. The forecaster must consider the often widespread and transitory nature of turbulence. PIREPs are the only means of validating the forecast.

"The wind bloweth where it listeth, and thou hearest the sound thereof, but canst not tell whence it came, and whither it goeth: . . ." John 3:8.

SIGNIFICANT CLOUDS AND WEATHER

The SIGNIFICANT CLOUDS AND WEATHER section includes sky condition, cloud heights, visibilities and obstructions to visibility, mountain obscurement, weather, surface winds, and a six-hour categorical outlook. Like other sections in the FA, it begins with issuance and valid times.

```
SFOC FA 141140
SGFNT CLDS AND WX VALID UNTIL 150000 . . . OTLK 150000 – 150600
```

This SFOC FA was issued on the 14th at 1140Z, valid at 1500Z until the 15th at 0000Z, a 12-hour forecast. The outlook is valid on the 15th from 0000Z to 0600Z.

When HAZARDS contains IFR or mountain obscurement, the first paragraphs of this section provide details on the phenomena.

```
IFR . . . MT
FROM 70NW FCA TO 50N FCA 30SE MSO TO 40SW MSO TO 70NW FCA
```

82

OCNL CIG BLO 10 OBSCD VSBY BLO 3F. CONDS IPVG ARND 20Z.

Occasional ceiling below 1,000 feet, skies obscured, visibility below three miles in fog; conditions improving around 20Z.

MTN OBSCN . . . CA
FROM PIH TO ABQ TO YUM TO SAN TO 40W SBA TO FOT TO MFR TO PIH
MTNS OCNL OBSCD IN CLDS/PCPN. CONDS CONTG BYD 00Z.

Mountains are forecast to be occasionally obscured by clouds and precipitation. This condition is expected to continue beyond 00Z, the end of the FA forecast period.

Flight precautions in the previous example have been plotted in FIG. 5-2. The mountain obscurement example illustrates a hazard covering more than one FA area. Details on the phenomena in Nevada, Utah, and Arizona would be found in the Salt Lake City FA.

A pilot planning a VFR flight from Santa Barbara, CA (SBA), to Amarillo, TX (AMA), can easily see the direct route might not be possible, due to mountain obscurement. However, flying south through San Diego, Tucson, and El Paso, not only will terrain be lower, but most of the route will be clear of the flight precaution area. (This example is taken out of context, in a real flight situation all available data must be evaluated and the flight planned accordingly.)

Sky condition contains cloud height, amount, and tops. Heights are normally MSL, with AGL and CIG generally limited to layers within 4,000 feet of the surface. Tops of building cumulus, towering cumulus, and cumulonimbus are quite variable, therefore only upper limits appear (TOPS TO 350, CB TOPS 300). When multiple or merging layers are forecast, which would prevent VFR flight between layers, only the top of the highest layer appears (80 – 100 BKN – OVC LYRD TO 200, MEGG/NMRS LYRS TO 180). Because of its scope, FA tops cannot be more precise. TWEB route forecasts might contain more detail.

Surface visibility and obstructions, usually combined with weather, are forecast when expected to be five miles or less. For example, 3 – 5R – F (visibility three to five miles in light rain and fog), or VSBY 3 – 5RW – AND WDLY SCT TRW – (visibility three to five miles in light rain showers and widely scattered light rain showers and thunderstorms). TABLE 5-2 defines WDLY SCT as less than 25 percent of the area. Because of the scope of this report, the forecast cannot be more precise. A pilot can interpret this forecast to mean the thunderstorms should be circumnavigable.

The absence of a visibility forecast only implies general visibilities greater than five miles. Widespread visibilities of six miles, or local visibilities less than five miles, may exist and not be included in the FA. TWEB route and Terminal Forecasts might contain greater detail.

Widespread areas of surface winds expected to reach sustained speeds of 30 knots or more are forecast. Direction is true, referenced to the eight points of the compass (N, NE, E). The lack of a wind forecast only implies widespread sustained speeds less than 30 knots. TWEB route and Terminal Forecasts can often be used to determine winds of lesser speeds and local conditions. Gusts expected to exceed sustained speeds by 10 knots or more are specified (G35). TRW G40 translates to wind gusts of 40 knots expected to accompany thunderstorms.

AREA FORECASTS (FA)

The forecaster divides the FA area using standard geographical designators. The most common designators can be found in Appendix D, Geographical Area Designators. The extent and detail will depend on the weather situation. The example below illustrates a standard division of the Dallas/Fort Worth FA.

```
SWRN TX
WEST OF PECOS RVR . . . CLR OR SCT CI.
EAST OF PECOS RVR . . . AGL 30 SCT 100 SCT. ISOLD RW – /TRW – .
```

This portion of the DFW FA covers southwestern Texas (SWRN TX). The forecaster has further divided the area into west and east of the Pecos River. This is a common feature in this FA. (If the Pecos River ever dries up, I don't think forecasters will be able to write a DFW FA.)

Below is another example of a SIGNIFICANT CLOUDS AND WEATHER section. The synopsis indicates midlevel moisture, with a stable air mass in the valleys. A typical situation during the winter months for Northern and Central California.

```
NRN/CNTRL CA
CNTRL VLYS AND CSTL VLYS SFO NWD . . GENLY CIG BLO 10 OVC/OBSCD VSBY
BLO 3F. ST TOPS 020 – 025 CNTRL VLYS AND 010 – 020 CSTL VLYS. CONDS
IPVG CSTL PTN 18 – 21Z.
ELSW . . 150 SCT CI ABV. OCNL 100 BKN 150 NRN CSTL WTRS AND CSTLN
WITH CHC R – .
```

The meteorologist has divided California, specifying this portion for Northern and Central sections. The forecaster will further divide the area within the text of the FA. Figure 5-3 pictorially displays the forecast. Below each excerpt from the Geographical Area Designators map in FIG. 5-3 is a portion of the written forecast. The gray shaded area represents the affected area. The forecast for the central valleys (Sacramento and San Joaquin) and coastal valleys (San Francisco northward): Generally ceiling below 1,000 feet (AGL because ceiling is specified), skies obscured, visibilities below three miles in fog; stratus tops are expected between 2,000 to 2,500 feet in the central valleys, and 1,000 to 2,000 feet in coastal valleys (tops are always MSL); coastal valleys are forecast to improve between 1800Z and 2100Z. Notice how the forecaster specifies a period (18Z – 21Z), rather than an exact time, which is another reflection on the limitations of forecasts.

Radiation fog has formed from the moisture of previous storms trapped in valleys and cooled at night under stable air. The relatively shallow layer in the coastal valleys is expected to improve by midday. Conditions in the central valleys will continue. VFR flights will be delayed until afternoon in the coastal valleys, and most probably not possible at anytime in the central valley.

Ceilings less than 1,000 feet and visibilities less than three miles are the lowest values found in the FA, so TWEB route and Terminal Forecasts should be consulted. It is not within the scope of this product to provide more detail. Therefore, a pilot planning IFR into an airport without an FT must specify an alternate. Additionally, airports within this

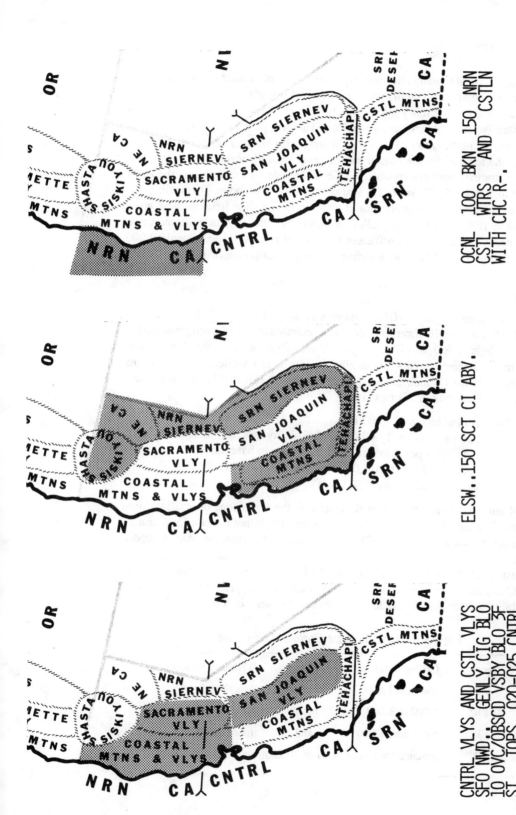

CNTRL VLYS AND CSTL VLYS
SFO NWD.. GENLY CIG BLO
10 OVC/OBSCD VSBY BLO 3F
ST TOPS 020-025 CNTRL
VLYS AND 010-020 CSTL
VLYS. CONDS IPVG CSTL
PTN 18-21Z.

ELSW..150 SCT CI ABV.

OCNL 100 BKN 150 NRN
CSTL WTRS AND CSTLN
WITH CHC R-.

Fig. 5-3. DUAT users will have to determine which parts of the forecast apply to an intended route. A copy of the Geographical Area Designators map will be extremely helpful.

area, without an FT, do not satisfy alternate requirements. A pilot must specify an airport with an FT forecasting alternate minimums, or an airport out of the affected area.

VFR operations above the valley fog will not be restricted despite VFR and IFR pilots flying above extensive areas of zero-zero conditions. This will pose a risk to single-engine operations in case of engine failure. Pilots should weigh this weather situation.

Elsewhere, the forecast for the coastal mountains (including northern coastal mountains above the stratus), northern mountains, Sierra Nevada mountains, and the coast south of San Francisco is 15,000 feet MSL, scattered, with cirrus above. There will be no restrictions to either VFR or IFR operations in these areas. Landing fields in these areas would be suitable IFR alternates for valley airports. Additionally, over the northern coastal waters and coast line, due to sufficient moisture at midlevels, occasional 10,000 feet MSL broken tops 15,000 MSL with a chance of light rain is expected.

OUTLOOK

A six-hour categorical outlook (OTLK) appears at the end of each 12-hour SIGNIFI-CANT CLOUDS AND WEATHER statement. The OTLK consists of the following categories: IFR (Instrument Flight Rules), MVFR (Marginal Visual Flight Rules), and VFR (Visual Flight Rules); these categories do not necessarily correspond to FAR definitions. Refer to TABLE 5-3, Area Forecast Outlook Categories. References to IFR or MVFR explain the phenomena causing the condition. For example:

IFR CIG   =   ceiling less than 1,000 feet.
IFR CIG F   =   ceiling less than 1,000 feet and visibility less than three miles.
MVFR HK   =   visibilities between three and five miles in haze and smoke.
VFR WIND   =   ceiling greater than 3,000 feet and visibility greater than five miles; sustained wind 30 knots or greater.

A "categorical outlook" is another direct reflection on the limitations of aviation forecasts. The outlook is based on synoptic scale events and might not contain local conditions. Differences between the FA and FT outlooks are to be expected, due to report scope, and are not inconsistent.

Pilots must carefully consider an outlook. VFR cannot be interpreted as clear, although conditions might actually be clear. VFR translates ceiling greater than 3,000 feet AGL and visibility greater than five miles; how much "greater" is not specified. Often,

Table 5-3. *Area Forecast Outlook Categories.*

Category	Ceiling (feet)		Visibility (miles)
IFR:	less than 1,000	and/or	less than three
MVFR:	1,000 to 3,000	and/or	three to five
VFR:	more than 3,000	and	more than five
WIND:	Sustained winds or gusts of 30 knots or greater.		

mountain obscurement is not considered. VFR might be expected in valleys, while VFR flight through mountainous areas might not be possible. This category is an indicator that airports within the area will not require an IFR alternate.

MVFR cannot necessarily be interpreted as allowing VFR flight. If conditions are at the lower limit of the category, IFR, most often, would be required. This category is an indicator that airports will be above instrument minimums, but require an alternate. IFR indicates that VFR flight is out. The IFR pilot, however, cannot interpret this category as indicating an airport will be above instrument minimums. It indicates an IFR alternate will be required.

A word of caution to the IFR pilot: outlooks are merely indicators. Categorical outlooks can never be used to determine IFR alternate requirements or suitable IFR alternate airports. FAR requirements must be met based on the latest forecasts prior to departure.

AREA FORECAST AMENDMENT CRITERIA

Weather advisories (AIRMETs, SIGMETs, CWAs, etc.) automatically amend the Area Forecast. Although appropriate sections of the FA (HAZARDS, icing, turbulence, and clouds) will also be amended when conditions develop that warrant the issuance of an AIRMET or SIGMET. HAZARDS, however, are not amended if conditions requiring a Convective SIGMET develop. In this case, the advisory itself serves to amend the FA. The SYNOPSIS will normally be amended with a significant change in the synoptic pattern. Other sections are amended whenever the weather improves or deteriorates.

This is a broad statement and pilots must remember the FA describes conditions over large areas. We should not expect amendments for local or localized changes, which might be reflected in TWEB route or FTs, or their amendments. When wide-scale changes do occur the FA will be amended. The OTLK will be amended when a change from IFR to VFR, or VFR to IFR is expected. A change in the wind outlook alone, however, is not sufficient for an amendment.

A DAY ON THE FA DESK

Figure 5-4 shows the National Aviation Weather Advisory Unit, FA position, at the NWS Kansas City office. The following article appeared in the FAA's June 1988 *Air Traffic Bulletin* by NAWAU meteorologist Paul Smith.

A typical day shift begins at 6:45 a.m. with a briefing from the midnight forecaster. We keep this as brief as possible, explaining current conditions and any expected trouble spots for the upcoming day.

Three forecasters start the shift together, one each for the East, Central, and West. (Each forecaster is responsible for two FAs: East – BOS and MIA, Central – CHI and DFW, and West – SLC and SFO). The three forecaster's work areas are adjacent to one another to allow easy coordination.

Several things are routine on every shift. For instance, surface maps are analyzed every two hours to keep up with current weather conditions over the area. PIREP collectives alarm at our consoles twice an hour and are displayed both in text form and graphically on a computer-generated map. (This emphasizes the importance of PIREPs.) Surface and upper

Fig. 5-4. *Located in Kansas City, meteorologists of the National Aviation Weather Advisory Unit, prepare Area Forecasts for the contiguous United States.*

level guidance material is received from NMC in Washington, D.C.

Many other things are not routine and occur as weather conditions warrant. When SIGMETs are in effect, or are being considered, coordination with the CWSUs occurs regularly. AIRMETs and amendments must be issued if forecast conditions go sour. When things of this type occur on a shift, the forecaster may become rushed to meet product deadlines.

Product composition is accomplished on computer terminals. Once composed and checked, our products are transmitted to WMSC [FAA's Weather Switching Center in Kansas City, MO.] for nationwide dissemination. While we do not have backup procedures in case of computer failure, delayed FAs can and do occur due to computer or communications failure.

Each forecaster has a different routine in preparing a forecast. Usually, the meteorologist spends the first hour or so on shift analyzing the current weather situation and reviewing computer guidance concerning the evolution of weather systems over the following six to 24 hours. SIGMETs, AIRMETs, and forecast amendments have high priority and are issued as needed to keep briefers up-to-date.

Approximately three hours prior to FA issuance, the forecasters begin work in earnest on the two FAs being written. Most forecasters draw up tentative outlines for their flight precaution areas, then consult with the person writing the adjacent forecast to develop a common set of VOR points to describe the entire area. Transmission times are staggered; the BOS and MIA FAs are transmitted first, followed an hour later by CHI/DFW and finally SLC/SFO. The issue time differences make early coordination a necessity. Thus, for flight precaution areas extending from the Rockies to the East Coast, the west forecaster must make decisions very early on the aerial outline of expected weather conditions. IFR areas, because of their changeable nature, are often the last VOR outline to be "nailed down." Negotiation and point changes are made right up to our transmission deadline.

The SGFNT CLDS AND WX portion of the FA is usually the last section to be composed. The forecaster makes use of many separate sources of information to develop the FA including SAs, PIREPs, FTs, TWEBs, satellite imagery, radar, radiosonde data, prognostic charts, standard level charts, and CSIS (the NWS) interactive computer system. During periods of extensive adverse weather conditions with multiple flight precautions and frequent conversations with CWSU meteorologists, the FA forecaster is particularly busy as transmission deadline approaches.

USING THE AREA FORECAST

Below is an example of a Boston Area Forecast used for the following discussion. Refer to FIG. 5-5 to better visualize conditions.

```
BOSH FA 301745
HAZARDS VALID UNTIL 010600
ME NH VT MA RI CT NY LO NY PA OH LE WV MD DC DE VA AND CSTL WTRS
FLT PRCTNS . . . IFR . . . ME NH MA RI AND CSTL WTRS
             . . . MTN OBSCN . . . ME NH VT MA NY WV VA
             . . . TURBC . . . NY PA OH LE LO WV MD
             . . . TSTMS . . . VA
TSTMS IMPLY SVR OR GTR TURBC SVR ICG AND LLWS.
NON MSL HGTS NOTED BY AGL OR CIG.
THIS FA ISSUANCE INCORPORATES THE FOLLOWING AIRMETS STILL IN
EFFECT . . . QUEBEC 1.
BOSS FA 301745
SYNOPSIS VALID UNTIL 011200
AT 18Z LOW WAS OVER LH WITH CDFNT CURVG THRU LO ERN PA CNTRL NC
NRN AL BCMG STNRY TO SRN TX. BY 12Z CDFNT WILL MOVE OFF NRN AND
MID ATLC CST CURVG ACRS SC NRN GA BCMG STNRY TO SRN TX.
BOSI FA 301745
ICG AND FRZLVL VALID UNTIL 010600
LGT TO LCL MDT RIME ICGIC ABV FRZLVL TO 150 OVER ME AND NEW ENG
CSTL WTRS.
OTRW . . . NO SGFNT ICG XPCD OUTSIDE CNVTV ACTVTY.
```

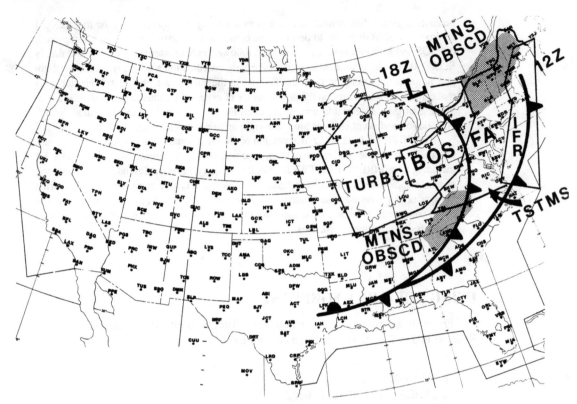

Fig. 5-5. *Plotting Area Forecast adverse conditions and synopsis is the next best thing for DUAT and FSS users that do not have access to weather graphics.*

FRZLVL . . . 50 – 80 ME. 80 – 100 NH VT MA RI CT NY LO LE OH. 100 – 110
NJ PA WV MD DC DE VA.
BOST FA 301745
TURBC VALID UNTIL 010600
NY PA OH LE LO WV MD
FROM MQT TO YOW BGM TO EKN TO LOZ TO ARG TO MCW TO MQT
MDT TO LCL SVR TURBC 200 – 400. CONDS DMSHG BY 06Z.
. . . . .SEE CHI FA FOR DETAILS IN THAT AREA . . . . .
BOSC FA 301745
SGFNT CLDS AND WX VALID UNTIL 010600 . . . OTLK 010600 – 011200Z.
IFR . . . ME NH MA RI AND CSTL WTRS
FROM MLT TO YSJ TO 150SE ACK TO ORF TO PVD TO CON TO MLT
OCNL CIG BLO 10 VSBY BLO 3F. CONDS CONTG NEW ENG AND CSTL WTRS
BYD 06Z.
MTN OBSCN . . . ME NH VT MA NY

FROM CAR TO CON TO 40SE ALB TO BGM TO YOW TO CAR
MTNS OBSCD IN CLDS. CONDS IPVG BY 01Z.
MTN OBSCN . . . WV VA
FROM BKW TO LYH TO GSO TO ATL TO CHA TO BKW
MTNS OBSCD IN CLDS AND PCPN. CONDS DVLPG 00 – 03Z AND CONTG BYD 06Z.
. . . . . SEE MIA FA FOR DETAILS IN THAT AREA . . . . .
ME NH
W OF MLT – CON . . . 30 BKN 100 BKN. MTNS OCNLY OBSCD. TOPS 150. AFT
01Z 50 SCT/BKN. OTLK . . . VFR.
E OF MLT – CON . . . 10 – 20 OVC. VSBY 3 – 5F. CHC R – . TOPS 150. OCNL
CIG BLO 10 OVC VSBY BLO 3R – F. AFT 00Z 20 SCT/BKN. VSBY 3 – 5F.
CONL CIG BLO 10 OVC/OBSCD VSBY BLO 3F. TOPS 40. OTLK IFR CIG F.
MA RI CT
CT WRN MA . . . 20 – 30 BKN. MTNS OCNLY OBSCD. TOPS 60. AFT 00 – 03Z
CLR. OCNL VSBY 3 – 5F. LCL VSBY BLO 3F. OTLK . . . IFR F.
RI ERN MA . . . 20 OVC. VSBY 3 – 5F. OCNL CIG BLO 10 OVC VSBY BLO 3F.
TOPS 50. AFT 21 – 00Z 20 SCT/BKN. VSBY 3 – 5F. AFT 00 – 03Z 20 SCT.
VSBY 3 – 5F. OCNL CIG BLO 10 OBSCD VSBY BLO 3F. TOPS 40.
OTLK . . . IFR CIG F.
VT
30 BKN. TOPS 80. MTNS OCNLY OBSCD. AFT 01Z 40 SCT. OCNL VSBY
3 – 5F AFT 03Z. OTLK . . . MVFR F.
NY LO
LO WRN AND NERN NY . . . 30 BKN. TOPS 60. MTNS OCNLY OBSCD. AFT
01Z 40 SCT. OCNL VSBY 3 – 5F AFT 02Z. OTLK . . . MVFR F.
SERN NY . . . 30 SCT/BKN. TOPS 60. MTNS OCNLY OBSCD. AFT 22Z CLR.
AFT 02Z CLR. VSBY 3 – 5F. LCL VSBY BLO 3F. OTLK . . . IFR CIG F.
NJ PA
40 SCT/BKN. TOPS 60. ISOLD TRW SRN NJ SERN PA TIL 00Z. CB TOPS
350. VSBY 3 – 5F. AFT 00Z CLR. VSBY 3 – 5F. OTLK . . . MVFR F.
OH LE
40 SCT. AFT 00Z CLR. CONL 100 SCT/BKN WRN AND SRN PTNS OH.
TOPS 150. OTLK . . . VFR.
WV
NRN . . . 50 SCT. AFT 00Z CLR. AFT 03Z 100 SCT/BKN. VSBY 3 – 5F.
TOPS 150. OTLK . . . VFR BCMG MVFR CIG F BY 10Z.
SRN . . . 50 SCT/BKN. AFT 00 – 03Z 30 – 40 BKN 100 BKN. VSBY 3 – 5F.
WDLY SCT RW/TRW. TOPS 180. CB TOPS 350. OTLK . . . IFR CIG TRW F.
MD DC DE VA
MD DC DE NRN VA . . . 40 – 50 SCT/BKN. WDLY SCT RW/TRW. OCNL 20
BKN/OVC CSTL SXNS. CB TOPS 350. OTLK . . . MVFR CIG F.
SRN VA . . . 40 – 50 BKN. WDLY SCT TRW. OCNL 20 OVC WDLY SCT TRW ERN
PTN WITH CHC SVR TSTMS. AFT 00 – 03Z 20 – 30 BKN. WDLY SCT RW/TRW.

MTNS BCMG OBSCD. CB TOPS 450. OTLK . . . IFR CIG TRW F.
CSTL WTRS
N OF ACK . . . 10 – 20 OVC. VSBY 3 – 5F. CHC R – . OCNL CIG BLO 10 OVC
VSBY BLO 3F. TOPS 150. AFT 00 – 03Z 10 – 20 OVC. VSBY 3 – 5F. OCNL
CIG BLO 10 OVC VSBY BLO 3F. TOPS 40. OTLK . . . IFR CIG F.
S OF ACK . . . 20 OVC. VSBY 3 – 5F. WDLY SCT RW/TRW. OCNL CIG BLO 10
OVC VSBY BLO 3RW/TRW/F. AFT 00 – 03Z 20 – 30 BKN. TOPS 60.
OTLK . . . MVFR CIG.

A pilot's first task is to determine the valid time of the forecast. Old forecasts occasionally remain in the "system" due to late revisions or computer trouble. This Boston FA was issued on the 30th day of the month at 1745Z, becomes effective at 1800Z, and is valid until the 1st at 0600Z.

Next, does the report cover the proposed flight? Notice the Boston FA includes Lake Erie (LE), Lake Ontario (LO) and the District of Columbia (DC). The forecast area has been outlined in FIG. 5-5. With valid time and coverage established, move to the flight precautions paragraph.

All or parts of the states, during all or part of the forecast period, are expected to contain the listed adverse conditions. The SYNOPSIS follows the standard thunderstorm and height statements, and the fact that AIRMET QUEBEC 1 has been incorporated. To visualize conditions the synopsis has been plotted in FIG. 5-5. The main weather feature is a cold front forecast to move through the FA area. Notice the 18-hour valid time through the outlook period.

The ICING AND FREEZING LEVEL paragraph forecasts light to locally moderate rime icing in clouds from the freezing level to 15,000 feet MSL over Maine and New England coastal waters. The forecaster does not expect extensive moderate icing and, therefore, icing is not included in HAZARDS. The absence of flight precautions does not exclude the possibility of hazardous weather. Otherwise, no significant icing—trace or no icing—is expected, except with convective activity (thunderstorms), which implies moderate or greater icing.

The freezing level paragraph states that the freezing level is expected to slope from around 5,000 feet in northern Maine to 8,000 feet in the south. This condition would be a definite consideration for aircraft without ice protection equipment. Freezing levels are always included, whether or not icing is forecast.

The TURBULENCE AND LOW-LEVEL WIND SHEAR paragraph states that moderate to locally severe turbulence is forecast between 20,000 and 40,000 feet within the delineated area (FIG. 5-5). Notice that only portions of New York and Pennsylvania are affected, with turbulence expected to diminish by 0600Z. The paragraph refers to the Chicago FA for details in that area. Severe turbulence will only be localized, so a SIGMET has not been issued. If a SIGMET is in effect, a statement following the paragraph will refer to the advisory (. . . . . SEE SIGMET ALPHA 1 FOR DETAILS . . . . .). This is not the only area where significant turbulence can be expected. Remember that thunderstorms imply moderate or greater turbulence and low-level wind shear, which are not addressed separately.

SIGNIFICANT CLOUDS AND WEATHER follow. When IFR or mountain obscurement appear in HAZARDS, the first paragraphs of this section contain details. Occasional ceiling below 1,000— AGL because CIG is specified—visibilities below three in fog is forecast. The outlined section in FIG. 5-5 labeled IFR over New England represents this area. Conditions will continue beyond 0600Z. The gray shaded areas of FIG. 5-5 depict mountain obscurement. The mountains of New York and New England are expected to be obscured in clouds. Here, conditions are expected to improve by 0100Z.

A second mountain obscuration paragraph provides details on conditions in West Virginia and Virginia. Mountains are expected to become obscured in clouds and precipitation between 0000Z and 0300Z, and continue beyond 0600Z. Notice that the condition will develop during the period. The forecaster has provided a time frame rather than a specific time for conditions to develop. This should be translated as mountain obscurement will develop between 0000Z and 0300Z. The paragraph refers to the MIA FA for details in that area.

Flight precautions for IFR and mountain obscurement are generally synonymous. The precautions represent low ceilings and visibilities that will preclude VFR flight within all or part of the affected area. Pilots, especially those used to flying over flat terrain, must use caution with mountain obscurement forecast. Weather reports from valley stations might indicate good VFR flying conditions, but VFR flights through passes and over the mountains might be impossible. Again, it is imperative for the pilot to have a sound knowledge of terrain. When the forecast indicates the phenomena will be occasional, for example the IFR paragraph in the BOS FA, the probability of occurrence is greater than 50 percent but expected to occur for less than half the forecast period. A forecast for "occasional" should not warrant the cancellation of VFR. All available information must be considered and caution exercised, with suitable alternates available. The absence of a conditional term indicates the phenomena will be widespread, for example the BOS FA mountain obscurement paragraphs. This means a greater than 50 percent probability occurring for more than half the forecast period. VFR flight probably will not be possible.

Next come the paragraphs describing expected weather for the forecast area. Areas are usually described using Geographical Area Designators, Appendix D, or the VORs on the In-flight Advisory Plotting Chart, Appendix C. In Maine and New Hampshire, west of a MLT CON line—the mountains—30 BKN 100 BKN, MTNS OCNLY OBSCD, TOPS 150 (all MSL) are expected from 1800Z until after 0100Z. With mountain peaks in the 3,500-to-5,000 foot range, they will be obscured; where minimum en route altitudes (MEA) are above 5,000 feet, icing in clouds can be expected.

After 0100Z, conditions are forecast to improve to 50 SCT/BKN, consistent with the mountain obscurement paragraph. General visibilities through the period will be five miles or greater, with no significant precipitation. The outlook is VFR.

East of MLT – CON line—the coastal plain—10 – 20 OVC, VSBY 3 – 5F, CHC R – , with TOPS 150, OCNL CIG BLO 10 OVC/OBSCD (skies obscured) VSBY BLO 3R – F are expected from 1800Z until after 0000Z. Conditions will not instantly change at 0001Z. The forecaster expects conditions to begin to improve, but not until *after* 0000Z. VFR will be iffy. MEAs are lower and, with flights below 5,000 feet ice should not be a factor.

After 0000Z, conditions will improve somewhat, but remain marginal VFR to IFR. Tops will drop significantly in the coastal areas. The outlook indicates the ceilings below 1,000 and visibilities below three miles in fog will persist.

Moving to the New Jersey, Pennsylvania paragraph (NJ PA), notice that the isolated thunderstorms and rain showers are forecast for southern NJ and southeastern PA. However, these states were not included in the HAZARDS section. The aerial coverage of thunderstorms must be at least scattered, or expected to meet Convective SIGMET criteria to warrant inclusion as a flight precaution. Because they are expected to be isolated storms, circumnavigation should be possible; but do not poke around in clouds without storm detection equipment in the aircraft. Under the circumstances, climbing above the lower layer where visual separation from convective activity can be maintained would be a prudent procedure. The outlook, MVFR F, indicates visibilities will be between three and five miles in fog and the ceiling greater than 3,000 feet.

Refer to the Maryland, District of Columbia, Delaware, Virginia (MD DC DE VA) paragraph. VA was included in HAZARDS for thunderstorms and notice for southern VA the forecast indicates OCNL 20 OVC WDLY SCT TRW ERN PTN WITH CHC SVR TSTMS. Over the eastern portion of southern VA a chance of severe thunderstorms is expected. This meets the criteria for a Convective SIGMET, therefore, HAZARDS contains a flight precaution for this phenomena. The outlook, IFR CIG TRW F, indicates ceiling less than 1,000 feet, visibilities less than three in fog, rain showers, and thunderstorms.

The final paragraph forecasts conditions for the CSTL WTRS. The area is divided into north and south of Nantucket, MA (ACK).

This FA describes a distinct weather system. Notice how flight precautions, synopsis, and significant clouds and weather are all tied together. FAs will not always be this detailed or consistent, but the example has provided most variables used in the report.

THE HIGH ALTITUDE SIGNIFICANT WEATHER PROG

The high altitude significant weather prog provides a pictorial view of forecast weather from 400 mbs to 70 mbs, approximately 24,000 through 63,000 feet. All heights are pressure altitudes (flight levels). The prog is manually prepared at the National Meteorological Center, the chart depicts cumulonimbus clouds, tropical cyclones, severe squall lines, moderate or severe turbulence, widespread sandstorms or dust storms, surface fronts, tropopause height, and jet streams. Charts are valid at 0000Z, 0600, 1200Z, and 1800Z.

Scalloped lines enclose areas of forecast cumulonimbus development, divided into three categories: isolated (ISOL) less than one-eighth coverage, occasional (OCNL) one-eighth to four-eighths coverage, and frequent (FRQ) five-eighths to eight-eighths coverage. Cumulonimbus clouds imply hail, and moderate or greater turbulence and icing. Bases and tops are shown by numerical figures below and above a short horizontal line. Bases below 24,000 feet are indicated by XXX below the line. For example, in FIG. 5-6, along the southwestern coast of Mexico, the forecast indicates an area of isolated (less than one-eighth coverage), embedded cumulonimbus with tops to 40,000 feet, bases below 24,000 feet. Clear Air Turbulence, not associated with cumulonimbus clouds, is

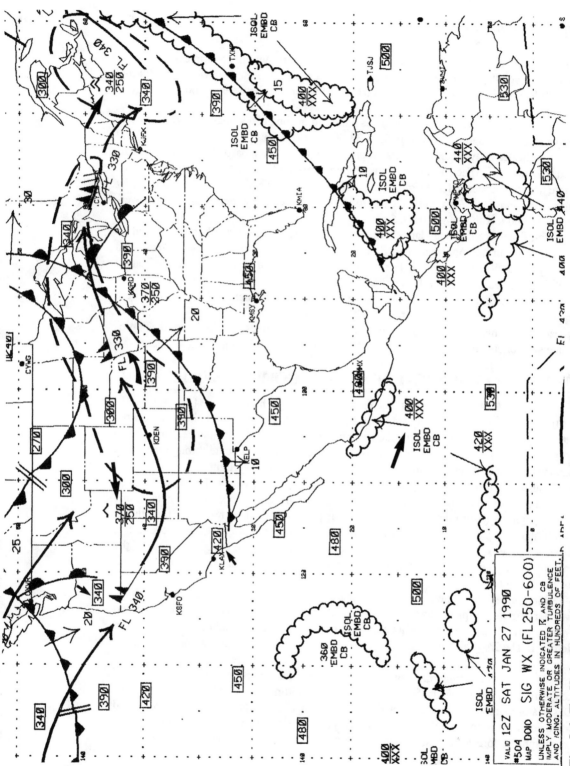

Fig. 5-6. *The High Altitude Significant Weather Prog pictorially displays weather above 24,000 feet. The chart is not amended, so the Area Forecast and weather advisories must be consulted to complete the forecast weather picture.*

indicated by a dashed line containing a turbulence intensity symbol and forecast height. In FIG. 5-6, over the central U.S., moderate turbulence is expected between 25,000 and 37,000 feet. Off New England, severe turbulence is forecast between 25,000 and 34,000 feet.

The expected location of jet streams is indicated by long black lines. Figure 5-6 shows the jet stream through the central U.S. at 33,000 feet (FL 330), with a core speed of 100 knots, indicated by two flags (each flag represent 50 knots, each barb 10 knots). The chart also contains the expected height of the tropopause—the boundary between the troposphere and stratosphere. The height of the tropopause over the West Coast is indicated by numerals enclosed in a box and forecast around 42,000 feet in Southern California, lowering to 34,000 feet in Oregon (FIG. 5-6).

Significant frontal boundaries are depicted using standard symbols contained in TABLE 10-2, Surface Analysis Chart Symbols, with movement indicated by an arrow and speed printed by the arrowhead. For example, the cold front in FIG. 5-6, in the central U.S., is expected to move to the southeast at 20 knots.

The names of tropical cyclones, when relevant, are entered next to the symbol. Severe squall lines are depicted within areas of CB by the symbol: − V − V − V. And, widespread sandstorms or dust storms are enclosed by scalloped lines, labelled with the appropriate symbol contained in TABLE 10-1, Station Model Symbols, and vertical extent.

USING THE HIGH ALTITUDE SIGNIFICANT WEATHER PROG

The chart is often an excellent place to begin planning a high altitude flight (above FL 240). For example, a pilot flying from San Francisco to New York might plan to follow the jet stream over the Great Lakes to take advantage of tail winds. If turbulence, for example a lifeguard flight, were a significant factor, the pilot might plan a route through the Texas panhandle then to New York to avoid wind shear turbulence. A flight from east to west might also select this route to avoid maximum jet stream head winds. The chart can also be used to determine areas of cumulonimbus, cloud tops, and tropopause heights. If aircraft equipment (storm detection equipment) or performance does not allow the pilot to climb above thunderstorms, he or she might wish to avoid areas where coverage is expected to be occasional or frequent. The pilot should note the expected height of the tropopause. If thunderstorms develop, the isothermal layer of the tropopause caps all except severe activity.

Pilots, like FSS briefers, can use the chart for the en route portion of a high altitude weather briefing but pilots, as well as briefers, must not substitute the chart for the FA and weather advisories. The chart is not amended and severe weather might develop that is not depicted. The FA is also needed to provide weather details for climb out and descent.

The pilot is becoming more and more responsible for report interpretation, as well as acquisition. He or she needs the In-flight Advisory Plotting Chart and Geographical Area Designator maps to determine affected areas. A Flight Service Station should be consulted when any item is not completely understood. Forecasters make mistakes, usually omitted paragraphs or forecast areas, or data inadvertently left over from the previous FA. The

NWS is virtually out of the pilot briefing business, so a pilot's only access to a forecaster will be through an FSS.

Weather advisories automatically amend the FA. Pilots must understand that the FA will only be amended when a significant change occurs. With few exceptions, hazardous weather must be extensive to warrant an advisory or amendment.

Issuance and valid times reflect the limitations on aviation forecasts.

Forecast Section, Valid Hours
Hazards, 12
Synopsis, 18
Icing, 12
Turbulence, 12
Clouds and Weather, 12 with a 6 hour outlook

FAs are issued at six to eight hour intervals and pilots should become familiar with these times. Most sections are only valid for 12 hours, so pilots checking with flight service or using DUAT just prior to the next issuance will only have five to six hours of valid forecast, excluding the outlook. Pilots interested in conditions for the following day, should call for or request the forecast after 9 p.m. This will usually ensure receipt of the latest information.

There is no question that the FA has improved. When the San Francisco WSFO issued the FA there was invariably a flight precaution for occasional moderate turbulence within 5,000 feet of rough terrain. Pilots and briefers became equally disgusted with this generalization. The NWS decision to consolidate in Kansas City and the commitment of NAWAU forecasters has resulted in standardization and consistency. And, in spite of criticism that flight precautions cover too much area, their issuance has become more conservative. Ironically, certain pilots and briefers criticize the forecast for not containing enough flight precautions. Virtually all criticism, however, is due to misconceptions and misunderstanding the product. The FA is a valuable and useful tool as long as the purpose, format, conditional terms, and limitations are understood.

Never rely on a single piece of data. The FA is only one product, one piece of the weather picture. Local conditions might not be included. Flight decisions should never be based solely on this or any other product. The FA must be used along with all available information. Forecast limitations cannot be over emphasized along with using all available sources.

> "Whatever may be the progress of the sciences, never will observers who are trustworthy and careful of their reputations venture to forecast the state of the weather."
>
> Dominique Argo
> French Astronomer-Physicist
> (1786−1853)

Dick Williams obviously hasn't heard this; you might recall he puts his name on the forecast.

6
TWEB Forecasts

TWEB AVIATION FORECASTS WERE DEVELOPED AS SCRIPTS FOR THE FAA'S *Transcribed Weather Broadcast Route Forecast* (TWEB) and *Pilots Automatic Telephone Weather Answering Service* (PATWAS). TWEB use has expanded with the *Interim Voice Response System* (IVRS), and the introduction of the *Telephone Information Briefing Service* (TIBS), which is available at Automated Flight Service Stations (AFSS).

Forecasts are available by phone from PATWAS and TIBS, broadcast continuously over selected low and medium frequency radio beacons, and VORs, and available on an individual basis from IVRS. Telephone numbers can be found in the FAA and NWS Telephone Numbers section of the *Airport/Facility Directory*; frequencies, most easily found on aeronautical charts, are also available in the directory, although not separately listed. (Refer to Chapter 11, Obtaining Meteorological and Aeronautical Information.) TWEB route forecasts might also be provided during preflight, in-flight and Flight Watch briefings. TWEB route numbers and locations are contained in Appendix B, Weather Report and Forecast Locations.

TWEB forecasts were revised in February 1988, and issuance and valid times standardized. TWEBs are issued three times a day and valid for 15 hours. Time references transmitted with the product remain UTC, but they are issued for local times in all time zones, and normally available just prior to valid time: 5 a.m.−8 p.m., (morning); 2 p.m.−5 a.m., (afternoon); and 9 p.m.−noon (evening).

```
403 TWEB 200419 RNO−BOI. ALL HGTS MSL XCP CIGS.
    GENLY CLR.
```

TWEB route number 403 forecasts conditions from Reno, NV, to Boise, ID (RNO--BOI). The forecast, the evening issuance (9 p.m.–noon), was valid on the 20th day of the month, from 04Z until 19Z the following day (200419). TWEB routes describe a corridor 50 nm wide, 25 miles either side of the route. The 403 route forecast covers conditions 25 miles either side of a line from Reno to Boise. It is important not to extrapolate and use the forecast beyond its designated area.

The loss of reporting stations has caused revisions to the TWEB network resulting in the issuance of certain routes on a part-time basis.

```
426 TWEB 250520 TSP MTNS SOLEDAD – CAJON – BNG PASSES AND ADJ MTNS.
   DLAD.
```

This evening issuance of the 426 route, for the Tehachapi Mountains, Soledad, Cajon, Banning Passes and adjacent mountains will be delayed due to lack of observations. Additionally, amendments might not be available for selected routes which will contain a remark, (NO AMDTS AFT 04Z). Significant changes can occur without an amendment, so this serves the same purpose as NO SPL on SAs. It's a warning that caution must be exercised, especially during marginal and deteriorating conditions.

Pilots, FSS specialists, and forecasters have been instrumental in revising TWEB routes. For example, the 420 route at one time forecast conditions from Concord to Arcata to Crescent City, CA (CCR – ACV – CEC). However, with the loss of 24-hour observations at Crescent City and only part-time observations at Concord, the forecast was suspended during the night. But, by changing the *anchors*—end points on the route—to Oakland and Arcata (OAK – ACV), with 24-hour observations, the route once more became available full-time. Other routes in the area have also been revised, as a direct result of pilot input. This is an excellent example of how pilots, briefers, and forecasters, working together, can improve the system.

SYNOPSIS

In addition to route forecasts, NWS offices responsible for TWEBs prepare a *synopsis*. The synopsis contains a brief description of fronts, pressure systems, and local climate or terrain factors affecting the routes, valid for the same period as the route forecasts. The *TWEB synopsis* often contains more detail than the FA; and, therefore, might be of more value describing local conditions. More detail is possible because the TWEB synopsis only covers about one-fifth the area of the FA. Refer to Appendix B for TWEB synopses locations.

```
LAX SYNS 191203
UPR RDG ALG W CST WITH NLY FLO ALF. SFC HI CONTS
TO BLD OVER GT BASIN FOR CONTG SANTA ANA CONDS.
```

This Los Angeles (LAX) synopsis covers the routes issued by the Los Angeles WSFO. An upper level ridge is along the west coast with a northerly flow aloft. Surface high pressure continues to build over the Great Basin—the high plateau generally consisting of Nevada, Utah, and southern Idaho—for continuing Santa Ana conditions, strong, sometimes warm, northeasterly winds over Southern California.

The detail of a TWEB synopsis depends on the weather pattern.

> ATL SYNS 301809 STNRY FNT NR MYR – ABY – PAM. HI PRES CNTRD OH DRFTG
> SEWD.

This Atlanta (ATL) synopsis describes a stationary front from Myrtle Beach, SC (MYR) to Albany, GA (ABY) to Panama City, FL (PAM). High pressure centered over Ohio is drifting southeastward.

A more complex weather system is reflected in a longer synopsis.

> IND SYNS 041809 CD FNT XTNDS FRM NRN LK ERIE THRU CNTRL OH INTO
> NRN AL. WK TROF EXTNDS FRM SFC LO SW LWR MI THRU W CNTRL
> IN. UPPR LVL LOW OVER NRN IL WL BRNG SCT TRW MAINLY OVR WRN
> AND NRN RTES THIS AFTN AND EVE. PRZYBYLINSKI

In this Indianapolis synopsis a cold front extends from northern Lake Erie through central Ohio into northern Alabama. A weak trof extends from a surface low in southwest Lower Michigan through west central Indiana. The upper level low over northern Illinois will bring scattered rain showers and thunderstorms mainly over the western and northern routes this afternoon and evening. The synopsis was prepared by Przybylinski.

Pilots using DUATs will have to contact an FSS for clarification of contractions or phrases they do not understand. One evening I had a pilot call the FSS with such a question. He didn't understand the last word of the synopsis. I explained it was the name of the meteorologist who wrote the forecast.

SIGNIFICANT CLOUDS AND WEATHER

TWEBs use the same terminology and contractions as the FA. Forecasts contain significant clouds and weather, with significant defined as phenomena affecting at least 10 percent of a route, or in the forecaster's judgment important to flight planning. Forecasts consist of sky condition, visibility, weather, including mountain obscurement, strong surface winds, and non-thunderstorm low-level wind shear. Cloud types might be included (CU, SC, CIFM)

Cloud heights are based on a standard reference: ALL HGTS MSL XCP CIGS (all heights mean sea level except ceilings) or ALL HGTS AGL XCP TOPS (all heights above ground level except tops). The use of AGL and CIGS are normally limited to layers within 4,000 feet of the surface. TWEBs were basically a low altitude forecast—below 15,000 to 18,000 feet. That no longer necessarily applies, but forecasters emphasize cloud conditions below 12,000 feet. With no clouds, or scattered clouds above approximately 12,000 feet, the forecaster might use the phrase NO SGFNT CLDS/WX (no significant clouds or weather); any clouds present should be easily circumnavigable.

Mountain obscurement has been added (MTNS OBSCD ABV . . . , MTN RDGS OBSCD, or ALL PASSES OBSCD), and geographical features might be specified (TSP

(Tehachapi) MTNS, CSTL MTNS). Because of the local nature of the forecast, not all locations appear on the Geographical Area Designators map. Pilots unfamiliar with locations on TWEB forecasts will have to consult an FSS.

When forecast, tops will normally only be included for layers with bases below 12,000 feet. Like the FA, for multiple or merging layers, that would not permit VFR flight between layers, only the top of the highest layer appears. However, because of the local nature of the product, tops are often more specific and, therefore, useful.

Surface visibilities are forecast when expected to be six miles or less. However, to prevent misunderstanding, 6+ might be used to indicate unrestricted visibility. Weather and obstructions to vision appear as necessary.

Sustained surface winds are normally forecast when expected to be 25 knots or greater. Notice the TWEB threshold for winds is five knots less than the FA. Direction is referenced to true north and given as cardinal headings (LO LVL WNDS W TO SWLY LCLY TO 25 KT.), or in degrees (30–3415–25, wind 300° to 340° at 15 to 25 knots). Gusts might also appear (WNDS G40). The lack of a wind forecast only implies sustained speeds less than 25 knots over 90 percent of the forecast area.

TWEB conditional terms describe variability; refer to TABLE 6-1, Conditional Terms used on TWEB Forecasts. Conditional terms have been intentionally changed to coincide with the FA. Also used in briefings, it is important to note interchangeable terms: *widely scattered* and *locally*; *scattered* and *areas*; *numerous* and *widespread*. These conditional terms can lead to confusion.

> 414 TWEB 312213 RDD – SAC – FAT – BFL . . .
> . . . AFT 02Z – 05Z BCMG 30 – 50 SCT SCT 30 BKN RW – SRN SAN
> JOAQUIN VLY. . . .

This would seem to say that after the period 02Z to 05Z conditions will become 3,000 to 5,000 feet scattered, scattered 3,000 feet broken with light rain showers in the southern San Joaquin Valley. The forecaster's intent is to describe conditions becoming 3,000 to 5,000 feet scattered, areas (25 percent to 54 percent of the route—the *conditional* term scattered) 3,000 feet broken with light rain showers. In this case the forecaster could have

Table 6-1. *Conditional Terms used on TWEB Forecasts.*

Term	Contraction	Definition
Isolated	ISOLD	Single cells or localized conditions (no percentage). Implies circumnavigable.
Widely Scattered or Local	WDLY SCT LCL	Less than 25 percent of area/route affected.
Scattered or Areas	SCT AREA	25 percent to 54 percent of area/route affected.
Numerous or Widespread	NMRS WDSPRD	More than 54 percent of area/route affected.

written BCMG 30–50 SCT AREAS 30 BKN RW– to prevent any confusion. In spite of this example, forecasters do attempt to avoid ambiguity when preparing forecasts.

As an FSS supervisor, I counsel specialists to keep briefings clear and concise. One area of excess verbiage is high thin *cirroform* clouds; all cirroform clouds are high. But, leave it to the National Weather Service when sure enough, one day I find 426 TWEB . . . HI THIN CIFM CLDS. What's a mother to do?

The length and detail of TWEB forecast varies widely. Beyond examples of one-liners, this is an example of the other extreme:

```
418 TWEB 250520 OAK–SAC–RNO. ALL HGTS MSL EXP CIGS. VCNTY OAK
    40–60 SCT. PTCHY FOG FRMG WITH AREAS CIG/VSBY BLO 10/3F.
    PCPN SPRDG TO AREA AFT 18Z WITH CIGS 10–20 AND SCT CIG/VSBY
    BLO 10/3R–F. MTNS BCMG OBSCD. SAC VLY CIG 30–50 VSBY 3–5F
    WITH SCT CIG/VSBY BLO 10/3F. FOG BCMG MORE XTSV AFT ABT 08Z
    WITH WDSPRED CIG/VSBY BLO 10/3F. PCPN SPRDG TO AREA AFT 18Z
    WITH CIGS 10–20 AND SCT CIG/VSBY BLO 10/3R–F. OVR SIERNEV TO
    RNO 100–200 SCT–BKN WITH SCT SW–. LATE IN PD PCPN SPRDG ACRS
    MTNS WITH SCT CIG/VSBY BLO 10/3R–/S–F. MTNS OCNL OBSCD BCMG
    OBSCD.
```

Well, try getting that and a half-dozen more like it on a three-minute tape for the transcribed weather broadcast and you get some idea why FSS specialists speak so fast. This example does show, however, how detailed a TWEB can be, and how it can relate to a geographical area. It begins with conditions in the vicinity of Oakland, through Sacramento Valley, and then over the Sierra Nevada Mountains to Reno. Forecast conditions are marginal at the beginning of the period, then deteriorate as precipitation spreads over the route.

LOCAL VICINITY FORECASTS

Local Vicinity Forecasts have been developed to cover metropolitan areas; locations are contained in Appendix B. They normally cover a radius of 50 nm.

```
358 TWEB 200419 SEA–PGTSND LCL VCNTY. ALL HGTS MSL XCP CIG. 20
    SCT 30–50 SCT–BKN . . . AFT 10Z CONDS BCMG 15 SCT–BKN 20–30
    BKN . . . AFT 17Z CONDS BCMG 30 SCT.
```

This Local Vicinity Forecast covers the Seattle and Puget Sound area. The forecast indicates scattered to broken clouds deteriorating after 1000Z and then improving after 1700Z.

Exceptions to the 50-mile radius occur in Southern California where large, irregular, homogenous geographical areas exist (FIG. 6-1). The 431 TWEB covers the Los Angeles Basin, from the San Fernando Valley along the San Gabriel and San Bernardino Mountains to Hemet, and back to Santa Ana. The 426 route forecasts conditions over the Tehachapi Mountains, and mountains and passes north and east of Los Angeles. This includes a specific forecast for the SOLEDAD, CAJON, and BNG (Banning) PASSES. The 429 route

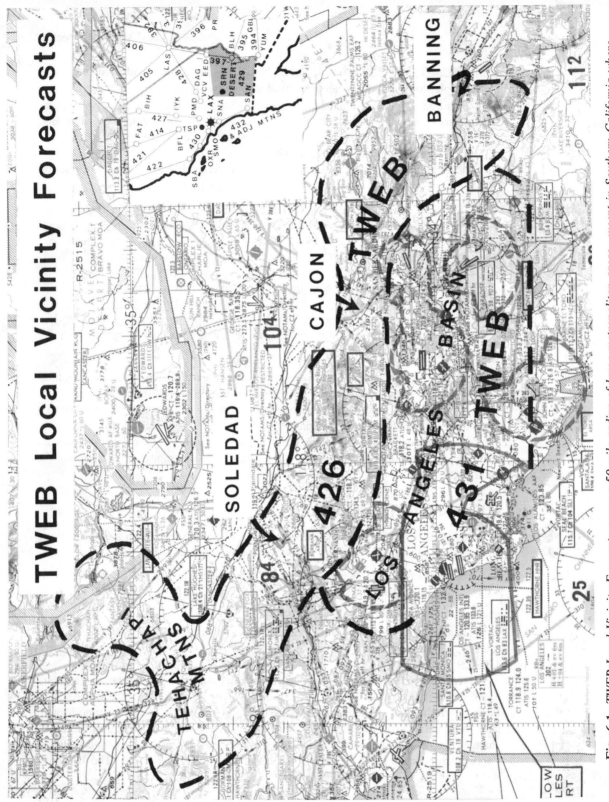

Fig. 6-1. *TWEB Local Vicinity Forecasts cover a 50-mile radius of large metropolitan areas, except in Southern California where*

for the Southern California deserts, south of a Palm Springs-Needles line is illustrated by the shaded portion of the inset in FIG. 6-1.

Compare the 431 TWEB, for the LAX BASIN route, with the San Francisco Area Forecast for the same time and location.

```
431 TWEB 071203 LAX BASIN. ALL HGTS MSL XCP CIGS.
    20 – 50BKN – SCT. ISOLD SHWRS. CIGS LCLLY AOB 10 . . . VSBY LCLLY
    AOB 3HF. HIR INLD MTNS OBSCD. AFT 18Z INCRG SHWRS WITH LCL
    EMBDD TSTMS.
CA
CST . . . 15 – 25 SCT – BKN 50 – 70 SCT – BKN 140 – 160 OVC 180 WITH SCT VSBYS
3 – 5RW – AND WDLY SCT TRW – . CB TOPS TO 300. MTNS OCNL OBSCD.
```

Sky conditions are comparable. The TWEB includes local ceilings and visibilities below 1,000 feet and three miles, these conditions are too localized for inclusion in the FA. The TWEB predicts increasing showers and thunderstorms after 18Z. The FA includes the same forecast, but without the time reference. The TWEB indicates mountains obscured, the FA occasionally obscured. This is consistent, given that the FA must cover conditions for all of California's coastal sections, the TWEB is only the L.A. Basin. The FA might contain more detail on tops, as in this case (tops 18,000 feet with CBs to 30,000 feet. Both forecasts are consistent within the scope of each product.

AMENDMENT CRITERIA

TABLE 6-2 contains TWEB amendment criteria. When phenomena occurs, is expected to develop, or is no longer anticipated, an amendment will be issued. Amendments are also required for thunderstorms and low-level wind shear. Routes will also normally be amended when trends indicate, in the forecaster's judgment, that the forecast will be substantially in error or unrepresentative. FSS specialists make inquiries when discrepancies develop, or significant differences occur between FA and TWEB forecasts. Amendments can originate in this manner.

Table 6-2. *TWEB Forecast Amendment Criteria.*

Ceiling with a forecast of:	amend if:	Visibility with a forecast of:	amend if:
ceiling more than 3,000	less than 3,000*	more than five miles	less than five*
3,000 or less	increase to or above 3,000	five miles or less	increase to above five
3,000 to 1,000	less than 1,000	three to five miles	less than three
less than 1,000	increase to or above 1,000	less than three miles	increase to or above three

*Or, in the forecaster's judgment is not representative.

Forecasters consider issuance times in the decision to amend. Because it takes time to write and distribute an amendment, if the next issuance is in less than two hours, the forecaster might elect to delay and issue the new forecast, rather than amend. As can be seen from TABLE 6-2, amendments are directed at low altitude changes. If these criteria are not met, the forecast is considered accurate, and will not be amended.

USING THE TWEB ROUTE FORECAST

Figure 6-2 compares and contrasts the Area Forecast with a TWEB route. Notice in the NERN OH portion of the 072 TWEB that AFT 16Z the forecast becomes 30 OVC VSBY 6 + . VSBY 6 + is included to prevent confusion or misunderstanding. The previous portion of the forecast includes VSBY 3 – 5RF . . . AREAS . . . VSBY BLO 3R – F. . . . The inclusion of 6 + indicates that during that portion of the forecast, after 16Z, visibilities are expected to be unrestricted. The absence of 6 + would be interpreted as ceiling improving after 16Z, but visibilities remaining predominately three to five miles, with AREAS below three miles.

Let's plan a flight from Pittsburgh's Allegheny County Airport (AGC) to Harrisburg's Capital City Airport (CXY) using the Pennsylvania portion of the Boston FA and the Pittsburgh to Harrisburg (PIT – HAR) portion of the 072 TWEB CLE – PIT – HAR. A pilot's first task is to determine the valid time of the forecast. The BOS FA Significant Clouds and Weather section was issued on the 29th day of the month at 0845Z, valid at 0900Z until 2100Z. The TWEB, also issued on the 29th, is valid from 0900Z until 2400Z. (Only used to indicate the end of a time period, 2400Z may be written as 2359Z. Almost always, when 2400Z is intended, it will be written as 0000Z.)

With valid time nailed down, a pilot's next job is to ensure the forecast covers the intended route. The FA divides the area into NW and SE of a Johnstown, PA, Saranac Lake, NY, (JST – SLK) line. The line is drawn on the excerpt from the In-flight Advisory Plotting Chart (FIG. 6-2). The PIT – HAR portion of the 072 TWEB is divided: southwestern PA west of the ridges; ridges and east of the ridges. Notice from the excerpts of the Geographical Area Designators map and TWEB Routes map in FIG. 6-2 that a JST – SLK line coincides with the west slopes of the Allegheny Mountains. The FA and TWEB cover the same geographical area.

BOSC FA	072 TWEB
NW JST – SLN LN	SWRN PA W OF RDGS
20 – 30 SCT – BKN 40 – 60 OVC 120	
OCNL CIG BLO 10 OVC/OBSCD AND	CIGS BLO 10 OVC VSBY BLO
VSBY BLO 3RW – F. MTNS OCNLY OBSCD.	3RW/TRW F . . .
18Z 30 – 50 BKN – OVC 100 BKN – OVC	AFT 14Z CIGS 20 BKN VSBY
120.	5RW – . . . AREAS 45 BKN VSBY
	BLO 3RWF . . . WDLY SCT TRW.

Ceilings below 1,000 feet and visibilities below three miles are expected to prevail over the TWEB route during the beginning of the forecast period, whereas the FA only forecasts occasional IFR. VFR flight will be doubtful based on the TWEB forecast. The TWEB expects improvement AFT 1400Z, the FA around 1800Z. Therefore, a VFR pilot

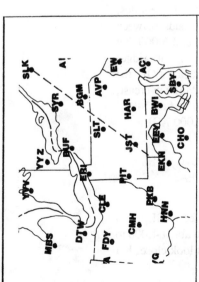

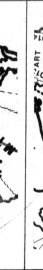
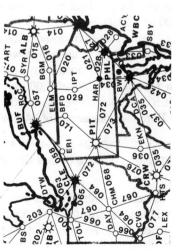

BOSC FA 290845
SGFNT CLDS AND WX VALID UNTIL 292100...

NY LO NJ PA
NW OF JST-SLK LN..20-30 SCT-BKN 40-60 OVC 120 WITH OCNL CIG BLO 10
OVC/OBSCD AND VSBY BLO 3RW-F. MTNS OCNLY OBSCD. 18Z 30-50 BKN-OVC
100 BKN-OVC 120...
SE OF JST-SLK LN...15-25 SCT-BKN 40-60 BKN-OVC 150 WITH OCNL CIG BLO
10 OVC/OBSCD AND VSBY BLO 3RW-F. MTNS OCNLY
OBSCD. TSTMS BCMG SCT AND PSBLY SVR AFT 18Z. CB TOPS ABV 450.

072 TWEB 290924 CLE-PIT-HAR. ALL HGTS AGL XCP TOPS. NERN
OH...CIGS 20-40 OVC VSBY 3-5R-F...AREAS CIGS 12 OVC VSBY BLO 3R-
F...WDLY SCT CIGS BLO 10 OVC. AFT 16Z CIGS 30 OVC VSBY 6+..WDLY
SCT R-. AFT 19Z 45 SCT. SWRN PA W OF RDGS...CIGS BLO 10 OVC VSBY
BLO 3RW/TRW F... AFT 14Z CIGS 20 BKN VSBY 5RW-..AREAS 45 BKN
VSBY BLO 3RW-..WDLY SCT TRW. RDGS AND E...45 OVC VSBY 5R-..
AREAS 12 OVC VSBY BLO 3RF. AFT 14Z CIGS 10-20 OVC...AREAS BLO
10 OVC...WDLY SCT TRW. RDGS OBSCD.

Fig. 6-2. *TWEB forecasts often contain more detail than the FA, although, they are usually perfectly consistent within the scope of each product.*

can expect a delay, although VFR flight should be possible after 1400Z to 1800Z, with excursions around scattered areas of lingering IFR conditions. The FA is of more value to the IFR pilot because it indicates layered clouds with tops to 12,000 feet MSL. However, the widely scattered thunderstorms predicted in the TWEB must be considered. For an aircraft without storm detection equipment, flight between layers or on top would be advisable.

After 1400Z, ceiling 2,000 broken, visibilities five miles in light rain showers are expected to prevail over the route according to the TWEB. However, one-quarter to one-half of the route (AREAS) are forecast 4,500 feet broken AGL, visibilities below three miles in rain showers and fog. The higher clouds and lower visibilities would not necessarily coincide. Given that terrain elevations are around 1,000 feet, FA and TWEB cloud heights are perfectly consistent. This illustrates the importance of determining whether forecast heights are MSL or AGL. Finally, less than one-quarter of the route (WDLY SCT) is expected to be affected by rain showers and thunderstorms. The TWEB forecaster covers the possibility of thunderstorms, whereas the FA forecaster does not. This is a matter of professional judgment.

```
BOSC FA                             072 TWEB
SE OF JST – SLN LN                  RDGS AND E
15 – 25 SCT – BKN 40 – 60 BKN – OVC 45 OVC VSBY 5R – . . . AREAS
WITH OCNL CIG BLO 10 OVC/OBSCD      12 OVC VSBY BLO 3RF.
AND VSBY BLO 3RW – F
WDLY SCT EMBDD TRW.
MTNS OCNLY OBSCD.
TSTMS BCMG SCT AND PSBLY SVR        AFT 14Z CIGS 10 – 20
AFT 18Z. CB TOPS ABV 450.           OVC . . . AREAS BLO 10
                                    OVC . . . WDLY SCT TRW. RDGS
                                    OBSCD.
```

The FA forecasts occasional ceilings and visibilities below 1,000 feet and three miles, skies obscured in light rain showers and fog, with scattered to broken clouds between 1,500 and 2,500 feet MSL, and broken to overcast clouds between 4,000 and 6,000 feet MSL. Terrain varies from about 500 feet around Harrisburg and in the valleys, with ridges to about 2,500 feet in the Johnstown area. Remembering that TWEB heights are AGL, the TWEB forecasts predominately 5,000 and 7,000 feet MSL (converted to MSL) overcast, with scattered AREAS of 2,000 to 3,500 MSL overcast (approximately). After 1400Z TWEB cloud heights become 2,000 to 4,000 MSL, with AREAS below 1,000 AGL.

Here is a comparison of FA/TWEB heights converted to MSL:

```
FA:     15 – 25 SCT – BKN 40 – 60 BKN – OVC OCNL CIG BLO 10 OVC
TWEB:   50 – 70 OVC AREAS 20 – 35 OVC . . . 14Z. 20 – 40 OVC AREAS
                                                     BLO 10 OVC
```

In general both forecasts predict occasional ceilings below 1,000 feet AGL, with higher clouds at about 2,000 to 3,000 feet MSL, and another layer between about 4,000 to 7,000 feet MSL. For people who deal with exact numbers, this might not look close, but from a meteorological forecast point of view, these forecasts are perfectly consistent, given the scope of each product. The TWEB can usually be more specific about the probability and coverage of weather. The FA, covering a larger area, forecasts thunderstorms increasing to scattered and possibly severe after 1800Z. However, the TWEB expects coverage to remain widely scattered.

VFR flight will be marginal, with the mountains occasionally obscured in clouds, rain, and possible thunderstorms. Other factors, primarily current conditions, would have to be considered to determine the advisability of a VFR flight.

For an IFR flight, again, the major concern will be convective activity. The FA indicates widely scattered embedded thunderstorms becoming scattered and possibly severe after 1800Z; the TWEB only contains widely scattered thunderstorms. This, again, is consistent given that the FA must cover a larger area. This can be interpreted as thunderstorm activity increasing and possibly becoming severe somewhere within the FA delineated area, which includes portions of New York and New Jersey, as well as Pennsylvania, but not within the area covered by TWEB route. This is a distinct advantage, due to the smaller aerial coverage, of TWEB forecasts. Often, TWEBs can be used to determine where within an FA area specific phenomena (thunderstorms) will occur. As well as current conditions, the advisability of an IFR flight would depend on current radar reports. A flight decision can never be made solely with the limited information in this example. Weather advisories, the synopses, and other portions of the FA, as well as current conditions, must be considered.

TWEBs do not directly forecast turbulence or icing. However, turbulence, and strong updrafts and downdrafts are implied by weather associated with these phenomena. For example, strong winds and mountain wave activity indicate turbulence. Icing can be expected above the freezing level where visible moisture exists, or in areas of freezing precipitation. And, like the FA, thunderstorms imply severe or greater turbulence and icing, and low-level wind shear. Specific forecasts for turbulence and icing must be obtained from the FA and weather advisories. The TWEB route forecast is not a substitute for, but rather a supplement to, the Area Forecast.

TWEB routes and synopses often provide more precise timing and detail than is possible in the FA. They provide additional specific information on visibility, surface winds, and local conditions that is not possible in the FA. But, like other forecast products, TWEBs cannot cover every instance of hazardous weather. Although the number of TWEB routes is extensive, many areas are not covered. Never extrapolate nor extend the forecast beyond its defined area.

Revised TWEB standards were adopted to standardize the product. However, as is often the case, interpretation of the new instructions was not consistent. Just after implementation, a message appeared from one weather service office: TWEB ROUTES DELAYED DUE TO RIDICULOUS NEW FORMAT.

7
Terminal Forecast
(FT)

ON SEPTEMBER 16, 1988, HURRICANE GILBERT, ONE OF THE CENTURY'S strongest, was approaching the Texas Gulf coast. With Gil's arrival, several San Francisco area oil companies planned to fly to Brownsville, presumably to check the fate of their oil rigs. Similar to the weather, there really wasn't much anyone could do; the rigs were either going to be there or gone. The following Terminal Forecast for Brownsville, TX (BRO), was written just prior to Gilbert's arrival.

At the end of the chapter we'll decode, translate, and interpret this BRO FT.

BRO FT 160808 20 SCT C60 OVC 4RW 0220G30 OCNL C20 BKN 2RW+
CHC C5 X 1/2TRW+ Q50. 00Z 3 SCT C12 OVC 2RW+ 0860Q75
OCNL C3 X 1/4 T+RW+ G120. 02Z LIFR CIG TRW WND . .

Some think the only place a pilot will actually see a Terminal Forecast is on an FAA exam. This might have been true in the past, but with FSS automation and DUAT, responsibility for decoding, translating, and interpreting this product will rest with the pilot. Incorrect interpretation could lead to anything from an embarrassing chat with an inspector from the local Flight Standards District Office (FSDO) to an aircraft accident.

Prepared by local Weather Service Forecast Offices, such as the Redwood City, CA, office in FIG. 7-1, Terminal Forecasts contain specific information for individual airports. FTs forecast cloud heights and amounts, visibility and obstructions to visibility, weather, wind, and low-level wind shear. FT locations are contained in Appendix B, Weather Report and Forecast Locations.

Fig. 7-1. *Meteorologists at local NWS offices prepare and monitor Terminal Forecasts. This forecaster at Redwood City, CA, is responsible for FTs in Northern and Central California.*

The meteorologist must have at least two consecutive SAs before issuing a Terminal Forecast. As a minimum, these observations must contain sky condition, visibility and obstructions to visibility, weather, temperature, dew point, wind, and altimeter setting. Part-time observations normally require three hours after the first observation for the FT to be written, distributed, and become available. The FT will not be issued if any element is missing. For example, with a missing dew point, pilots could expect to see XYZ FT 071919 FT NOT AVBL DUE MSG DEW PT. Some say this practice is foolish and dangerous, but the fact remains, just as pilots must abide by FARs, controllers must abide by the *Air Traffic Control* handbook, and FSS specialists by the *Flight Services* handbook, forecasters must comply with their *Operations Manual*. Our litigation-happy society means even the slightest transgression from procedures can result in a lawsuit and we all know who ends up paying the bill.

FT time references are UTC, with specific intervals specified. For example, 18Z, 23Z, 02Z–06Z, etc., which might be qualified using BY, AFT (after) or TIL (until). Terminal Forecasts for the contiguous states and Alaska are valid for 24 hours, an 18 hour forecast with a six-hour categorical outlook. Hawaiian FTs, valid for 12 hours, do not contain an outlook.

FTs are issued in the contiguous United States three times a day. Times vary with time zone, based on operational and other considerations. Refer to TABLE 7-1 for FT issuance times.

FTs have been criticized for not being written more often and not being valid for a longer period: written every three hours, valid for 24 hours. This is really nothing more than amending the forecast every three hours whether necessary or not. Issuance and valid times are based on available resources, and directly reflect the limitations on aviation weather forecasts. It's not logical to expect the last six hours of a forecast that is valid for 24 hours to be any more accurate than the categorical outlook on domestic FTs. In any case, for the foreseeable future, pilots will have to deal with the present system.

```
TUL FT 190909 250 – SCT 0410. 15Z 60 SCT C150 OVC 0515.
   23Z 30 SCT C80 BKN 0712 SCT OCNL BKN CHC C10 OVC 1TRW.
   03Z MVFR CIG . .
```

This Tulsa, OK (TUL) FT was issued on the 19th day of the month, valid from 0900Z until 0900Z on the 20th (190909). The first forecast section (250 – SCT 0410) is valid at 0900Z until the next forecast section becomes effective at 1500Z. The FT contains an 18-hour forecast (09Z–03Z) with a six-hour categorical outlook (03Z–09Z). The FT forecasts conditions within five nautical miles of the center of the runway complex, except in areas where thunderstorms, showers, or fog regularly develop beyond five miles, but directly affect operations. For these locations the term (*vicinity*) is used. VCNTY indicates phenomena occuring beyond five miles, but within 25 miles of the airport.

BODY AND REMARKS

The forecast group—as opposed to the outlook—is divided into *body* and *remarks*. Remarks amplify or describe conditions that differ from that in the body of the forecast

Table 7-1. *Terminal Forecast Issuance and Valid Times.*

Time Zone	Issued/UTC	Local
Eastern	0730/0830	3:30 a.m.
	1630/1730	12:30 a.m.
	2330/0030	7:30 p.m.
Central	0730/0830	2:30 a.m.
	1630/1730	11:30 a.m.
	2330/0030	6:30 p.m.
Mountain	0030/0130	6:30 p.m.
	0830/0930	2:30 a.m.
	1730/1830	11:30 a.m.
Pacific	0130/0230	6:30 p.m.
	0930/1030	2:30 a.m.
	1830/1930	11:30 a.m.

Note: UTC issuance times change one hour with daylight-saving time in the contiguous states.

Alaska (most locations)	0340	6:40 p.m.
	1040	1:40 a.m.
	1540	6:40 a.m.
	2040	11:40 a.m.
Hawaii	0540	7:40 p.m.
	1140	1:40 a.m.
	1740	7:40 a.m.
	2340	1:40 p.m.

group. Conditional terms describe variability TABLE 7-2, Terminal Forecast Conditional Terms, defines terms used on the FT.

The body contains sky cover (CLR, 250 – BKN, C50 OVC, etc.). FTs are similar to SAs in that they report cloud heights above ground level (AGL). This is important when using an FT product or comparing it with observations, PIREPs, or other forecasts. The letter C designates the ceiling; its definition is the same as used on SAs. FTs are specifically intended for arriving and departing aircraft, therefore cloud layers above 15,000 feet might not be included when a lower ceiling appears. Visibility will be forecast when prevailing visibility is expected to be six miles or less; the omission of a visibility forecast implies visibilities greater than six miles.

Visibilities greater than six miles are often referred to as unrestricted by FSS briefers. The symbol 6 + indicates that unrestricted visibility is intended, which prevents misunderstanding C10 OVC 2RW OCNL 10 SCT will be written C10 OVC 2RW OCNL 10 SCT 6 + to

Table 7-2. *Terminal Forecast Conditional Terms.*

No Conditional Term	Greater than 50 percent probability of occurrence during more than $1/2$ of the forecast period.
OCNL (occasional)	Greater than 50 percent probability but only expected to persist for $1/2$ or less of the forecast period.
CHC (chance)	50 percent probability or less.
VCNTY (vicinity)	Phenomena expected to occur beyond five miles and up to 25 miles from the airport
Probability of Precipitation	
CHC (chance)	30 percent to 50 percent
SLGT CHC (slight chance)	10 percent to 20 percent

clearly indicate that visibility is expected to be occasionally unrestricted. Weather and obstructions to vision appear with a visibility forecast (3HK, 5TRW, etc.). Weather and obstructions to vision use the same contractions, with the same definitions, as those on SAs.

A popular aviation magazine reported that winds received from a tower were miles per hour and on FTs winds were knots. Let's settle the matter: wind direction true or magnetic, blowing from or toward the reported direction, speed knots or miles per hour. *All official aviation wind observations and forecasts are reported in relation to true north, given as the direction from which the wind is blowing, with speed in knots.* The only time a pilot will receive winds in relation to magnetic north is from a tower, AWOS broadcast, or as part of an airport advisory because runway headings are magnetic.

Omission of a wind forecast implies speed less than six knots; otherwise, wind direction and speed will appear on the FT. Gustiness is a forecast for rapid fluctuations of 10 knots or more indicated by the G following the wind group: 3425G40 (mean wind speed 25 knots with peak gusts to 40 knots), 0720G (wind speed variable between 10 and 30 knots), or G50 (wind gusts to 50 knots). Unlike the FA or TWEB, the FT does provide a specific wind forecast.

Low-level wind shear on Terminal Forecasts refers to non-thunderstorm shear. Wind direction, speed, and height might be included. LLWS appears when PIREPs report an airspeed gain or loss of 20 knots or more, or vertical shears of 10 knots or more per 100 feet are expected or reported:

    CLR LLWS TIL 13Z WND 1505 AT SFC 1935 AT 1500 FT

TERMINAL FORECAST (FT)

LLWS is forecast until 1300Z due to surface winds from 150° at five knots and winds at 1,500 feet AGL from 190° at 35 knots. Non-thunderstorm LLWS is described in Chapter 4, The Area Forecast.

Refer to the 2300Z portion of the TUL FT. The body forecasts 30 SCT C80 BKN 0712 and the remarks contain SCT OCNL BKN CHC C10 OVC 1TRW. The body decodes, 3,000 scattered, ceiling 8,000 broken, wind 070° at 12 knots. The remarks indicate that the 3,000-foot AGL scattered layer might be occasionally (greater than 50 percent probability but expected for 50 percent or less of the period) broken, and a chance (50 percent probability or less) of ceiling 1,000 overcast, visibility one mile in moderate rain showers and thunderstorms exists.

A word of caution, it's dangerous to extrapolate the FT beyond five miles. Over flat terrain, such as the Midwest, chances are that nearby airports might have similar conditions. This does not relieve the pilot, however, of checking appropriate FA or TWEB forecasts. In hilly or mountainous terrain this practice can be disastrous. For example, afternoon surface winds during the summer are routinely strong and gusty at San Francisco International Airport, whereas, at other Bay Area airports winds remain relatively calm due to wind direction and terrain.

Conversely, an airport in the middle of a valley might have benign surface winds, however at a nearby airport below a canyon, surface winds can prevent landings altogether. This is not uncommon in the Los Angeles Basin when Santa Ana winds blow; winds at the Ontario, CA, airport might be out of the west less than five knots, but at Rialto, about 10 miles away, winds might be out of the north gusting to more than 40 knots. Rialto lies just below the Cajon Pass.

From the discussion thus far let's decode, translate, and interpret the following FT.

18Z 35 SCT C80 BKN OCNL C35 BKN 2312 CHC RW/TRW.
23Z CFP C25 BKN 80 OVC 0808 CHC C15 OVC 1TRW.
02Z 45 SCT 100 SCT 1713 LYRS SCT OCNL BKN TRW VCNTY.

At 18Z greater than 50 percent probability, during more than one-half the period (18Z–23Z), exists for scattered clouds at 3,500 feet, ceiling 8,000 feet broken. However, there is greater than 50 percent probability for one-half or less of the period that the scattered clouds at 3,500 feet will be broken, winds 230° at 12 knots, and a 30 to 50 percent probability of rain showers, or rain showers and thunderstorms. The winds would not necessarily coincide with broken clouds. Conditions are expected to deteriorate around 2300Z, so expect the remarks portion of the forecast to be more prevalent during the later portion of the period.

Cold front passage is expected around 2300Z. But, from our discussion thus far, conditions will not instantly change. Limitations on Aviation Weather Forecasts (TABLE 3-1), reveals the best that could be expected would be frontal passage within two hours, sometime between 2100Z-0100Z. At that time conditions are forecast to deterioration to (greater than 50 percent probability, during more than one-half the period 2300Z-0200Z) ceilings 2,500 feet broken, 8,000 feet overcast, wind 080° at eight knots. Remarks indicate a 50 percent probability or less of ceilings 1,500 feet overcast, visibility one mile in rain showers and thunderstorms. Here we could reasonably expect the remarks (CHC C15

OVC 1TRW) to be more prevalent during the beginning of the period, associated with frontal passage.

By 0200Z greater than 50 percent probability, during more than one-half of the period, exists for conditions to improve to 4,500 scattered, 10,000 scattered, wind 170 at 13, scattered layers broken for one-half or less of the period. Rain showers and thunderstorms are expected beyond five miles, but within 25 miles of the airport.

It's extremely important to understand the synoptic situation and obtain frequent updates. Remember the limitations on aviation forecasts in TABLE 3-1. Timing is a major problem and if observations reveal that frontal passage occurred at 2100Z, we could reasonably expect the conditions described at 2300Z to prevail. Conversely, if frontal passage occurs at 01Z, expect the improvement advertised in the 0200Z portion of the forecast to be delayed. Within the scope of this product, frontal passage within two hours is considered accurate and, under most circumstances, will not generate an amendment.

The lowest conditions forecast, CHC C15 OVC 1TRW, are associated with frontal passage. Even under these conditions special VFR should be possible—assuming special VFR is allowed in the control zone (Chapter 14, VFR Flight Planning). To be safe, however, based solely on the forecast, VFR flight should be planned either before 2100Z or after 0100Z. The thunderstorm activity would be of concern to both VFR and IFR flights. Convective activity should be circumnavigable, but could cause arrival and departure delays; fuel reserves and alternatives for both VFR and IFR flight plans should be planned accordingly.

Remarks must be considered when determining IFR alternatives. Therefore, a forecast of CLR 5F CHC C5 X 2L – F would require an alternate. Additionally, this airport would not qualify as a legal alternate because the ceiling is forecast less than 600 feet (FAR Part 91.169). Forecasters are aware that remarks, as well as the body, must be considered when determining legal destinations, alternates, and fuel loads. This makes remarks operationally more significant when they describe lower conditions. Forecasters will use remarks sparingly and be as concise as possible, to allow the use of an airport as an alternate.

Provisions of FARs Part 135 (Air Taxi) and Part 121 (Air Carriers) are also considered. Both regulations state: "No person may . . . begin an IFR . . . operation unless the latest weather report or forecast, or any combination of them, indicate that weather conditions at the ETA at the next airport of intended landing will be at or above authorized IFR landing minimums." Forecasters could effectively close airports to certain operations. Below is an example how forecasters deal with this situation. The SAs and FT are for Monterey, CA (MRY), from a controller at the part-time tower.

```
MRY SA 1250 W3 X 1/4F
MRY SA 1345 W0 X 1/4F
MRY SA 1449 W0 X 1/8F
MRY SP 1522 W1 X 1/2F
MRY FT RTD 061410 1420Z C0 X 1/4F OCNL C3 X 1F. 17Z C4 X 2F OCNL
     5 SCT 6F. 19Z . . .
```

Monterey's first report was observed at 1250Z. The FT is, therefore, routinely delayed (RTD). When two consecutive observations became available, the FT was written, valid at 1420Z. However, due to transmission and distribution time, a pilot wouldn't expect the FT to be available until some time after 1420Z. Notice the 1420Z forecast C0 X 1/4F OCNL C3 X 1F, even though W0 X 1/4F is reported. When actual conditions improve to landing minimums (ceiling 200 and visibility 1/2 mile) FAR 135 and 121 operations can legally land. The forecaster said: Between 1420Z and 1700Z conditions will improve to IFR landing minimums, between 1700Z and 1900Z the weather will become VFR.

Pilots continually demand to know *exactly* when an airport will improve to IFR landing minimums or VFR conditions. Accuracy simply is not possible. FAR alternate airport and fuel reserve minimums take these limitations into consideration. However, departing with appropriate alternates and adequate fuel does not relieve the pilot of updating weather information en route.

Forecasts Based on AWOS Observations

With the implementation of automated observations the FT forecast will change somewhat, due to differences in observational techniques. FTs based on automated observations will be labeled as such (INW FT 211818 AUTOB—a forecast based on an NWS AUTOB system). All the cautions that apply to automated SAs must be considered using an FT based on those observations. And, like the FAA with respect to operational requirements, the National Weather Service has concluded that augmentation—remarks—are not a factor in forecasting. The following criteria reflect the limitations of automated observations discussed in Chapter 1.

Forecasts based completely on automated observations will only report sky condition up to two-thirds of the reporting range of the cloud height sensor. For example, the NWS AUTOB system does not report clouds above 6,000, therefore, the highest sky condition forecast will be CLR BLO 40 (clear below 4,000 feet AGL). Although, the forecaster might include higher cloud layers determined from other sources. Visibilities are similar to other FTs, except when minimum sensor visibility is less than one mile, the lowest forecast visibility will be BLO 1 (below 1 mile). Precipitation normally will be forecast as a "yes" or "no" proposition: if yes, indicated by the letter P (1PF, visibility one in precipitation and fog). Obstructions to visibility and obscurations are based on visibility, usually less than two miles. They might or might not be representative of actual conditions.

With cloud heights forecast more than 6,000 feet and visibility less than two miles, CX 1PF might be forecast. This is translated as no significant clouds, with an obscuration—partial obscuration—produced by precipitation and fog reducing visibility to one mile. AUTOB might be satisfactory for airports like Winslow, AZ, where minimum visibility for the approach is one mile. The system would not be effective for an airport with a precision approach, or minimums less than one mile. AWOS, however, will satisfy the ceiling and visibility requirements to generate an FT for precision approach minimums.

OUTLOOK

The final six hours of an FT, issued for the contiguous states or Alaska, consists of a categorical forecast group. Only prevailing conditions—greater than 50 percent probability of occurrence during more than $1/2$ of the period—are included. Outlook categories are similar to the Area Forecast with two exceptions. (Refer to TABLE 7-3, Terminal Forecast Outlook Categories.) First, in addition to three basic categories (IFR, MVFR, and VFR), FTs might contain Low Instrument Flight Rules (LIFR). Second, wind (WND) is defined as sustained winds or gusts of 25 knots or greater. Like the FA, the cause of the condition for an outlook of LIFR, IFR, or MVFR will be specified: LIFR CIG ceiling less than 500 feet; IFR SW visibility one to less than three miles in snow showers, or, MVFR HK visibility three to five miles in haze and smoke. VFR may be modified by one of the following: VFR CIG ABV 100, indicating a ceiling above 10,000 feet; VFR NO CIG, clouds covering less than $6/10$ of the sky or thin clouds; or VFR CLR, clouds covering less than $1/10$ of the sky. Thunderstorms, precipitation, and wind are added when required (. . . TRW, . . . SW, . . . WND).

TABLE 7-3 Outlook Definitions do not necessarily correspond to those in the Federal Aviation Regulations. VFR indicates ceiling *more* than 3,000 feet and visibility *more* than five miles. How much *more* is unknown unless one of the VFR modifiers appears (VFR CLR).

Table 7-3. *Terminal Forecast Outlook Categories.*

Category	Ceiling (feet)		Visibility (miles)
LIFR (Low IFR)	less than 500	and/or	less than one
IFR	500 to less than 1,000	and/or	one to less than three
MVFR (Marginal VFR)	1,000 to 3,000	and/or	three to five
VFR	more than 3,000	and	more than five
WIND	Sustained winds or gusts of 25 knots or greater.		

When applying the outlook to a proposed flight, remember that sky condition is above ground level within five miles of the airport.

Consider an airport located in a valley with an FT outlook of VFR. Surrounding terrain could make VFR flight out of the valley impossible. VFR flight might or might not be possible with an outlook of MVFR, depending on whether the weather is at the upper or lower limit of the category. In either case the capability for IFR, or possibility of delay, is indicated.

IFR indicates a non-precision approach (VOR, NDB) might be possible. Whereas, LIFR would generally require a precision approach (ILS). Of course, the outlook is for planning purposes only and must never be used in place of a briefing just prior to departure.

AMENDMENT CRITERIA

The NWS forecast manual states:

"Forecasters should strive to amend FTs prior to the occurence of expected changes which meet these criteria. If this cannot be done, amendments to the body and/or remarks portion of FTs shall be issued promptly whenever conditions meeting the criteria occur, and, in the forecasters judgment, these conditions will persist."

Reviewing TABLE 7-4, Terminal Forecast Amendment Criteria, to perhaps notice why forecasters tend to create strategic forecasts. Ceilings above 4,000 feet and visibilities more than five miles must change drastically before an amendment is required. And, as conditions lower, becoming more significant, criteria intervals decrease. Changes in wind speed less than 15 knots do not require an amendment (TABLE 7-4). At speeds of 15 knots or greater the speed must differ by 10 knots or more. Therefore, a forecast of 20 knots would have to decrease to 10 knots or increase to 30 knots before an amendment is required.

Basically, FT wind speeds are considered accurate when within 10 knots of the forecast. A pilot competent enough to handle 20 knots must consider that with a forecast of 20 knots, actual winds could increase to almost 30 knots without a requirement to amend. And, within these parameters the forecast is considered accurate. The only weather phenomena requiring amendments are thunderstorms, freezing precipitation, ice pellets, and LLWS. The unforecast occurrence or ending of rain or snow does not require an amendment. This fact has led many people to erroneously criticize the forecast.

When phenomena described in VCNTY moves, or is expected to move, within five miles of the airport, an amendment is required. The phenomena can appear in the body or remarks of the amendment. Outlook Categories are amended when expected to change by two increments. For example LIFR is expected to become MVFR or VFR. At locations with part-time observations the remark NO AMDTS AFT (time)Z will appear; like TWEBs, this serves as a warning that significant changes can occur without an amendment. Extra caution must be exercised operating into these airports, especially during marginal or deteriorating conditions.

The following example illustrates a forecaster applying amendment criteria. The observations and forecasts are for San Francisco International Airport (SFO).

```
SFO FT 061111 C12 BKN OCNL 12 SCT 30 SCT C200 OVC. 15Z C15 BKN
    OCNL 15 SCT C30 BKN. 20Z . . .
SFO SP 1222 9 – SCT 200 – BKN 10 . . .
SFO SA 1251 11 SCT E200 BKN 10 . . . /FEW LWR ST N
SFO SA 1351 11 SCT 200 – BKN 10 . . . /VSBY NW 1/2V11/4 SHLW FBNK
SFO RS 1501 – X E200 BKN 1/4F . . . /F4/F INCR RAPIDLY
SFO FT AMD 1 061511 1433Z 11 SCT 200 – OVC OCNL – X 3F.
    1530Z 11 SCT 200 – OVC 3F OCNL – X 1/2F. 18Z . . .
```

The SFO SAs, sky condition, and remarks, indicate unforecast fog increasing; expecting fog to continue to develop an amendment was issued, effective at 1433Z. The forecaster expects conditions to further deteriorate at 1530Z. In fact, that did occur with

Table 7-4. *Terminal Forecast Amendment Criteria.*

With a forecast of:	Amend if:	With a forecast of:	Amend if:
Ceiling		**Visibility**	
No ceiling/ceiling more than 8,000	4,000 or less	More than five miles	Three miles or less
More than 4,000 through 8,000	Decreases to 1/2 or less	More than one mile through five miles	Decreases to 1/2 or less, or increases to twice or more
More than 1,000 through 4,000	Increases to twice or more/decreases to 1/2 or less	One mile or less	More than 1/2 mile difference
1,000 feet	Decrease by 300 ft. or more, or increase to twice or more		
Less than 1,000	300-ft. difference or more		
Wind		**Weather**	
Speed 15 knots or more	Direction differs by 30 degrees or more	Thunderstorms, freezing precipitation; or ice pellets	Does not occur or no longer expected
	Speed differs by 10 knots or more	No thunderstorms, freezing precipitation or ice pellets	Occurs or is expected
Gusts with mean speed of 12 knots or more	Gust 10 knots or more above forecast	LLWS	No LLWS expected
Categorical Outlook		No LLWS	LLWS occurs or is expected
LIFR	MVFR or VFR		
IFR	VFR		
MVFR	LIFR		
VFR	LIFR or IFR		

the 1501 RS. The amended forecast indicates occasional visibilities half-mile in fog. With this forecast, visibility can vary from zero to one mile. This accomplishes two things. First, conditions between zero and one mile are covered, such as the 1501 RS visibility of 1/4, and, second, when RVR or prevailing visibility indicate minimums, FAR Part 135 and Part 121 operators can legally land.

The preceding example points out the significance of remarks. If this had been an AWOS observation, the first clue the forecaster might have had to notice the deteriorating conditions would have been the 1501 RS. This could have delayed an amendment by hours.

Applying Amendment Criteria to VFR.

Below are examples of how ceiling and visibility can vary without requiring an amendment.

Forecast	Variability
Ceiling 1,500 feet	800 to 2,900
Visibility four miles	greater than two to less than eight (2 1/4 to 7)

The forecast is considered accurate as long as conditions remain within these values. The implications are, and pilots must understand, that conditions can deteriorate below basic VFR without a requirement to amend. Low-time pilots, student pilots, and flight instructors (who must endorse student cross-country flights) should consider the following. With an understanding of amendment criteria, and that forecasters tend toward strategic forecasts, what would be a reasonable forecast for VFR operations? A ceiling forecast of 3,000 feet would have to decrease to 1,500 or lower, and a visibility of more than five miles would have to decrease to three miles or less to require an amendment (TABLE 7-4). Therefore, these pilots should strongly consider FT ceilings 3,000 feet and visibilities six miles as minimums.

Don't forget the winds. A forecast wind of 15 knots could increase to 24 knots without a requirement to amend. If a pilot's personal limits are in the 15 to 20 knot range, he or she might well consider a forecast of 15 knots or more as a no-go indicator. There are no guarantees, but these values do give a margin of safety. These minimums would apply to the remarks of the forecast as well as the body.

Interestingly, FARs don't require VFR alternates, whereas IFR alternates are specified. Don't interpret this to mean that VFR alternates need not be considered. Pilots who fail to consider options, and get into trouble will very likely be faced with the FAA's catch-all regulation, FAR Part 91.13 Careless or reckless operation. When the weather is close to legal or personal minimums, a solid VFR alternate and frequent weather updates are a must.

Applying Amendment Criteria to IFR.

IFR pilots must be just as cautious as VFR pilots when applying Terminal Forecasts close to minimums. The IFR pilot, however, has Federal Aviation Regulations as a hedge against forecast limitations. FAR Part 91.169 IFR flight plan: Required information specifies IFR alternate airport weather minimums.

Refer to the Fresno, CA (FAT), FTs and SAs for the following discussion.

```
FAT FT 132323 C7 BKN 1F CHC 7 SCT 2F. 07Z C2 X 1/2F. 17Z LIFR
    CIG F.
FAT SA 2254 −X M9 BKN 1F
SA 2353 −X 9 SCT 11/4F
```

```
        SA 0053 M8 OVC 3/4F
        SA 0352 M4 OVC 11/2F
        SA 0451 W3 X 1F
        SA 0652 W2 X 1/2F
        SA 0852 W0 X 0F
  FAT FT 141010 C1 X 1/4F OCNL C4 X 1F. 04Z LIFR CIG F . .
  FAT FT 141616 C1 X 1/4F OCNL C4 X 1/2F. 20Z C5 OVC 1F OCNL C10
        OVC 2F . . . .
```

To require an amendment with the 132323 forecast (C7 BKN 1F . . .), ceiling would have to decrease to 400 feet or less and/or visibility to less than one-half mile, or increase to four miles or more. With the remark (. . . CHC 7 SCT), sky condition could improve to clear without an amendment. This portion of the forecast can be interpreted as conditions are expected to remain above IFR landing minimums (ceiling 200, visibility one-half) and possibly improve to VFR. In fact, conditions did improve at 2353Z: 9 SCT 11/4F.

Special VFR would be possible, but don't bet your life on it. Conditions deteriorated below special VFR minimums the following hour. Based on the forecast, Fresno would require an alternate if filed as the destination, but, could not be used as an alternate for another airport. According to FAR Part 91.169(c), IFR alternate airport weather minimums, Fresno must forecast at least ceilings 600 feet and visibilities two miles to be filed as an alternate, assuming standard alternate minimums for a precision approach. Visibilities in the body of the forecast do not meet this requirement. Pilots should note that to qualify as an alternate, the forecast must indicate appropriate alternate minimums for the pilot's ETA at the alternate airport.

Notice that conditions just meet amendment criteria at 0352Z. It appears the forecaster was hoping conditions would not continue to deteriorate until the 0700Z portion became effective. Conditions did lower slightly at 0451Z. Since there was no significant operational impact—the field remained above ILS minimums—the forecaster apparently decided not to amend with the 0700Z forecast effective in two hours. With the 0700Z (C2 X 1/2F) forecast, ceiling could increase to 400 feet and/or visibility to one mile, or decrease to C0 X 0F. The latter occurred at 0852Z.

With the 141010 forecast ceiling could vary between zero and 600 feet, visibility between zero and one-and-one-half. The 141616 forecast is much more realistic. Unfortunately, as previously mentioned, the 1600Z to 2000Z portion omits the information needed most—when will conditions improve to landing minimums? This example of a strategic forecast is a major operational problem, but reflects the limitations on aviation weather forecasts. However, again, FAR fuel reserves and alternate requirements are based on these limitations.

A forecast of landing minimums is no guarantee those conditions will exist at the estimated time of arrival. An alternate affected by the same weather pattern as the destination might satisfy FARs, but leave a pilot on the proverbial limb with a busted forecast. For example, if a pilot's destination was Fresno, as in this example, Bakersfield might qualify as a legal alternative. However, with Tule Fog—a local name given to this condition—in California's Central Valleys, a viable alternate might be along the coast, which is normally not affected by this phenomena. This would also apply to airports affected by upslope fog or frontal systems. If at all possible, a pilot should select an alternate not affected by the weather pattern at the destination. At the risk of being redundant, know the synopsis and continually update weather en route.

TERMINAL AERODROME FORECASTS (TAF)

The National Weather Service issued TAFs for airports served by long, usually over-water, international flights in International Civil Aviation Organization (ICAO) format. Forecasts are issued four times a day, valid for 24 hours. Forecasts using TAF (World Meteorological Organization—WMO) codes are also issued by many local military weather offices. Military TAFs have different criteria than those issued by the NWS, therefore some differences will occur. Conditions are described using an alphanumeric code and numerical indicators. TABLE 7-5, Terminal Aerodrome Forecasts (TAF), provides an explanation of TAF format and conditional terms.

Below is an example of a TAF for Denver, CO.

```
KDEN 1818 VRB05KT 9999 5CI250 GRADU 2021 06008KT 2CU060 6CI250
    INTER 2105 6CU060 PROB40 2105 06008/30KT 6000 96TSGR 8CB050
    GRADU 0506 VRB05KT 2AC100 5CI250=
```

Notice the four letter international identifier KDEN. Valid time appears next, 1800Z to 1800Z the following day. The first code group describes wind conditions. At 1800Z wind is forecast to be variable (VRB) at five knots. Visibility in meters follows wind. TABLE 7-5 can be used to convert meters to statute miles. Values range from 0000 meters to 9999 meters (greater than six miles). Sky cover is expressed in octas (or eights). In the example, 5/8 sky cover is forecast at 25,000 feet. Also, the type of cloud appears using standard contractions, in this case cirrus (CI). In the sky condition group, 9 indicates sky obscured. This is followed by a double solidus (or slants), (//), and vertical visibility into the obscuring phenomena (9//000—sky obscured, indefinite ceiling zero, W 0 X). Conditions are expected to gradually change (GRADU) between 2000Z and 2100Z (2021).

Wind is forecast 060° at eight knots, sky condition 2/8 cumulus at 6,000 feet and 6/8 cirrus at 25,000 feet. Frequent but brief changes from prevailing conditions (INTER) are expected between 2100Z and 0500Z (2105). During this period 6/8 cumulus at 6,000 feet is forecast. Probability of occurence is expressed in percent.

The next portion of the forecast decodes, a 30 percent to 50 percent probability (PROB40) between 2100Z and 0500Z (2105) of wind 060 degrees at eight knots with gusts to 30 knots (06008/30KT), visibility 6,000 meters (four miles) in thunderstorms, rain showers, and hail (96TSGR—WMO term, refer to TABLE 7-6, Terminal Aerodrome Forecast (TAF) Weather Codes), sky condition 8/8 cumulonimbus at 5,000 feet. Conditions will gradually improve between 0500Z and 0600Z, continuing through the remainder of the forecast period. The equal sign (=) indicates the end of the forecast.

Now compare the TAF format with the domestic DEN FT for the same period. Keep in mind the parameters and limitations discussed thus far.

```
DEN FT 1018118 250 –BKN. 20Z 60 SCT C250 BKN 0608 OCNL C60 BKN
    CHC C50 OVC 4TRWA G30. 05Z 100 SCT 250 –BKN. 12Z VFR . .
```

Table 7-5. *Terminal Aerodrome Forecasts (TAF).*

KSAV 212200 (Savannah, GA)

```
TAF
KSAV  (TIME) (WND)    (VSBY)         (CLDS & WX)
KSAV  0024   16009KT  9999 2SC030 6AS100  INTER 0004 6SC025  PROB40  0004  16009/35KT 0800 95TS 81XXSH 9//005  GRADU  0304  VRB05KT 2SC045 2AS120
SAV 210024  1609      6+   30 SCT C200 BKN (VRBLTY) 00-04Z C25 BKN (PRBLTY) 00-04Z   1/2  TRW/R44+ W5 X  (WX CHG) 03-04Z  (WND)  45 SCT 120 SCT

6CI250  INTER  0408 6000 10BR 6SC045  GRADU  0708 6000 10BR 2ST005 6SC045  INTER  0814  3200 10BR 6ST005  GRADU  1314  9999  WX NIL...
C250 BKN (VRBLTY) 04-08Z 4  F  C45 BKN (WX CHG) 07-08Z  4  F  5 SCT C45 BKN (VRBLTY) 08-14Z  2  F  C5 BKN (WX CHG) 13-14Z  6+  (CLDS/WX)
```

Wind (WND): dddss/ggKT Direction True-three digits (ddd), Speed Knots (ss), Gusts when expected follow a slant (/gg).

Visibility (VSBY) In Meters:

Meters	Miles
0000	0
0100	1/16
0200	1/8
0300	3/16
0400	1/4
0500	5/16
0600	3/8
0800	1/2
1000	5/8
1200	3/4
1400	7/8
1600	1
1800	11/8
2000	11/4
2200	11/2
2400	13/8
2600	13/4
2800	15/8
3000	17/8
3200	2
3600	21/4
4000	21/2
4800	3
6000	4
8000	5
9000	6
9999	6+

Clouds (CLDS): Sky cover is given in OCTAS (eights), cloud type specified, and height AGL in hundreds of feet. An obscuration is indicated by "9//hhh", where "hhh" represents the vertical visibility.

Note: The following is a summary and general translation of TAF alphanumeric codes and numerical indicators.

Significant Weather Change Indicators (WX CHG):

GRADU – A gradual change occurring during the period.

RAPID – A rapid change occurring.

Probability (PRBLTY):

PROB (%) – Probability of occurrence expressed as a percent.

PROB20 – 10% to 20% ("SLGT CHC").

PROB40 – 30% to 50% ("CHC").

Variability Terms (VRBLTY):

TEMPO – Temporary change from prevailing conditions.

INTER – Frequent, but brief, change from prevailing conditions.

Cloud and Weather Terms (CLDS/WX):

CAVOK – No significant clouds or weather.

WX NIL – No significant weather.

SKC – Sky clear.

They are identical. This shouldn't be a surprise because both were written by the same forecaster. The TAF, however, directly reflects the limitations on aviation forecasts through the use of weather change indicators and variability terms not used on domestic FTs. The lack of TAF indicators and terms on domestic FTs does not mean the forecast is more accurate. As we've seen, they're implied, and must be considered when applying the forecast.

Rather than the previous example, pilots often can expect to see the TAF code used with military forecasts. Below is an example of the March Air Force Base, Riverside, CA (RIV), forecast.

```
RIV 2323 30008KT 4000 05HZ SKC QNH2982INS SKY – X
     GRADU 2324 33008KT 4800 05HZ SKC QNH2980INS SKY – X
     GRADU 0507 VRB03KT 2400 10BR 8ST008 QNH2980 CIG008
     GRADU 1214 VRB03KT 3200 10BR 8ST012 QNH2984INS CIG012
     GRADU 1820 30008KT 4800 05HZ SKC QNH2980INS SKY – X =
```

This RIV forecast is valid from 2300 to 2300 the following day. Wind forecast 300 degrees at eight knots, visibility 4,000 meters (2.5 miles) in haze (05HZ), sky clear (SKC)—no clouds—but partially obscured (SKY – X). Notice that the military also forecasts altimeter setting 29.82 (QNH2982INS) and adds a remark with a ceiling forecast (third line: CIG008). Below is a translation of the RIV TAF into domestic format.

```
RIV FT 142323 – X 21/2H. 00Z – X 3H 3308. 06Z C8 OVC 11/2F. 13Z
       C12 OVC 2F. 17Z MVFR H . .
```

Naval TAFs use a slightly different format to describe a partial obscuration. Following the altimeter setting forecast, the TAF contains amount of sky obscured, obscuring phenomena, and three solidi or slants. For example, in this TAF for Alameda Naval Air Station (NGZ).

```
NGZ 0303 . . . QNH3035INS 2BR/// . . .
```

The forecast indicates that $2/8$ of the sky will be obscured by mist and fog (BR, refer to TABLE 7-6).

Whether international or military, TAFs suffer from the same limitations as domestic FTs, or any forecast for that matter. It really can't be said that one or the other is necessarily more accurate. However, comparing a domestic FT with a nearby military TAF, provides a second opinion.

Certain optional codes might appear on TAF forecasts. These optional numerical groups forecast operationally significant temperature, icing, and turbulence. Table 7-6, Terminal Aerodrome Forecast (TAF) Optional Codes, decodes these phenomena.

USING THE TERMINAL FORECAST

Apparent inconsistencies arise because different forecasts serve different purposes. The following example compares FA and TWEB forecasts with a Terminal Forecast.

Table 7-6. Terminal Aerodrome Forecast (TAF) Weather Codes.

Note 1: TAF conversions to Domestic FT codes are approximations.
Note 2: Fog, Codes 40 through 47, include both fog (F) and ice fog (IF).

TAF Code	Domestic Code	Remarks
04FU	K	
05HZ	H	
06HZ	D	
07SA	BD	Blowing Dust
08PO	BD	Dust Devil
10BR	F/GF	Mist/Fog
11MIFG	GF	Shallow Fog
12MIFG	GF	Shallow Fog
17TS	T	Thunderstorm
18SQ	Q	Squall
19FC	TORNADO	Funnel Cloud/Water Spout
30SA	BD/BN	Dust/Sandstorm/DCRG
31SA	BD/BN	Dust/Sandstorm
32SA	BD/BN	Dust/Sandstorm/INCRG
33XXSA	BD/BN	SVR Dust/Sandstorm/DCRG Decreasing
34XXSA	BD/BN	Severe Dust/Sandstorm
35XXSA	BD/BN	SVR Dust/Sandstorm/INCRG
36DRSN	BS	Drifting Snow
37DRSN	BS	Drifting Snow
38BLSN		
39BLSN		
40BCFG	F	Patchy Fog
41BCFG	F	Patchy Fog
42FG	F	
43FG	F	
44FG	GF	
45FG	F	
46FG	F	
47FG	F	
48ZFFG	F	Fog Depositing Rime Ice
49FZFG	F	Fog Depositing Rime Ice
50DZ	L–	Intermittent
51DZ	L–	Continuous
52DZ	L	Intermittent
53DZ	L	Continuous
54XXDZ	L+	Intermittent
55XXDZ	L+	Continuous
56XXDZ	ZL–/ZL	
57XXFZDZ	ZL/ZL+	
58RA	L–/R–	
59RA	R/L	Moderate or Heavy
60RA	R–	Intermittent
61RA	R–	Continuous
62RA	R	Intermittent
63RA	R	Continuous
64XXRA	R+	Intermittent
65XXRA	R+	Continuous
66FZRA	ZR/ZL	Light or Moderate
67XXFZRA	ZR	Moderate or Heavy
68RASN	R/S	Light or Moderate
69XXRASN	R+/S+	
70SN	S–	Intermittent
71SN	S–	Continuous
72SN	S	Intermittent
73SN	S	Continuous
74XXSN	S+	Intermittent
75XXSN	S+	Continuous
77SG	SG	
79PE	IP	
80RASH	RW	Light or Moderate
81XXSH	RW	Moderate or Heavy
82XXSH	RW+	
83RASN	RW/SW	Light or Moderate
84XXRASN	RW+/SW+	
85SNSH	SW	Light or Moderate
86XXSNSH	SW	Moderate or Heavy
87GR	IPW–	
88GR	IPW	Moderate or Heavy
89GR	A	
90XXGR	A	Moderate or Heavy
91RA	R–	
92XXRA	R	Moderate or Heavy
93GR	RW–/SW–/IPW–	
94XXGR	RW/SW/IPW	Moderate or Heavy
95TS	TRW–/TRW/TRW+	
96TSGR	TRWA	
97XXTS	T+RW/T+RW+	
98TSSA	T	Dust/Sandstorm
99XXTSGR	T+RWA/T+RW+A	

Table 7-7. Terminal Aerodrome Forecast (TAF) Optional Codes.

TAFs may contain the following optional numerical groups for temperature 0 t t T T, icing 6 i h h h d, and turbulence 5 i h h d.

KJFK 1818 22015/30 5000 80RASH 7CU125 02125 621300 510309 GRADU ...

Temperature: 02125

    0 – (0) Temperature group

    21 – (tt) Time UTC temperature is expected to occur.

    25 – (TT) Temperature in Degrees Celsius.

Icing: 621300

    6 – (6) Icing group

    2 – (i) Icing Intensity (Light icing in cloud)

    130 – (hhh) Base height hundreds of feet (13,000 feet)

    0 – (d) Thickness in thousands of feet*

      * 0 indicates to top of clouds.

Icing Intensity (TAF Group 6)

0	No icing
1	Light icing
2	Light icing in cloud
3	Light icing in precipitation
4	Moderate icing
5	Moderate icing in cloud
6	Moderate icing in precipitation
7	Severe icing
8	Severe icing in cloud
9	Severe icing in precipitation

Turbulence: 510309

    5 – (5) Turbulence group

    1 – (i) Turbulence Intensity (Light Turbulence)

    030 – (hhh) Base height hundreds of feet (3,000 feet)

    9 – (d) Thickness in thousands of feet* (9,000)

      (Turbulence expected from 3,000 through 12,000 feet)

Turbulence Intensity (TAF Group 5)

0	None
1	Light turbulence
2	Moderate turbulence in clear air, infrequent
3	Moderate turbulence in clear air, frequent
4	Moderate turbulence in cloud, infrequent
5	Moderate turbulence in cloud, frequent
6	Severe Turbulnece in clear air, infrequent
7	Severe turbulence in clear air, frequent
8	Severe turbulence in cloud, infrequent
9	Severe turbulence in cloud, frequent

CHIC FA 141845
SGFNT CLDS AND WX VALID UNTIL 150700 . . . OTLK 150700 – 151300Z.
IN
AGL 45 SCT – BKN. CHC 3 – 5R – . 04Z CIGS 40 BKN VSBY 3 – 5F. OCNL
CIGS 12 BKN VSBYS 3 – 5R – /RW. WDLY SCT TRW – . TOP CBS 400.

220 TWEB 141910 HUF – STL. ALL HGTS AGL EXCP TOPS. 40 SCT – BKN 100
    SCT – BKN. AFT23Z . . . CIG 20 – 30 BKN – OVC . . . AREAS VSBY 4RW – F. HUF
    VCNTY AFT 06Z . . . AREAS CIG 10 OVC VSBY 3TRW – F.

Below is the Terre Haute Terminal Forecast.

HUF FT 141717 45 SCT C100 BKN 200 OVC 2410 OCNL C45 BKN 100 OVC
    CHC 5R – F. 02Z C30 BKN 70 OVC 2309 OCNL 10 SCT C25 OVC 4R – F.06Z 10
    SCT C25 OVC 4F 2908 OCNL C10 OVC 3TRW – F . . .

The following discussion is an analyzation of the forecasts.

FA: AGL 45 SCT – BKN. CHC 3 – 5R – . 04Z . . .
TWEB: 40 SCT – BKN 100 SCT – BKN. AFT 23Z . . .
FT: 45 SCT C100 BKN 200 OVC 2410 OCNL C45 BKN 100 OVC
          CHC 5R – F. 02Z . . .

The TWEB and FT contain more detail with respect to the second cloud layer (100 SCT – BKN and C100 BKN OCNL 100 OVC respectively). The FA forecaster does not consider this layer to be extensive enough for inclusion in the FA, for the entire state of Indiana. Both the FA and FT forecast reduced visibilities in light rain. The TWEB omits this phenomena because the forecaster doesn't expect it to cover 10 percent of the route. The FT provides a surface wind forecast of 10 knots. Ten knots is not within the scope of either the TWEB or FA. All three forecasts are consistent given the scope of each product.

Products for the next time period:

FA: 04Z CIGS 40 BKN VSBY 3 – 5F. OCNL CIGS 12 BKN VSBYS 3 – 5R – /RW.
          WDLY SCT TRW – .
TWEB: AFT23Z . . . CIG 20 – 30 BKN – OVC . . . AREAS VSBY 4RW – F. HUF
          VCNTY AFT 06Z . . . AREAS CIG 10 OVC VSBY 3TRW – F.
FT: 02Z C30 BKN 70 OVC 2309 OCNL 10 SCT C25 OVC 4R – F . . 06Z 10 SCT
          C25 OVC 4F 2908 OCNL C10 OVC 3TRW – F . . .

All three forecast deteriorating conditions (FA 0400Z, TWEB AFT 2300Z, FT 0200Z). Ceilings are, generally, expected to be between 2,000 and 4,000 feet. FA and FT expect occasional ceiling between 1,200 and 2,500 feet. Both the TWEB and FT, however, provide a more specific time when conditions will further deteriorate at 0600Z to occasional ceilings 1,000 feet. Visibility forecasts are comparable, FA three to five, TWEB more than six to areas of four, and FT more than six to occasionally four. All three forecasts indicate rain, fog, and thunderstorm activity.

From the forecasts, a pilot can conclude that the lower conditions and thunderstorm activity advertised in the FA will not occur in the HUF area until around 0600Z. This is not inconsistent given that the FA must cover the whole state. From the FA, a pilot could only conclude that surface winds are expected to be less than 30 knots, and from the TWEB, less than 25 knots. However, from the FT, surface winds in the HUF area are expected southwest to northwesterly around 10 knots. Otherwise, sky cover, ceiling, visibility and obstructions, weather, and wind forecasts are comparable. All three forecasts are perfectly consistent, given the scope and purpose of each product.

A pilot should never base a flight decision solely on the information provided. However, from these forecasts, there is no significant impact for either VFR or IFR operations in the Terre Haute area until 0600Z. From the FT, surface winds are expected to remain around 10 knots. This might be significant for student pilot operations. And, thunderstorms are not expected within five miles of the airport until between about 0600Z and 0800Z. This time frame is deduced from the TWEB forecast AFT 0600Z and the FT 0600Z.

Let's say we're planning an IFR arrival to the Sullivan Co. Airport, about 25 miles southwest of Terre Haute. In accordance with FARs, we must determine if an alternate airport is required, and, if so, select a suitable alternate. Our ETA is 2200Z. Because Terre Haute is farther than five miles, the HUF FT cannot be used to determine destination weather. The TWEB and FA, however, both cover the destination. Both forecasts, from one hour before until one hour after ETA, predict ceilings of at least 2,000 feet and visibilities at least three miles. Therefore, based on both the TWEB and FA, an alternate airport is not required.

What about an ETA of 0500Z? The FA forecasts OCNL CIGS 12 BKN, based on the FA, an alternate would be required. But, take a look at the TWEB. For the ETA, the TWEB forecasts CIG 20 – 30 BKN – OVC . . . AREAS VSBY 4RW – F. If we derive our destination forecast from the TWEB, an alternate airport would not be required. Is the TWEB a legal destination forecast? Absolutely.

Finally, let's look at an 0800Z arrival. Now both FA and TWEB forecast a ceiling less than 2,000 feet. An alternate airport is required. Could Terre Haute be used as a legal alternate? Assuming standard alternate minimums for Terre Haute, the lowest forecast is contained in the remark OCNL C10 OVC 3TRW – F. Terre Haute would satisfy FAR requirements for an alternate airport.

The preceding comparison contradicts a misconception that in the absence of an FT there is no forecast on which to base destination, alternate, and fuel requirements. If not TWEBs, FAs are always available; maybe not very detailed, requiring additional alternates and fuel, but nonetheless available.

Forecasters consider four elements when writing FTs:

1. Expected weather.
2. Local effects.
3. Climatology.
4. Amendment criteria.

Attention to detail places a premium on the forecaster's time and judgment.

Due to a number of factors, inconsistencies with reported conditions are to be expected. The forecaster might not believe observations are representative or the forecaster might expect conditions to change rapidly. Even in the body of the forecast there is only a greater than 50 percent probability of occurrence, during more than one-half the forecast period. Amendment criteria gives the forecaster quite a bit of latitude. The forecaster might be waiting until FT amendment criteria are reached—reported or expected. The time required to write and distribute an amendment is also a consideration; saturated computer and communications systems can hinder timely updates. If there is less than two hours between the time an amendment is required and a new forecast becomes effective or the next portion of the forecast becomes effective, an amendment might not be issued. Time parameters on domestic FTs usually indicate phenomena will change within two hours of the specified time. And, forecasters have other duties that might hinder timely amendments.

FAs, TWEBs, and FTs are usually perfectly consistent given their individual purpose and criteria. Apparent inconsistencies arise because cloud heights in the FA are generally MSL, whereas in the FT cloud heights are always AGL; FTs can consider local effects not within the scope of other products; or a pilot attempts to extrapolate an FT beyond five miles. When inconsistencies develop, FSS specialists and forecasters coordinate to resolve differences. Pilots using DUAT will have to consult an FSS for resolution.

Domestic FTs do not directly forecast turbulence or icing. However, like SAs, these phenomena are implied. Strong surface winds, LLWS, and thunderstorms indicate turbulence; surface temperatures close to freezing with cloud layers, freezing precipitation, and thunderstorms suggest icing.

Recall the beginning of the chapter where an FT was presented and the reader was asked to translate and interpret its meaning; Hurricane Gilbert was approaching the Texas Gulf Coast.

```
BRO FT 160808 20 SCT C60 OVC 4RW 0220G30 OCNL C20 BKN 2RW+
     CHC C5 X 1/2TRW+ Q50. 00Z 3 SCT C12 OVC 2RW+ 0860Q75
     OCNL C3 X 1/4 T+RW+ G120. 02Z LIFR CIG TRW WND . .
```

At 0800Z 2,000 scattered, ceiling 6,000 overcast, visibility four in moderate rain showers, wind 020° at 20 gusting to 30 is forecast. However, remarks indicate occasional ceilings 2,000 feet broken, visibility two in heavy rain showers, and a chance of ceilings 500 sky obscured visibility one-half mile in thunderstorms, heavy rain showers with wind gusts to 50 knots. VFR flight might be possible, but certainly not fun. An IFR pilot might get away with a non-precision approach, but he or she better be prepared for a precision approach with a chance of 500 and one-half. With either the OCNL or CHC forecast an alternate is required; this airport would not qualify for filing as an alternate. Thunderstorm activity would have to be considered for both VFR and IFR operations.

Conditions are expected to deteriorate around 0000Z so the remarks of the previous portion could be more prevalent during the end of that period. Hurricanes and other low pressure systems demand caution. These systems often have bands of weather that move through, causing conditions to deteriorate, improve, and deteriorate again. The ultimate example being the eye of the hurricane. (Refer to FIG. 10-18, in Chapter 10 for a satellite view of Gilbert.)

At 0000Z conditions are expected to deteriorate to 300 scattered, ceiling 1,200 overcast, visibility two in heavy rain showers, wind 080° at 60 with peak gusts in squalls to 75 knots.

Remarks indicate occasional ceilings 300 feet, sky obscured, visibility one-fourth in severe thunderstorms, heavy rain showers, with wind gusts to 120 knots. I don't think anyone will argue with the briefer that VFR flight is not recommended, and conditions will probably go below IFR landing minimums occasionally.

The outlook from 0200Z to 0800Z indicates ceilings less than 500 feet, visibilities less than one mile in thunderstorms and rain showers, wind 25 knots or greater. About the only thing that can be concluded is that conditions are not going to significantly improve.

The FT, the most detailed aviation forecast, is a valuable planning tool when used in conjunction with current reports and other forecasts, especially when limitations, and amendment criteria are understood and considered.

A hurried pilot poked his head into the FSS and requested destination weather and terminal forecast. The briefer provided that specific information, which contained nothing significant. The pilot was halfway out the door when the briefer mentioned thunderstorms en route. Needless to say, the pilot *was interested*.

8
Winds & Temperatures Aloft Forecasts (FD)

A NAVION PILOT CALLED FLIGHT SERVICE WITH HIS REQUEST, "WINDS aloft." The specialist asked, ". . . for what altitudes?" The pilot rather indignantly replied, "What ever's best for my direction of flight!" Well, let me tell you it's 51,000 feet every time.

Winds and Temperatures Aloft Forecasts (FD) for the contiguous U.S., Alaska, and many oceanic areas are computer generated at the National Meteorological Center outside Washington, D.C. FDs for the Hawaiian islands are produced by the Honolulu forecast office. Based on the twice daily radiosonde balloon observations (balloon with a radiosonde attached) are normally released at 1100Z and 2300Z daily. Launch sites can be found in the *Airport/Facility Directory*. Because these sites and times are published, pilots cannot expect to receive launch warnings in the form of NOTAMs or broadcasts, except for unscheduled releases. Figure 8-1 shows the balloon preparation building and launch site at Norman, OK. FD forecast locations are contained in Appendix B.

A computer program known as the *Nested Grid Model* (NGM) analyzes data. NGM is one of the latest forecast models and has replaced the *Limited Fine Mesh* (LFM) for FD-tabulated forecasts; with a smaller grid, thus better resolution, and terrain taken into account to a greater degree than the LFM, the NGM has improved forecast accuracy. However, the NGM can only consider synoptic (large scale) weather systems. The computer projects system movements and produces a forecast. And, although large scale terrain, to some extent, is considered, local features are not. Therefore, FDs tend to be less accurate in the western states, especially below 12,000 feet. The LFM is still used to produce winds aloft forecast charts.

Fig. 8-1. *Sites such as this launch balloons with a radiosonde attached twice daily from approximately 120 locations in the United States.*

Approximately 750 upper air stations worldwide—about 120 in the United States—take observations. Stations are generally located on land leaving great expanses of ocean without observations; satellite and aircraft reports help fill in the gaps. The computer must interpolate for locations without observations and sparse observational data hinders the accuracy of the forecast.

Winds and Temperatures Aloft forecasts can be obtained from a number of sources: Flight Service Stations, Transcribed Weather Broadcasts, Pilots Automatic Telephone Weather Answering Service, Telephone Information Briefing Service, Interim Voice Response System, Direct User Access Terminals, and commercial vendors.

TABULATED FORECASTS

FDs normally become available after their scheduled transmission times of 0440Z and 1640Z. They consist of three forecast periods: six, 12, and 24 hours. These periods are labeled FD1, FD2, and FD3 for levels through 39,000 feet, and FD8, FD9, and FD10 for 45,000 and 53,000 feet (TABLE 8-1).

Table 8-1.

Winds and Temperatures Aloft Forecast Schedule.

File Type		Valid	For Use
Forecasts based on 0000Z data, available at 0440Z.			
FD1	FD8	0600Z	0500-0900Z
FD2	FD9	1200Z	0900-1800Z
FD3	FD10	0000Z	1800-0500Z
Forecasts based on 1200Z data, available at 1640Z.			
FD1	FD8	1800Z	1700-2100Z
FD2	FD9	0000Z	2100-0600Z
FD3	FD10	1200Z	0600-1700Z

Note: FD1, FD2, FD3 for levels through 39,000 feet.

FD8, FD9, FD10 for levels 45,000 and 53,000 feet.

FAA Automated Flight Service Stations using Model 1 can display levels 3,000 through 53,000 feet. Although, the 45,000- and 53,000-foot levels are not available for all standard FD locations (Appendix B). Other FSSs usually post levels through 39,000; the two higher levels are normally available on request. FSSs usually post the six- and 12-hour forecasts (FD1 and FD2), with the 24-hour forecasts (FD3) available on request.

FD3s and FD10s are plagued with the same limitations as other forecasts and must be viewed with skepticism and used only for advanced planning, then updated with the latest forecasts prior to departure. This requires the pilot to become familiar with the issuance times in TABLE 8-1. For example, a pilot planning a 1900Z departure might obtain the FD3s, based on 0000Z data, the evening before departure. The FD1s, based on 1200Z data, become available at 1640Z. If the pilot fails to update the forecast, he or she could be wide open to a violation in the event of a problem.

Figure 8-2 contains FD1 and FD8 examples, based on the 30th day of the month 1200Z radiosonde data (DATA BASED ON 301200Z). The DATA BASED ON must always be checked. From time to time old FDs fail to be purged and remain in the system. It's possible to receive data that is 24 hours old. The next line states VALID 301800Z FOR USE 1700-2100Z. These FDs are for use between 1700Z and 2100Z. The computer does not forecast an average; the model predicts winds and temperatures for one specific time, in this case 1800Z (VALID 301800Z).

Forecasts based on expected movement of synoptic systems explains one reason for apparent errors. With rapidly moving or intensifying systems, FDs can change significantly during the FOR USE period. This would be especially true for flights at the beginning or end of the period.

Forecast levels are True Altitude—true height above sea level—through 12,000 feet.

WINDS AND TEMPERATURES ALOFT FORECASTS

DATA BASED ON 301200Z
VALID 301800Z   FOR USE 1700-2100Z.   TEMPS NEG ABV 24000

FT	3000	6000	9000	12000	18000	24000	30000	34000	39000
SFO	3513	3316+10	3220+06	3224+01	3138-11	3148-24	325539	315846	315954
RNO		0605	3308+02	3217-02	3134-16	3052-28	316542	316848	316853

DATA BASED ON 301200Z
VALID 301800Z   FOR USE 1700-2100Z.   TEMPS NEG ABV 24000

FT	45000	53000
SFO	314961	304263

Fig. 8-2. *Tabulated Winds and Temperatures Aloft Forecasts are available from just above the surface to 53,000 feet. These forecasts are based on the twice daily radiosonde observations.*

From 18,000 through 53,000 feet, levels are Pressure Altitude—height as indicated with an altimeter setting of 29.92 inches (1013.2 mb). Figure 8-2 shows FDs for SFO (San Francisco, CA) and RNO (Reno, NV).

Levels within the area of *frictional effect* between the wind and the earth's surface are omitted. Therefore, forecast levels within approximately 1,500 feet of the surface, plus temperatures for the 3,000-foot level, or levels within 2,500 feet of the surface, do not appear.

Refer to the SFO 12,000-foot winds in FIG. 8-2. The first two digits of a wind group represent true direction, from which the wind is blowing, to the nearest 10° ("32"24 + 01); the third and fourth digits indicate speed in knots (32"24" + 01); and the last two digits are temperature in degrees Celsius (3224" + 01"). Temperatures, plus or minus, are indicated through 24,000 feet; all temperatures above 24,000 are below 0° C and the minus sign is omitted. Therefore, 3224 + 01 is wind blowing from 320° true at 24 knots, temperature +01° C.

Forecast speeds less than five knots are encoded 9900, and referred to as light and variable. Briefers are periodically asked, "What's the direction and speed of the light and variable winds?" One extreme case had a rather irate pilot demand to know what was "actually written on the paper." The specialist replied, "niner-niner-zero-zero!"

Pilots must *interpolate*—compute intermediate values—to determine values between forecast levels and reporting locations. Plan to fly from Oakland to South Lake Tahoe at 13,500 feet; use the SFO and RNO FDs in FIG. 8-2. Average the 12,000-foot and then the 18,000-foot levels. At 12,000 feet direction is the same. A difference in speed of seven knots results in an average of 21 knots ($7/2 = 4$; $17 + 4 = 21$). The average temperature is zero. At 18,000, again the direction is the same. A difference in speed of four knots results in an average of 36 knots ($4/2 = 2$; $34 + 2 = 36$). The difference in temperature is five, resulting in an average of -14 ($-5/2 = -3$; $-11 + (-3) = -14$). Be careful with the algebraic sign. The final result: 12,000 feet, 320° at 21 -01, and at 18,000 feet, 310° at 36 -14.

The 13,500 level is one-quarter of the way between 12,000 and 18,000 feet. Therefore, divide the difference between levels by four and add the result to the 12,000 foot values. Wind direction is 320°, speed 25 knots ($15/4 = 4$; $21 + 4 = 25$) and temperature -04 ($-13/4 = -3$; $-1 + (-3) = -4$). Because direction is to the nearest 10°, speed in knots, and temperature in Celsius, the result cannot have a value in smaller increments than the original data; values are rounded off. As already noted, be careful of the algebraic sign. FAA exams might require calculating wind direction to the nearest five degrees, however, for practical purposes this is not necessary.

Is a forecast of 7Ø1548 a misprint or garbled transmission? With forecast winds of 100 knots or more, five is added to the first digit of the wind direction group. Therefore, to decode, subtract five from the first digit of the wind direction, and add 100 to speed. In this example wind direction, speed, and temperature are:

Direction	Speed	Temperature
70	15	48
$-$ 5	$+100$	
200	115 knots	$-48°$

(No mathematical sign ($+$ or $-$) was specified, so the temperature must be negative.) Maximum speeds for FD tabulated forecasts are 199 knots.

FORECAST CHARTS

Forecast winds and temperatures aloft are also available in graphic form, issued twice daily valid at 1200Z and 0000Z. FD charts are excellent for determining forecast winds for long distance flights. By visually depicting winds at various levels, favorable routes and altitudes can be determined. The eight panels contain forecast levels from 6,000 through 39,000 feet. Figure 8-3 illustrates the 24,000-foot pressure level panel VALID ØØZ 17 OCT 86. Because of valid times and computer models, some differences between the chart and tabular forecasts are to be expected.

Plotted data are standard. The inset in FIG. 8-3 shows the station model for DRT (Del Rio, TX). Forecasts are to the nearest 10° and five knots. Arrows with pennants and barbs are similar to those on other charts. The first digit of the wind direction is obtained from the general direction of the arrow. At DRT that is westerly, approximately 270°. The number below the arrow (8) represents the second digit. Therefore, wind blowing from 280°. Pennants (50 knots), barbs (10 knots) and half barbs (five knots) denote speed. At DRT the wind speed decodes as 35 knots. The temperature appears just above the station, $-21°$ C (-21).

AMENDMENT CRITERIA

Although FDs are generated in Washington, regional NWS offices are responsible for amendments. FDs are amended when, in the forecaster's judgment, there is a change or

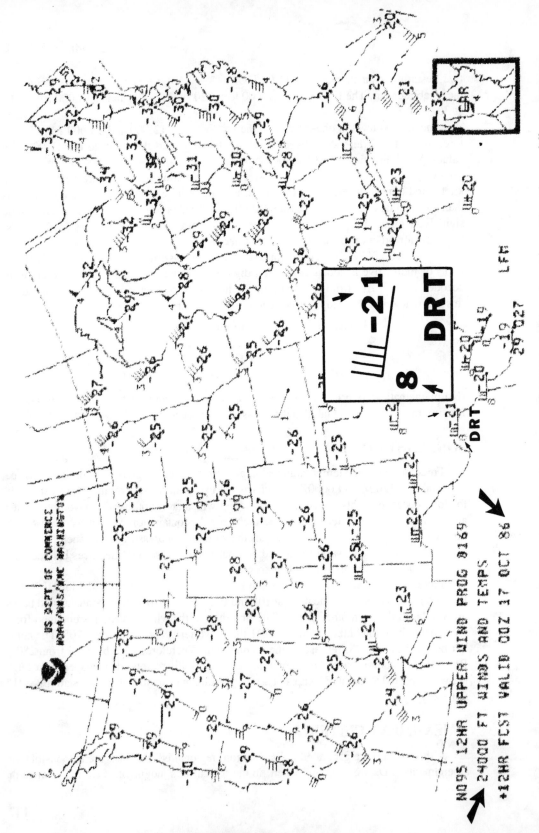

Fig. 8-3. *Winds aloft forecasts are available in chart form through 39,000 feet. Chart forecasts are based on a different computer model and have different valid times, therefore, differences between chart and tabulated values are to be expected.*

Table 8-2. *Winds and Temperatures Aloft Amendment Criteria.*

With a forecast of:	Amend if:
Wind Direction	
Wind speed 5 to less than 30 knots	Direction change of 45 degrees or more
Wind speed 30 knots or greater	Direction change of 30 degrees or more
Wind Speed	
Wind speed of less than 70 knots	Speed changes by 20 knots or more
Wind speed between 70 and 100 knots	Speed changes by 30 knots or more
Wind speed between 100 and 135 knots	Speed changes by 40 knots or more
Wind speed greater than 135 knots	Speed changes by 50 knots or more
Temperature	
Amend if observed or forecast temperature changes by 5° C or more.	

an expected change in the wind or temperature that would significantly affect aircraft operations. Amendment procedures are complex.

Reviewing TABLE 8-2, it can be seen there must be a considerable difference between forecast and actual winds to require an amendment. In general, forecasts within 30° of direction, and plus or minus 20 knots are considered accurate. As with turbulence and icing, the only way to verify the forecast is through pilot reports.

USING THE FD FORECAST

FDs provide the pilot with two valuable pieces of information: wind direction and speed, plus temperature. Both significantly affect aircraft operation and performance. Failure to properly consider and apply either can be potentially hazardous.

In spite of its limitations the FD can never be ignored. Pilots are required by FARs to consider ". . . fuel requirements . . .;" and, are prohibited from beginning a flight either VFR or IFR ". . . unless (considering wind and forecast weather conditions) . . ." the aircraft will have enough fuel to fly to destination, an alternate if required, and still have appropriate fuel reserves. FAR fuel reserve minimums, which do not necessarily equate to "safe," in no way relieve the pilot from keeping careful track of ground speed, and revising the flight plan accordingly.

When reserves are marginal, good operating practice dictates the careful tracking of position and ground speed. Marginal is not necessarily synonymous with legal; in sparsely populated areas, a fuel reserve of 30 minutes with clear weather reported and forecast might be sufficient. But with marginal weather or thunderstorms, and the nearest suitable alternate 35 minutes away, a 30-minute reserve doesn't make any sense. Chapter 7 discusses how legal alternates might not be satisfactory with a busted forecast. The same is true for legal fuel reserves.

WINDS AND TEMPERATURES ALOFT FORECASTS (FD)

The following situation illustrates how a series of small, at the time, seemingly insignificant factors have the potential to lead to disaster. The flight from Van Nuys, CA, to Tonopah, NV, was based on four hours of fuel and a 10-knot head wind, time en route estimated 3:15. My Cessna 150 was fueled Friday when I arrived at Van Nuys. During the preflight Sunday morning I noticed the fuel was not at the top of the fuller neck—factor one. This was not unusual because the airplane was parked on a slight incline and some fuel tends to vent overboard. The departure required an IFR climb to on top conditions, which added about 15 minutes to time en route—factor two.

Over Trona, CA, about halfway, ground speed checks indicated winds were as forecast. Calculations indicated adequate fuel for Tonopah based on four hours of fuel and ignoring the extra time required for departure.

The Cessna 150 climbs like a wet mop, so I decided not to land at Trona—factor three. The fuel gauges were bouncing on zero and I still had 30 minutes to destination and there were no suitable alternates—factor four. I made a straight-in approach and had everything stowed ready to crash, but landed safely in spite of some extremely poor planning. By the way, they put 22.6 gallons in my 22.5-gallon-usable airplane. Never again.

A Grumman Tiger pilot—instructor with student—was not so fortunate. On a flight from Salt Lake City to Tonopah they crashed short of the airport, out of fuel. The pilot couldn't understand why, after calculating the airplane had 2:45 fuel, the engine quit after only 2:31. Needless to say the FAA wanted to have a little chat with this gentleman.

The venturi effect at mountains and mountain passes accelerates winds over ridges and through passes. Stronger than forecast winds should be expected in these areas, especially within 5,000 feet of terrain.

Aircraft performance charts are based on the Standard Atmosphere, more precisely the International Standard Atmosphere (ISA). Standard atmosphere temperature and pressure at sea level are 15° C and 29.92 inches of mercury. The standard lapse rate—decrease of temperature with height—in the troposphere is approximately 2° C per thousand feet. Temperature decreases to a value of −57° C at the tropopause—the boundary between the troposphere and the stratosphere—at approximately 36,000 feet. An isothermal lapse rate occurs in the stratosphere to about 66,000 feet (FIG. 8-4).

Altitudes on the ISA chart are pressure altitudes. Pilots using the local altimeter setting fly indicated altitude for levels through 17,500 feet, and pressure altitude at 18,000 feet and above. Winds aloft forecasts are true altitude through 12,000 feet, so there will be a slight difference between the altitudes in the forecast (true altitude) and those flown by the pilot (indicated altitude). However, unless atmospheric pressure is extremely high or low, the difference is negligible. A variance of one inch of mercury from standard would only result in a 1,000 foot altitude difference. Temperature is the biggest factor.

Standard conditions rarely occur in the real world and performance charts are based on standard conditions; accommodation must be made for a non-standard environment, usually a temperature correction. Manufacturers sometimes provide an ISA conversion with cruise power setting charts for high, low, and standard temperatures or simply note that performance is based on standard conditions. The aircraft doesn't understand any of this and performs based on the environment—pressure altitude and temperature.

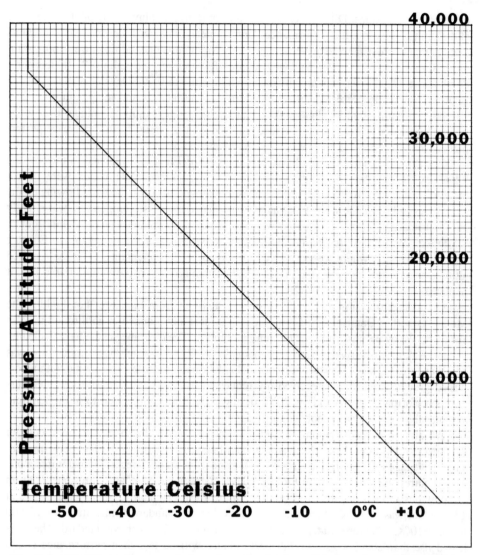

Fig. 8-4. *Aircraft performance is based on standard conditions and standard conditions rarely exist in the real atmosphere, so pilots need a means of calculating actual performance. This is most often accomplished by comparing standard conditions with actual conditions.*

Non-standard conditions affect true air speed (TAS) and performance, as well as power settings. (TAS is *calibrated*, or *equivalent*, airspeed corrected for air density—pressure altitude and temperature. TAS is used on flight plans, and is independent of wind direction and speed.) An aircraft with an advertised service ceiling of 13,100 feet is based on standard conditions. Differences are usually not significant unless the pilot is operating at the limit of the aircraft's performance. Unfortunately, this occurs every year with pilots that attempt to cross the Sierra Nevada or Rocky Mountains in conditions well above standard. Some pilots can't understand why an aircraft with a service ceiling 13,100 feet can't climb above 12,000 feet with an outside air temperature of 0° C. Density Altitude, which is pressure altitude corrected for temperature, at 12,000 feet and temperature 0° C is 13,100. And, this is an ideal case. A runout engine, poor leaning technique, over gross weight, and the possibility of turbulence and downdrafts would further decrease performance. You can't fool Mother Nature; attempts can be fatal.

My 1966 Cessna 150 had a book ceiling of 12,650 feet. We planned to traverse the 9,941-foot Tioga Pass in California's Sierra Nevada range. The winds were out of the northeast at only 10 knots, resulting in a slight downdraft from the wind flowing up the east slopes and down the west slopes as we approached the pass. Temperature was slightly above standard, and in combination with the wind, the airplane wouldn't climb out of 9,500 feet. We had to proceed north along the west slopes of the mountains to Ebbett's Pass at 8,732 feet, where we were able to safely cross the mountains. Gain the required altitude prior to reaching the crest, and with sufficient room to make a comfortable 180, if required.

On another occasion we had filed for an IFR flight from Lancaster Fox Field in the Mojave Desert to Ontario, CA. I requested 7,000 feet and planned to go through the San Fernando Valley because of lower minimum altitudes. The clearance came back, "cleared via the Cajon two arrival; climb and maintain 11,000." The surface temperature was 85° F and the Cessna 150 was not going to 11,000 that day. After negotiating with a perturbed ground controller, I received my requested routing. Pilots must know their aircraft's performance and not allow ATC, or anyone else for that matter, to push them into an untenable—in this case unobtainable—position.

All aircraft have limitations, including turbojet aircraft that often fly at the edge of their performance envelope where non-standard conditions critically affect performance. The pilot's task is to determine aircraft performance based on forecast temperatures aloft. This requires the information in FIG. 8-4, The International Standard Atmosphere. From the previous discussion, the average temperature from Oakland to South Lake Tahoe at 13,500 feet was −04° C. Figure 8-4 indicates that the standard temperature for 13,500 feet is −10° C. The forecast temperature is 6° warmer, which is above standard. The air is less dense than standard, so aircraft performance will be less than performance charts advertise. Based on the above conditions, density altitude is about 15,000 feet.

Certain performance charts require the pilot to determine temperature at altitude relative to ISA. For example, the forecast temperature over Reno at Flight Level 300 (30,000 feet) is −42° C. Figure 8-4 indicates that the standard temperature for that pressure altitude is −45° C. Certain flight computers can be used to determine ISA temperatures; the Jeppesen CR-3 has a true altitude computation window. With the scales aligned (10 on the outer scale with 10 on the inner scale), standard temperature is read under pressure altitude. Under 30,000 feet pressure altitude, −45 appears. Therefore, the forecast temperature is ISA +3.

FDs are a source of forecast freezing level. They should be in general agreement with the FA because they're based on the same data. Differences result from FD freezing levels representing only one point in time, whereas FA forecasts take into account changes during the period. However, if a significant difference occurs, be alert for other possible forecast errors. FSS specialists coordinate with forecasters under such circumstances. Pilots using DUAT would normally have to consult an FSS for resolution. Figure 8-2 indicates the expected freezing level at 1800Z is approximately 12,500 feet over SFO, lowering to 11,000 feet in the RNO area based on the standard lapse rate in the troposphere, approximately 2° C per thousand feet.

FDs can be used to determine the approximate height of the tropopause. Winds are strongest just below the tropopause. Checking FIG. 8-2, SFO winds at 39,000 feet are 59 knots and at 45,000 feet have decreased to 49 knots. Also note that speed continues to decrease at 53,000 feet and temperature remains almost constant. Therefore, the tropopause is between the 39,000 and 45,000 foot pressure levels.

FD forecast limitations and amendment criteria must be understood for effective flight planning. Product preparation, plus the advantages—and to some extent, the limitations—of computer models have already been discussed. Surface heating, as well as terrain affect winds aloft. Today's technology cannot account for the effects of land/sea and mountain/valley winds, nor frictional effects between wind and the surface. Other forecast problems include the extent and availability of data, and timing.

FDs are based on the expected movement of weather systems, so errors result when weather systems move faster or slower than forecast. This is one reason why Flight Watch specialists are required to continually solicit reports of winds and temperatures aloft. Specialists are specifically trained to recognize these situations and provide updated information. Careful tracking of position and ground speed will verify the accuracy of the FDs.

Inertial navigation, LORAN, and other computerized navigation systems can provide immediate wind readouts. Anyone remember how to calculate winds with the E6B flight computer? Electronic flight computers make the calculation easy. This is a reminder for pilots to become actively involved in the system with PIREPs. Observed winds aloft, whether they confirm or contradict the forecast, should be routinely passed to Flight Watch. Only two upper air observations are made each day, so PIREPs are the only other direct source of observed winds, and the only way to verify the forecast.

The situation might change in the future with wind profilers that will automatically and almost continuously provide high resolution upper-air wind measurements. Naturally, the closer to observation time, the more accurate the forecast. Accuracy normally deteriorates with time—the FD2s and especially the FD3s. The evening forecast becomes available after 0440Z it doesn't do much good to request winds any earlier for the following day. Flights departing after 1640Z, must consult the new FDs. Weather patterns can change significantly in 12 hours.

The pilot has no option but to use FDs in flight planning by regulation. Local or short flights might mean nothing more than an eyeball interpolation. Exams and flight tests require computer calculations. Flights toward the limit of aircraft range will require a careful interpolation and calculation.

WINDS AND TEMPERATURES ALOFT FORECASTS (FD)

With the general criticism of winds aloft forecasts, it's amazing how many pilots call and must absolutely have winds two or even three days in the future. Then there's the guy who calls Flight Watch and can't understand why the winds are 20° and five knots off forecast. Oh well, you can't please everyone. By now we should have some insight into FD limitations, the causes of inaccuracies, and perceived errors of this valuable, but often maligned product.

9
Radar and
Convective Analyses

A "DISASTEROUS THUNDERSTORM ACCIDENT CLOSE TO BOWLING GREEN, Kentucky, in 1943 that involved an American (Airlines) DC-3 started a chain of events that eventually led to the first systematic research into thunderstorm behavior. The plane crashed onto the ground either near or under a severe thunderstorm. Buell (C.E. Buell, chief meteorologist, American Airlines 1939–1946) initiated a letter to the Civil Aeronautics Board pointing out the appalling dearth of understanding of what actually occurs inside a thunderstorm, as evidenced by the accident investigation. He recommended a massive research effort be organized to probe into thunderstorms and document their internal structure," according to Peter E. Kraght in *Airline Weather Services 1931–1981.*

Radar was one of many projects and played a significant role, in the early 1950s. Early airborne radars had many technical problems, but by the beginning of the 1960s most airliners were equipped with airborne weather radar. Ground-based radar was also developed.

Access to radar information has increased over the years. NWS radars in the east, FAA radars west of the Rockies supplemented by a few NWS sites, are used to compile a national Radar Summary chart. An NWS network in the west was thought unjustified because severe weather is relatively rare in that area. Radar Weather Reports (RAREPS) and convective analysis charts are routinely transmitted on NWS and FAA circuits, and available through many private services. Many twin, and more and more, single engine aircraft are being equipped with airborne weather radar, Radair (a weather avoidance system), or Stormscope. And, by the early 1990s the next generation (NEXRAD) weather radar will become operational. Each system, product, or service has its own particular application and limitations that must be thoroughly understood for safe and efficient flight.

RADAR

Radar displays an image dependent on *reflected energy* or *back scatter*. Intensity depends on several factors and among them are particle or droplet size, shape, composition, and quantity. Particles must be at least precipitation size for detection on weather radars. Therefore, a precipitation-free area does not translate into a cloud-free sky. Droplets reflect more energy than snow. There is almost no relation between the intensity of snow and back scatter. Therefore, an intensity is never assigned a radar report of snow. On the other hand hail, coated with water, produces the best back scatter and the notation hail shaft may appear on reports and charts.

Three radars are used in the aviation weather system:

1. FAA ATC En Route
2. National Weather Service
3. Airborne

Each system has a specific purpose and its own application and limitations.

ATC radar is specifically designed to detect aircraft; a narrow fan-shaped beam reaches from near the surface to high altitudes. ATC radars have a wavelength of 23 centimeters (cm), ideal for detecting aircraft, but which reduce the intensity of detected precipitation; additional features reduce the radar's effectiveness to see weather.

To efficiently detect aircraft, and eliminate distracting targets, ATC radars use *circular polarization* (CP), *moving target indicator* (MTI), and *Sensitivity Time Control* (STC).

CP results in a low sensitivity to light and moderate precipitation. MTI only displays moving targets; unless droplets have a rapid horizontal movement they remain undetected; even rapidly moving precipitation will not be observed when advancing perpendicular (tangentially) to the radar beam. STC further eliminates light and decreases the intensities of displayed precipitation. Naturally, controllers, especially at approach facilities, engage these features during poor weather to accomplish their primary task—aircraft separation.

NWS radars, on the other hand, with wave lengths of five or 10 cm and a narrow linearly polarized beam, are ideal for detecting precipitation-size particles. Figure 9-1 shows a typical weather radar installation. This site houses a WSR-88, NEXRAD unit, at Norman, OK. Sensitivity Time Control on NWS radars compensates for *range attenuation*, which is loss of power density due to distance from echoes. STC-displayed intensity remains independent of range, therefore, targets with the same intensity, at different ranges, appear the same to the radar specialist. NWS radars can detect targets up to 250 nautical miles (nm), however, due to *range* and *beam resolution*, which is the ability of the radar to distinguish individual targets at different ranges and azimuth, an effective range of 125 nm is used.

Figure 9-2 shows a WSR-57 display console. The large center scope is the *Plan Position Indicator* (PPI). The PPI displays distance (range) and direction (azimuth) of the target in relation to the antenna. The smaller scope on the right is the *Range Height Indicator*

Fig. 9-1. *Wave length, beam shape, and power of NWS weather radars is designed to detect and display precipitation size particles.*

Fig. 9-2. *This is a WSR-57 display console. The PPI center screen displays echo azimuth and distance, RHI scope on the right shows echo height, and Amplitude Modulation scope on the left allows the radar specialist to determine echo type.*

The RHI determines approximate tops and occasionally determines bases of precipitation. Tops are approximate due to *non-standard refraction*—bending of the radar beam—by the earth's atmosphere. Tops can be in error as much as several thousand feet. The *Amplitude Modulation Scope* on the left of FIG. 9-2 is used to distinguish between liquid precipitation, snow, and hail. *Melting level* (MLT LVL), which translates into freezing level for aviation purposes, might appear in radar reports. This scope is also used to determine nonprecipitation echoes, such as aircraft and ground clutter, or *Anomalous Propagation* (AP), which is ground targets that are not normally present in the usual ground clutter pattern.

Next generation weather radar, NEXRAD, will be a quantum leap in providing early warning of severe weather. On December 1, 1987, Unisys Corporation of Detroit, MI, was selected to produce the system. NEXRAD will be the standard for the next 20 to 25 years with a wavelength of 10 cm. Implementation will begin in 1991 and is scheduled to be completed by 1995. The WSR-88 network should consist of up to 195 units, 113 NWS sights in the contiguous United States, with additional sites in Alaska, Hawaii, the Caribbean, and western Europe, and 22 Department of Defense (DOD) units. The NEXRAD network will fill radar gaps in the West.

NEXRAD is a doppler radar that detects the relative velocity of precipitation within a storm. It will increase the accuracy of severe thunderstorm and tornado warnings, and has the capability of detecting wind shear. The radar specialist using a WSR-88 will have *Radar Data Acquisition*, *Radar Product Generation*, and *Display* units, as shown in FIG. 9-3. Notice the trend in technology from the raw data *cathode ray tube* (CRT) to the computer-generated display era. NEXRAD will provide hazardous and routine weather radar data above 6,000 feet east of the Rockies and above 10,000 feet in the western United States, although the details of how this information will be relayed have not yet been established. It is also expected to be available to pilots directly through Mode S transponders with automatic data link capability.

Airborne weather radars are low power, generally with a wave length of three centimeters. Precipitation attenuation, which is directly related to wave length and power, can be a significant factor. *Precipitation attenuation* results from radar energy being absorbed and scattered by close targets and the display becomes unreliable in close proximity to heavy rain or hail. Intensity might be greater than displayed, with distant targets obscured. An accumulation of ice on the radome causes additional distortion.

Figure 9-4 illustrates the affects of precipitation attenuation, showing how a heavy precipitation pattern with a very strong gradient might appear on a NWS 10-cm radar, compared with the same weather system as seen on five- and three-centimeter units. A pilot seeing the pattern on a three-centimeter set might elect to penetrate the weather at what appears to be the weakest point only to find the most severe part of the storm, or find additional severe weather where the radar showed clear.

According to the National Transportation Safety Board (NTSB), precipitation attenuation was a contributing factor in the crashes of a Southern Airways DC-9 in 1977 and an Air Wisconsin Metroliner in 1980. Precipitation attenuation is not significant with NWS 10-cm high-power units such as the WSR-57 and WSR-74S, however, it can be a serious problem with units of five centimeters or less, especially in heavy rain. The NTSB recommends: ". . . in the terminal area, comparison of ground returns to weather echoes is a useful technique to identify when attenuation is occurring. Tilt the antenna down and observe ground returns around the radar echo. With very heavy intervening rain, ground returns behind the echo will not be present. This area lacking ground returns is referred to as a shadow and may indicate a larger area of precipitation than is shown on the indicator. Areas of shadowing should be avoided."

In August 1985 a Delta Air Lines L-1011 crashed at the Dallas/Fort Worth Airport. The NTSB was unable to determine if the crew had been using airborne weather radar at the time of the crash. The NTSB report did state however: "The evidence concerning the

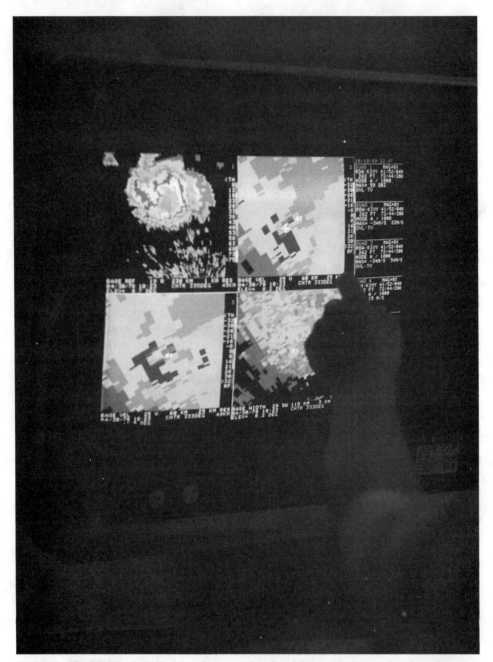

Fig. 9-3. *The NEXRAD WSR-88 radar provides the radar specialist with a computer display of radar echoes. This doppler radar allows the observer to see relative movement within the storm. The system has the potential to greatly improve storm prediction and warning.*

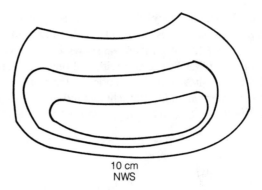

10 cm
NWS

Fig. 9-4. *Precipitation atten-uation, caused by close tar-gets absorbing and scattering the radar's energy, can be a serious problem with low power, short wave length sets. Attenuation is not significant with high power NWS radars.*

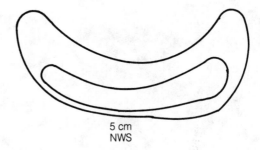

5 cm
NWS

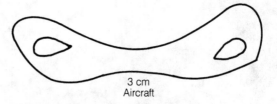

3 cm
Aircraft

use of the airborne weather radar at close range was contradictory. Testimony was offered that the airborne weather radar was not useful at low altitudes and in close proximity to a weather cell . . .;" although, "At least three airplanes scanned the storm at very close range near the time of the accident." The accident was probably caused by a microburst from a single severe storm cell, which illustrates how weather can develop rapidly, often without any severe weather warning.

When using an airborne weather radar it is imperative to understand the particular unit, its operational characteristics, and limitations. "Just reading through the brochure that comes with the equipment is certainly not enough to prepare a pilot to translate the complex symbology presented on the [airborne] scope into reliable data. A training course with appropriate instructors and simulators is strongly recommended," according to the March-April 1987 *FAA Aviation News*.

Flight Watch Control Stations, Center Weather Service Units, and many Flight Service Stations have access to direct weather radar through the *Radar Remote Weather Display System* (RRWDS). Figure 9-5 shows a typical RRWDS display. RRWDS provides the FSS or Flight Watch specialist with real time weather radar information from one of several different sites on high-resolution color monitors. Specialists are specially trained to interpret information for preflight and inflight briefings. FSS and Flight Watch specialists translate RRWDS echo coverage into the following categories:

- Widely Scattered   Less than $^1/_{10}$
- Scattered $^1/_{10}$ to $^5/_{10}$
- Broken $^6/_{10}$ to $^9/_{10}$
- Solid   More than $^9/_{10}$

Fig. 9-5. *The Radar Remote Weather Display System (RRWDS) provides FSS and Flight Watch specialists with real time weather radar.*

Limitations exist. West of the Rockies, the few NWS sites available suffer from extreme ground clutter, which renders them almost useless for real time RRWDS use; facilities using RRWDS with FAA radars suffer from the limitations of ATC units. Implementation of the NEXRAD network will help eliminate many of these limitations. NEXRAD will cover the contiguous United States and eliminate much of the ground clutter present with today's NWS radars. Many FSSs in the West have access to radar information through a *Radar Facsimile Circuit* (RAFAX) (FIG. 9-6). Observations are made 35 minutes past each hour and charts are normally available 15-20 minutes later. However, real-time information, which is available in the east, is not available in the West.

Private vendors also have access to radar data. The RADAIR Weather Avoidance System puts RRWDS in the cockpit. Information from radars is coded, transmitted to the aircraft, and displayed. The limitations of RRWDS apply to this system. When using a RRWDS it's important to know how the unit displays information such as intensity, whether it's displaying an ATC or NWS radar, and if it is indeed a real time observation, or a freeze or memory display.

The violent nature of thunderstorms causes gust fronts, strong updrafts and downdrafts, and wind shear in clear air adjacent to the storm out to 20 miles with severe storms and squall lines. Precipitation, which is detected by radar, generally occurs in the downdraft, while updrafts remain relatively precipitation free. Clear air or lack of radar echoes does not guarantee a smooth flight in the vicinity of thunderstorms.

STORMSCOPE

Stormscope, invented in the mid 1970s by Paul A. Ryan as a low-cost alternative to radar, must be mentioned. The Stormscope senses and displays electrical discharges in approximate range and azimuth to the aircraft. Stormscope also has limitations. One misconception proclaims that in the absence of dots or lighted bands there are no thunderstorms. However, NASA's tests of the Stormscope differed. Precipitation intensity levels of three and occasionally four (VIP levels) would be indicated on radar without activating the lightning detection system. A clear display only indicates the absence of electrical discharges. This does not necessarily mean convective activity and associated thunderstorm hazards are not present. Even tornadic storms have been found that produced very little lightning. The lack of electrical activity, as with the absence of a precipitation display on radar, does not necessarily translate into a smooth ride.

Many authorities agree that a combination of radar and Stormscope is the best thunderstorm detection system. It cannot be overemphasized that *these are avoidance, not penetration* devices. Thunderstorms imply severe or greater turbulence and neither radar nor Stormscope, at the present, directly detect turbulence.

RADAR WEATHER REPORTS (RAREPS)

The National Weather Service routinely takes radar observations from NWS and ATC radars at 35 minutes past the hour. These observations are coded and transmitted over the FAA's Service A weather distribution system. Locations are contained in Appendix B, and the inside back cover of the *Airport/Facility Directory*. All locations are not available on a

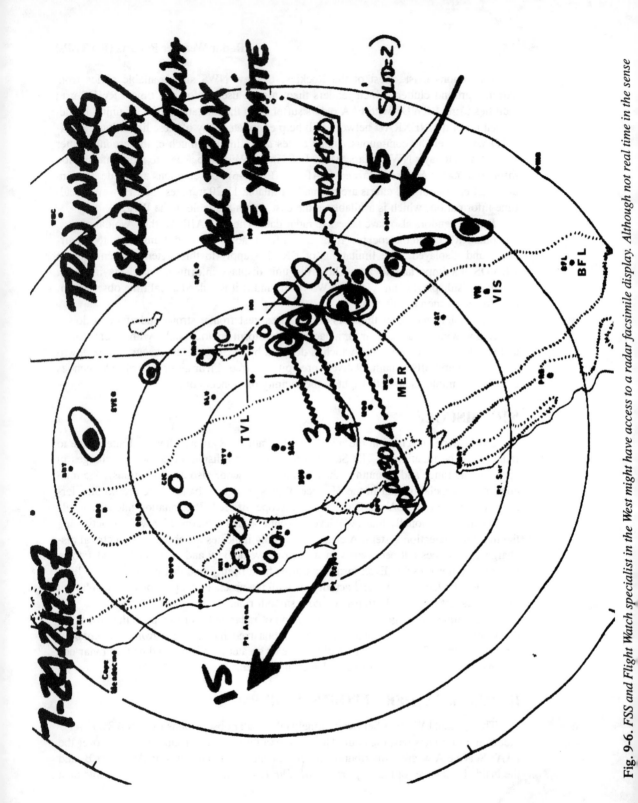

154

Fig. 9-6. *FSS and Flight Watch specialist in the West might have access to a radar facsimile display. Although not real time in the sense*

continuous basis. Local Warning Radars normally only report when convective activity occurs in the area. The radar report (or SD, Storm Detection) contains the following information:

1. The location of the radar.
2. The time of observation.
3. The configuration of echoes.
4. The coverage of echoes (subjective by the radar specialist).
5. The type of precipitation.
6. The intensity of precipitation.
7. The intensity trend.
8. The location of echoes.
9. The movement of echoes.
10. Height of echoes (not available from ATC radars).
11. Remarks.

The following illustrates a coded SD report. All reports begin with the radar site. This report for OKC (Oklahoma City, OK) was observed at 2235Z.

```
OKC 2235 LN 8TRWX/+ 350/100 230/112 25W L2930 C2535 MT 500 AT
   320/67 TOP 480 AT 235/100
AREA 3TRW/NC 080/75 110/100 140/100 170/75 100/50 A2525 C2330
MT 340 AT 155/75
   IK32 JK42 KK5 LK4 MP21 NJ11 NQ1 OJ4 OQ1 PJ5 PO21 QI13=
```

Echo Configuration and Coverage

Echo configuration falls into three categories: *cell, area,* and *line.* A single isolated area of precipitation, clearly distinguishable from surrounding echoes, constitutes a *cell.* The following illustrates how cells are indicated on a RAREP.

```
GGG 1057 SPL CELL TRWXXA/NC 323/95 D30 C2730 MT 550 HOOK
   321/91 . . .
```

The Longview, TX (GGG) 1057Z special (SPL) reports a cell with a 30 nm diameter (D30) exhibiting a hook echo. Cell diameter refers to precipitation, not necessarily the diameter of the cloud, which could be considerably larger. A hook echo is the signature of a mesolow, often associated with severe thunderstorms which produce strong gusts, hail, and tornadoes. An *area* consists of a group of echoes of similar type that appear to be associated. A *line* (LN) defines an area of precipitation more or less in a line—straight, curved, or irregular—at least 30 miles long, five times as long as it is wide, with at least 30 percent coverage. Echo coverage is estimated by the observer and reported in tenths. In OKC example, the line has $^8/_{10}$ (LN "8"TRWX/+) coverage and the area $^3/_{10}$ (AREA "3"TRW/NC) coverage.

Precipitation Type, Intensity, and Intensity Trend

The radar specialist determines precipitation type from scope presentations and other sources (SAs and satellite pictures). Standard aviation weather symbols are used. In the OKC example the line and the area contain thunderstorms and rain showers (TRW). Following precipitation type, one of the six standard Video Integrator and Processor (VIP) levels describe intensity. VIP level definitions and descriptions are contained in TABLE 9-1. The line is intense (TRW"X") and the area moderate (TRW—no symbol). Intensity trend follows the solidus (/). Refer to TABLE 9-2, RAREP/Radar Summary Chart Plotted Data for intensity trend symbols. The OKC example indicates that the trend of the line is increasing (+). The + indicates an increase of one or more VIP levels during the past hour. The intensity of the area has not changed (NC) during the preceding hour.

Echo Location and Movement

The RAREP defines the location of precipitation by points, azimuth (true), and distance (nm) from the reporting station (FIG. 9-7). The line extends from a point 350° at 100

Table 9-1. *Radar Precipitation Intensity (VIP) Levels.*

VIP* Level	RAREP Symbol	Echo Intensity	Precipitation Intensity	Rainfall Rate Stratiform**	Rainfall Rate Convective**	Associated Weather
1	—	WEAK	LIGHT	less than 0.1	less than 0.2	LGT-MDT TURBC PSBL LTNG
2	NO SYMBOL	MODERATE	MODERATE	0.1 - 0.5	0.2 - 1.1	LGT-MGT TURBC PSBL LTNG
3	+	STRONG	HEAVY	0.5 - 1.0	1.1 - 2.2	SVR TURBC & LTNG
4	++	VERY STRONG	VERY HEAVY	1.0 - 2.0	2.2 - 4.5	SVR TURBC & LTNG
5	X	INTENSE	INTENSE	2.0 - 5.0	4.5 - 7.1	SVR TURBC LTNG WIND GUSTS HAIL
6	XX	EXTREME	EXTREME	more than 5.0	more than 7.1	SVR TURBC LTNG EXTENSIVE WIND GUSTS LG HAIL

* VIP (Video Integrator and Processor) A system used to determine the intensity of precipitation.
** Precipitation in inches per hour.

nm (350/100) to a point 230° at 112 nm (230/112), 25 nm wide (25W). The points 080/75, 110/100, 140/100, 170/75 to 100/50 encompass the area. *Line* or *area* echo *movement* indicates the long-term progress of the system; *cell movement* indicates short-term motion of cells within the line or area. The line in FIG. 9-7 is moving from 290° at 30 knots (L2930); cell movement within the line is from 250° at 35 knots (C2535).

Echo Height

Maximum heights are reported in relation to azimuth and distance from the reporting station, with approximate elevation in thousands of feet MSL (MT 500 AT 320/67). Tops within a stable air mass are usually uniform indicated by the letter U (MT U120, uniform tops to 12,000 feet MSL). It's important to remember these are precipitation tops, not cloud tops. Precipitation tops will be close to cloud tops within building thunderstorms. However, precipitation in dissipating cells will normally be several thousand feet below cloud tops.

Remarks

Remarks, added by the radar specialist, elaborate on or explain the report in plain language or standard contractions. TABLE 9-2, RAREP/Radar Summary Chart Plotted Data, contains some of the remarks used on the report.

RAREP digital data appears at the bottom of the report. A grid, as shown in FIG. 9-8, centers on the reporting station. Each block, 22 nm on a side, is assigned the maximum

Table 9-2. *RAREP/Radar Summary Chart Plotted Data.*

		Intensity Trend		
Symbol	**Trend**		**Symbol**	**Trend**
−	Decreasing		NC	No change
+	Increasing		NEW	New echo
		Operational Status of Radar		
Symbol	**Meaning**		**Symbol**	**Meaning**
PPINE	Equipment normal—no echoes observed		PPIOM	Out of service for maintenance
PPINA	Observation not available		ROBEPS	Radar operation below standards
ARNO	Azimuth/range indicator inoperative		RHINO	Range/height indicator inoperative
NE	No echoes observed		NA	Observation unavailable
OM	Out for maintenance		NS	Nonsignificant echoes
		Remarks		
LEWP	Line echo wave pattern		BWER	Bounded weak echo pattern
WER	Weak echo region		MLT LVL	Melting level
MA	Echoes mostly aloft		PA	Echoes partly aloft

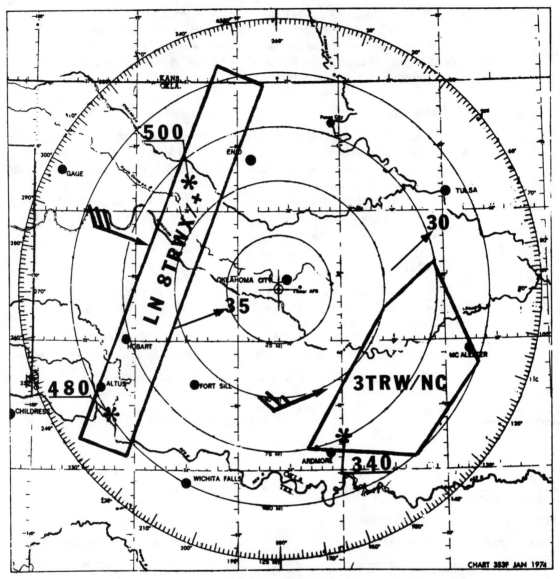

Fig. 9-7. *As with most coded data, plotting the RAREP helps visualize conditions.*

VIP level observed. When 20 percent of a block contains VIP level one, that level is assigned. Therefore, from digital data alone, all that can be concluded from VIP level one is that at least 20 percent of that grid contains weak echoes.

Letters represent coordinates; numbers indicate the maximum VIP level for that and succeeding coordinates to the right. The first block (FIG. 9-8) containing precipitation is IK ("IK"32). Grid IK contains VIP level three (IK"3"2). The next coordinate to the right

158

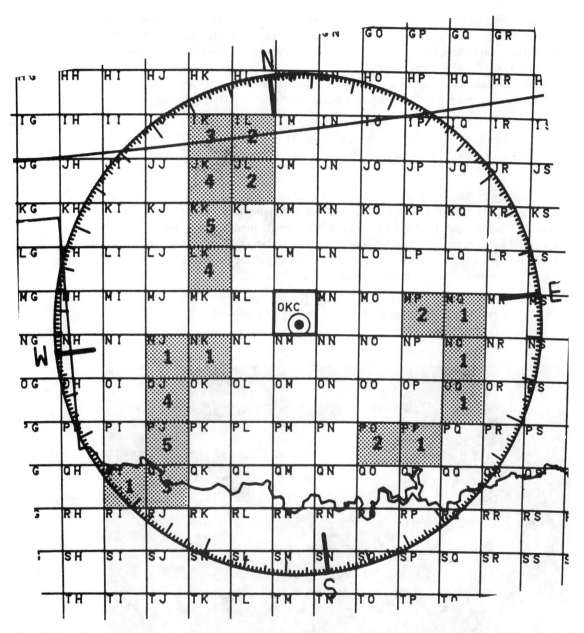

Fig. 9-8. *Plotting RAREP digital data provides additional insight into the strength and location of convective activity. This plot shows a weak area in the center of the line west of Oklahoma City.*

159

(IL) has a VIP level two (IK3″2″). Occasionally an eight or nine appears. This indicates a block outside the 125-nm operation range of the radar that contains precipitation. An eight indicates an echo believed to be severe, a nine a nonsevere echo. Figure 9-8 illustrates a plot of the OKC RAREP digital data.

Below is another example of a RAREP from the Sacramento, CA (SAC), NWS site. Sacramento radar was not showing any significant weather prior to the following observation.

SAC 0125 CELL TRW+ +/+ 349/80 D9 C2920 MT 250
  AREA 1R – S/NC 10/115 46/30 80W C2920 MT 130 AT 33/79
  IN41 KM101 =

Look what popped up, a level four (very strong) cell. Thunderstorms were not forecast. This single cell with a diameter of nine miles and approximate precipitation tops to 25,000 feet "didn't read the forecast." Figure 9-9, a single thunderstorm cell, illustrates what a pilot flying in this area could expect to see. The cell should be easily circumnavigable, and only present a hazard if it occurred in the vicinity of the departure or destination airport. A pilot should not fly into, close to, or under this cell.

SAC 0225 CELL RW/ – 346/81 D6 C2820 MT 170
  AREA 1R – S/NC 6/95/87/15 80W C2820 MT 120 AT 22/89
  IN21 LO1 =

Fig. 9-9. *Isolated and widely scattered thunderstorms are normally easily circumnavigable. But, don't get too close; severe turbulence and hail can reach many miles into the clear air surrounding the cell.*

One hour later (0225) the cell has deteriorated to moderate rain showers and continues to decrease in intensity, with maximum precipitation tops down to 17,000 feet MSL. Obviously convective activity can develop and dissipate, often unforecast, at an alarming rate.

RADAR SUMMARY CHART

The Radar Summary Chart graphically displays a computer-generated summation of RAREP digital data. The date and time of the observation—time is important because the transmission system might make the report several hours old—appear on the chart. Figure 9-10 illustrates a May 9, 1986, summary, based on 0935Z data. Similar to the RAREP, the chart contains information on precipitation type, intensity and trend, configuration, coverage, tops and bases, and movement.

Line and area movement, echo movement, and tops are depicted using the RAREP symbology. Arrows with flags, barbs, and half barbs indicate line or area movement (flag 50 knots, barb 10 knots, half barb five knots). Figure 9-10 shows the line in Texas is moving from the northwest at 50 knots; the area in Louisiana is moving from the west at 25.

An arrow with the speed printed at the arrowhead represents echo or cell movement. Echoes within the line (FIG. 9-10) are moving from the southwest at 25 knots and within the area from the northwest at 15 knots; the contraction LM (echoes in Idaho) indicates *little movement*. Maximum tops in FIG. 9-10 within the line vary between 37,000 and 53,000 feet MSL (*370, 440,* and *530*). When bases can be determined, the height MSL will appear below the line. West of the Rockies echo heights are usually missing because ATC radars are used, except when data are based on one of the NWS units.

Echo configuration is graphically depicted. Echoes reported as a line are drawn and labeled *solid* (SLD) when at least $8/10$ coverage exists, (FIG. 9-10) in southwestern Texas. The computer plots lines of equal value to indicate echo coverage and intensity. However, unlike the RAREP, the chart only contains three levels. The first contour includes VIP levels one and two (echoes in Utah), the second contour is levels three and four (echoes in Iowa) and the third contour is levels five and six (echoes in Louisiana and around the line in Texas).

Aviation Weather Services states: "When determining intensity levels from the radar summary chart, it is recommended that the maximum possible intensity be used." In the western United States nonsignificant weather echoes (VIP 1) might be indicated by the notation NS and contouring will not appear. This is interpreted as light precipitation occurring, without significant convective activity.

Precipitation type and intensity trend use the same symbology as the RAREP, with one exception. The + indicates an increase in intensity of at least one VIP level since the last observation or the + indicates a new echo. The Radar Summary Chart can contain remarks that have special significance (TABLE 9-2, with an explanation in the Glossary).

USING RAREPS, RRWDS, AND THE RADAR SUMMARY CHART

Pilots can expect to find holes in what the RAREP or Radar Summary Chart portray as an area of solid echoes. This apparent inconsistency is due to several factors. Targets

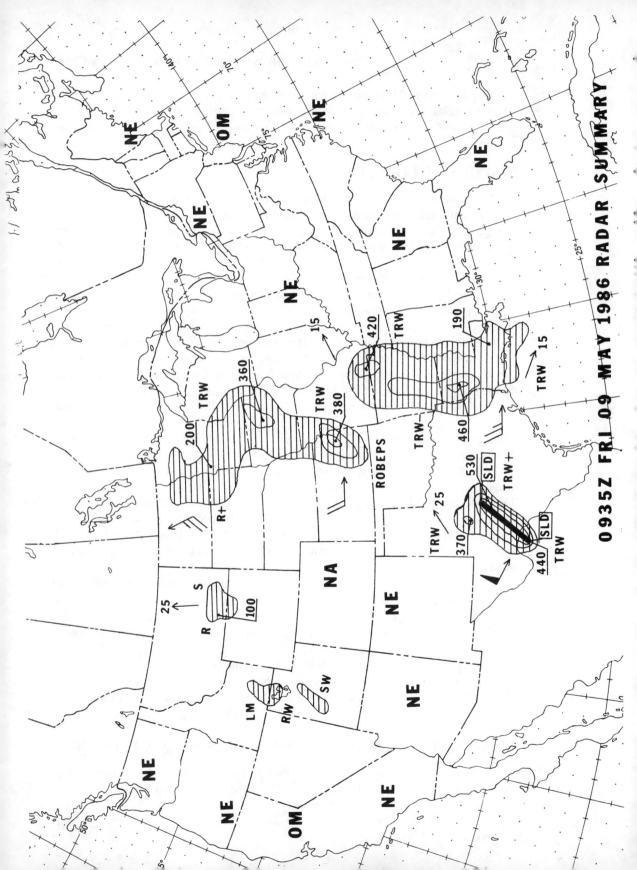

farther from the antenna might be smaller than depicted due to range and beam resolution. NWS weather radars, at a range of 200 miles, cannot distinguish between individual echoes less than seven miles apart. A safe flight between severe thunderstorms requires 40 miles, so this provides adequate resolution to detect a safe corridor. Recall that as little as 20 percent coverage of VIP one requires the entire grid to be encoded, so holes also occur with isolated and scattered precipitation. On the Radar Summary Chart large areas might be enclosed by relatively isolated echoes. This is especially true in the West, where ATC radars are used.

Assumptions can never be made with RAREPS or the Radar Summary Chart. Refer to FIGS. 9-7 and 9-8. Can a pilot fly west from Oklahoma City and avoid severe weather by at least 20 miles? Not without weather avoidance equipment, contact with a facility with real time RRWDS, or visual contact with the convective activity because RAREPs and the Radar Summary Chart are observations, not forecasts. They report what occurred in the past and convective activity can develop and move at an astonishing rate, as already demonstrated. Time of observation is an important consideration. RAREPs might be as much as two hours old and the Radar Summary Chart from two to four hours old. On the other hand, RRWDS observations are usually real time.

Most radar information west of the Rockies comes from ATC sites. SDs as such are not available from the ATC radars, but a summary of activity is distributed. Although some SDs from NWS sites are available, often the radar facsimile is of more use. Pilots will normally only have access to RAFAX through a Flight Service Station or Flight Watch: not real time, but the next best thing. Figure 9-6 illustrates a RAFAX display of the Sacramento, CA, NWS radar. Figure 9-11 illustrates a wall of clouds that a pilot in flight could expect to see based on the RAFAX chart in FIG. 9-6. A pilot, even with storm detection equipment, would be ill-advised to attempt to penetrate the activity south of Lake Tahoe (TVL) or north of Merced (MER); a Viscount—four-engine turboprop—reported severe turbulence during an attempt to penetrate. A southern route between Visalia (VIS) and Bakersfield (BFL) would be best because activity is increasing and moving toward the northwest. One purpose of Flight Watch is to interpret and relay information of this kind.

Refer to FIG. 9-10. A pilot can never assume there are holes in the solid line in southwestern Texas. The chart can only be interpreted as $8/10$ or more coverage within the line. A pilot could expect to see something similar to FIG. 9-11. By reviewing RAREP digital data, a pilot can quickly assess echo intensity and coverage. For example, let's say the digital data for the line read: MJ24542 NI23532 NH23632 PI3532. Notice that each consecutive group contains levels five or six. The line is continuous with $10/10$ coverage. No pilot, regardless of weather avoidance equipment, should attempt to penetrate this activity.

Nor should he or she assume they can fly through the weather in southern Kansas avoiding thunderstorms without weather avoidance equipment or visual contact with convective activity. If the RAREP for southern Kansas was JN13531 KM11311 LM1111, it would indicate weak activity at the southern end of the area. Interpreting the chart alone, a pilot must conclude that the echoes in Utah are solid with moderate precipitation (VIP level two). However, the areas might only contain scattered or widely scattered light precipitation. This could be verified from the RAREP.

The Radar Summary Chart provides general areas and movement of precipitation for

Fig. 9-11. *A pilot should never attempt to negotiate a line of convective activity without airborne storm avoidance equipment, or direct access to real time ground based weather radar information.*

planning purposes only, and must be updated by hourly RAREPs or RRWDs. Chart notations, such as OM (Out of Service for Maintenance) or NA (Not Available) must be considered. The chart must always be used in conjunction with other charts, reports, and forecasts. Once airborne, in-flight observations—visual or electronic (radar, RADAIR, or Stormscope)—and radar information from FSS or Flight Watch must be used.

Precipitation should not be cause to cancel a flight. However, the following must be considered. What is the coverage and intensity of precipitation? What is the weather expected to do (improve/deteriorate)? What is the pilot's experience level, the capability of his or her aircraft, and the time of day? It can be difficult to see clouds at night, although lightning flashes are visible, distances can be difficult to judge. How familiar is the pilot with the terrain and weather patterns over the intended route? Is an alternate available if the planned flight cannot be completed? Is the pilot mentally prepared to divert, should it become necessary? What about the pilot's physical condition? Tired and anxious to get home is a potentially fatal combination.

CONVECTIVE OUTLOOK AND SEVERE WEATHER OUTLOOK CHART

The Convective Outlook (AC) is prepared by the National Severe Storm Forecast Center at 0700Z, 1500Z, and 1930Z daily. The 0700Z issuance covers a 24-hour period from 1200Z to 1200Z, and the 1500Z and 1930Z ACs update the original issuance. The AC describes the potential for thunderstorm activity and describes areas where thunderstorms might approach severe limits. Risk categories are defined: slight risk 2 percent to 5 percent coverage, moderate risk 6 percent to 10 percent coverage, and high risk more than 10 percent coverage.

```
MKC AC 081500
CONVECTIVE OUTLOOK
VALID 081500 – 091200Z


THERE IS A SLGT RISK OF SVR TSTMS TNGT TO RT OF LN FM MEM CBM MCB IAH AUS
DAL PBF MEM.


GNL TSTMS TO RT OF LN FM 80 SW TUS ABQ AMA SGF CVG HTS MGI PNS.


SWRN UPR LOW NOW ACLTG ENEWD IN RESPONSE TO STG HGT FALLS MVG INTO
NRN PLAINS. STG INFLUX OF DP GULF MSTR SHLD CONT INTO LWR MS VLY THRU PD
WITH ASSOC GNL WAA. GOOD INSTBLTY AND MSTR NOW AVBL INTO ERN TX AND BY
TNGT WILL SPRD NEWD INTO MS. MRNG LIFTED INDICIES GNLY MINUS 4 IN ERN TX.
DURG NGT VERY STG WIND FIELD AT MID AND UPR LVLS ALG WITH INCRG LOW
WINDS WILL PROVIDE XLNT SHEAR ENVIRONMENT FOR SVR TSTMS. BEST SVR THRT
SHLD BE IN STG ANTICYCLONIC SHEAR ZN ON S SIDE OF STG POLAR JET WHICH
SHLD RUN FM DRT TO EVV BY 12Z TUE. THIS WOULD PUT SHEAR ZN OVR WM SECTOR
FM ERN TX NEWD INTO NRN MS. XPCT PRIMARY SVR THRT AFTER 00Z WHEN UVV
WITH EJECTING UPR LOW WILL BE CROSSING WM SECTOR.
```

This convective outlook is valid from the eighth day of the month at 1500Z through the ninth at 1200Z (VALID 081500 - 091299Z), the first paragraph describes the probability, or risk, and location of severe thunderstorms. A slight risk (two percent to five percent coverage) of severe thunderstorms tonight to the right of a line from Memphis, TN (MEM), to Columbus, MS (CBM), to Mc Comb, MS (MCB), to Houston, TX (IAH), to Austin, TX (AUS), to Dallas, TX (DAL), to Pine Bluff, AR (PBF), and to Memphis.

The second paragraph provides the location for probable general thunderstorms—not expected to reach severe limits. A probability for general thunderstorms exists to the right of a line from 80 SW of Tucson, AZ (TUS), to Albuquerque, NM (ABQ), to Amarillo, TX (AMA), to Springfield, MO (SGF), to Covington/Cincinnati, OH (CVG), to Huntington, WV (HTS), to Matagorda Island, TX (MGI), to Pensacola, FL (PNS). A pilot might have difficulty decoding these locations without a copy of FAA Handbook 7350.5 *Location Identifiers* or consulting a Flight Service Station, although most locations are on the In-flight Advisory Plotting Chart, Appendix C.

The subsequent paragraph provides synoptic details and the meteorologist's reasoning:

A southwestern upper low is now accelerating east-northeastward in response to strong height falls [drastically reduced elevation of the 500 mb level] moving into the northern Plains. A strong influx of deep Gulf moisture should continue into the Lower Mississippi

Valley through the period with associated general weather. Good instability and moisture now available into eastern Texas and by tonight will spread northeastward into Mississippi. Morning lifted indices generally minus four in eastern Texas. During the night very strong wind field at mid and upper levels along with increasing low winds will provide excellent shear environment for severe thunderstorms. The best threat should be in strong anticyclonic shear zone on south side of strong polar jet which should run from Del Rio, TX, to Evansville, IN, by 1200Z Tuesday. This would put shear zone over warm sector from eastern Texas northeastward into northern Mississippi. Expect primary severe threat after 0000Z when upward vertical velocity with ejecting upper low will be crossing warm sector.

This narrative falls into the same category as the outlook portion of Convective SIGMETs, providing synoptic details in meteorological terms directed toward forecasters more than pilots. It would be helpful to have surface and upper level analysis charts to help visualize the discussion.

The AC can be interpreted as follows:

An upper level low pressure area over the southwestern United States is accelerating east-northeastward as strong height falls move into the northern Plains. [Chart representations and the significance of pressure falls are discussed in Chapter 10.] A deep layer of moist air from the Gulf of Mexico continues to flow into the Lower Mississippi Valley. Unstable air and moisture are now available in eastern Texas and by tonight will spread into Mississippi. The morning lifted indices (1200Z observations) are generally minus four in eastern Texas, a moderate indicator of severe thunderstorms. A strong wind field at mid and upper levels with increasing low level winds will provide excellent shear environment for severe thunderstorms. [Most severe thunderstorms develop in an area where wind speed increases with height and direction turns clockwise—a shear environment. In a typical situation, the surface wind is from the southeast at about 20 knots, at 5,000 feet wind veers to the south and increased to about 30 knots, and the wind at 15,000 feet veers further becoming southwest at about 50 knots.] The greatest threat of severe thunderstorms exists along the south side of a strong polar jet in the anticyclonic shear zone between Del Rio, TX and Evansville, IN. This will put the shear zone over the warm sector [the area that lies between the cold front and warm front of a storm] from eastern Texas into northern Mississippi. The primary severe threat will occur after 0000Z when upward vertical velocity with ejecting upper low will cross the warm sector [factors that enhance the development of severe thunderstorms].

The Severe Weather Outlook Chart provides a preliminary 48-hour thunderstorm probability potential. The left panel gives a 24-hour outlook for general and severe thunderstorms. For example, from FIG. 9-12, a probability for general thunderstorms exists in the south central portion of the United States, with a slight risk of severe thunderstorms in southeastern Texas. The right panel, for the next 24 hours, only contains severe thunderstorm probability.

This chart indicates areas where conditions are right for the development of convective activity sometime during the period. The manually prepared chart is basically a pictorial display of the AC, however, it is not amended nor updated. Notice that the AC, the 1500Z update, is somewhat different from the 1200Z Severe Weather Outlook Chart. The forecaster has additional information for the 1500Z update, which includes the 1200Z upper air data.

A potential for thunderstorms exists within depicted areas. This does not necessarily

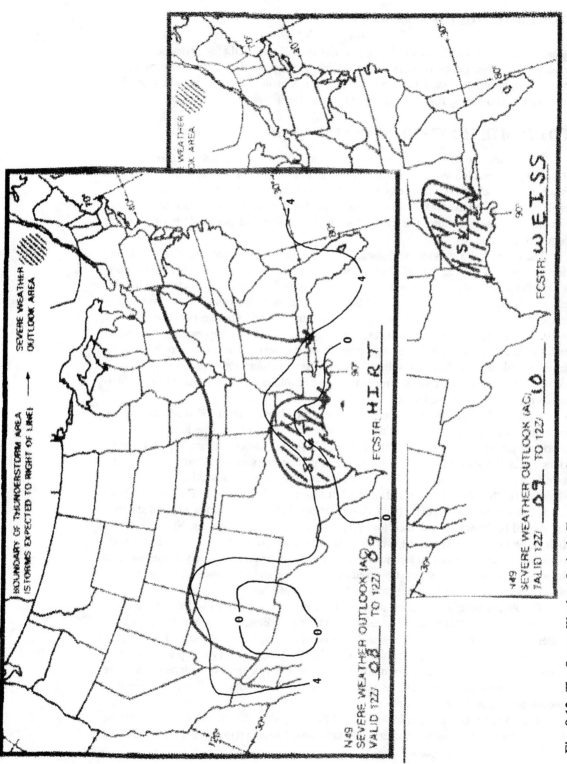

Fig. 9-12. *The Severe Weather Outlook Chart provides a preliminary look at general and severe thunderstorm potential for 24 hours, and severe thunderstorm potential for 48 hours.*

mean thunderstorms will develop. The chart, like the AC, is strictly for advanced planning to alert forecasters, pilots, briefers, and the public to the possibility of future storm development. Appropriate FAs, FTs, WSTs, and Severe Weather Watches must be consulted just prior to and during flight for details on convective activity.

COMPOSITE MOISTURE STABILITY CHART

The Composite Moisture Stability Chart consists of four panels: the Lifted Index Analysis, Precipitable Water, Freezing Level, and Average Relative Humidity. Available twice daily, the chart is computer-generated from radiosonde data. Notice in FIG. 9-13 the analysis is based on the 0000Z observation, Thursday, August 10, 1989. Due to computation and transmission times this chart is about four-and-a-half hours old by the time it becomes available.

The Lifted Index provides an indication of atmospheric moisture and stability—thunderstorm potential at the time of observation. The Lifted Index compares the temperature a parcel of air near the surface would have if lifted to the 500 mb level and cooled adiabatically, with the observed temperature at 500 mbs. The index indicates stability at the 500 mb level. The index can range from +20 to −20, but generally remains between +10 and −10 (The figures are strictly an index, not a representation of temperature). A positive index indicates a stable condition, high positive values, very stable air. A zero index indicates neutral stability. Negative values from zero to minus four indicate areas of potential convection, large negative values from minus five to minus eight very unstable air, which could result in severe thunderstorms.

The K Index evaluates moisture and temperature. The higher the K Index the greater potential for an unstable lapse rate and the availability of moisture. The K Index must be used with caution; it is not a true stability index. Large K Indexes indicate favorable conditions for air mass thunderstorms, during the thunderstorm season. K values can change significantly over short periods due to temperature and moisture advection.

Refer to the Lifted Index panel, upper left FIG. 9-13. The Lifted Index appears above the K Index in the plotted data. *Isopleths*—lines equal in number or quantity—of stability are plotted beginning at zero then for every four units (plus and minus). Negative Lifted Indexes and large K values exist over Florida and the desert southwest. The chart would, therefore, indicate a potential for thunderstorms in those areas. Conversely, positive Lifted Indexes and small K values were observed over New England and Washington state west of the Cascades indicating little moisture and a stable lapse rate.

The Precipitable Water panel, upper right of FIG. 9-13, analyzes water vapor content from the surface to 500 mbs. Darkened station circles indicate large amounts of available water. Isopleths of precipitable water are drawn at one-quarter intervals. The panel is more useful for meteorologists concerned with flash floods. However, a pilot can get an excellent indication of changes in moisture content. For example, considerable moisture exists over the central Rockies. Assuming a northwest to southeast flow, this moisture should be advected into the central plains.

The Freezing Level panel, lower left of FIG. 9-13, plots the lowest observed freezing level. Multiple entries indicate inversions, and above-freezing temperatures, aloft. This is

Composite Moisture Stability Chart

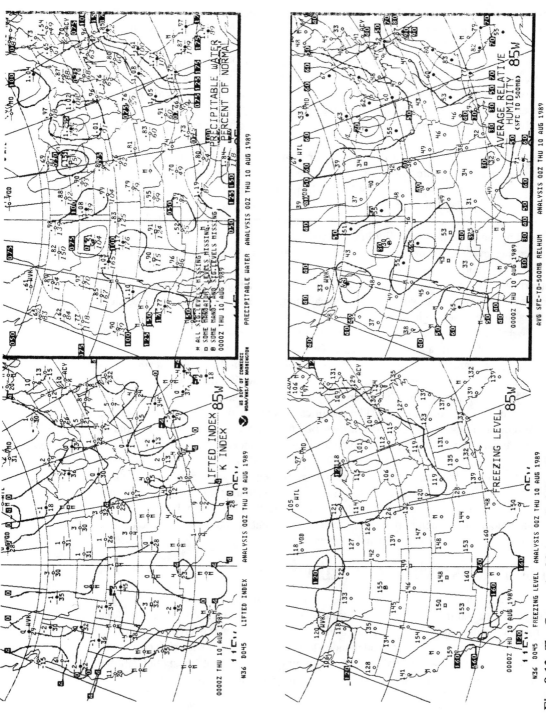

Fig. 9-13. *The Composite Moisture Stability Chart provides a pictorial analysis of stability, moisture, and freezing level based on the twice-daily radiosonde observations. The chart is always old by the time it becomes available, and must never be substituted for current observations and forecasts.*

169

a graphic plot of the RADAT discussed in Chapter 1. Implications and analysis are the same. Remember this is observed data and must be used with forecast information contained in the FA and other forecasts for flight planning.

The Average Relative Humidity panel, lower right of FIG. 9-13, analyzes the average relative humidity from the surface to 500 mbs. Darkened station plots indicate high humidity. *Isohumes*—lines of equal relative humidity—are drawn at 10 percent intervals. The chart indicates large-scale moisture content in the lower part of the troposphere. Clouds and precipitation are indicated in the southeast with a lifting mechanism available and 70 percent relative humidity.

Figure 9-13 indicates several likely areas for significant convective activity. Florida and the desert southwest are prime candidates, due to abundant moisture and instability. Considerable moisture exists over New England, but the air is stable. Any precipitation should be steady and clouds stratiform. Moisture and instability also exists over the Great Lakes for the possibility of convective activity. Thunderstorms for the central Rockies are indicated by moisture and instability in that area.

Freezing levels across the country vary from 10,000 feet in the north to 16,000 feet in the south. Therefore, potential icing exists in clouds and precipitation to 21,000 feet in the southern states. Icing intensities, and the height at which icing would be encountered, increase with convective activity. This is a typical summer case, where pilots must be alert for icing into the lower flight levels.

The Lifted Index Analysis is only one element used to develop the AC, Severe Weather Outlook Chart, and other forecasts. This is illustrated in FIG. 9-12 where Lifted Index Analysis isopleths of stability have been superimposed on the Severe Weather Outlook Chart. Note only a general correlation. Instability below 500 mbs might not be indicated. The chart is several hours old when received and the Lifted Index does not consider a lifting mechanism, nor, can it consider modifications by the development, dissipation, and movement of systems. AC 00-45 *Aviation Weather Services* states: "It is essential to note that an unstable index does not automatically mean thunderstorms."

Certain pilots have attached great significance to the AC and Lifted Index Analysis. They infer some additional insight into thunderstorm activity and severity from these products. The Lifted Index is an observation and only one element used to prepare the AC and other products. The Convective Outlook and Severe Weather Outlook Chart are just that, an outlook. They merely provide a statement of potential and must never be used in place of weather advisories or area and terminal forecasts.

MICROBURSTS AND LOW-LEVEL WIND SHEAR

As aircraft instruments and navigational system capabilities improved, pilots began taking on more and more weather. Hazards of fog and low clouds were solved with the Instrument Landing System (and increased fuel reserves). Icing was overcome in the '30s and, for the most part, turbulence and thunderstorms were mastered with high cruise altitudes and radar. With these hazards solved, major air carrier accidents most often fall into the categories of mechanical failure, pilot error, and wind shear.

The hazards of wind shear can be even more critical to general aviation. *Wind shear*, a rapid change in wind direction or speed, has always been around. Convective activity produces *severe shear*, which is defined as a rapid change in wind direction or velocity causing airspeed changes greater than 15 knots or vertical speed changes greater than 500 feet per minute. The microburst produces the most severe wind shear threat.

Rain cooled air within a thunderstorm produces a concentrated rain or virga shaft less than one-half mile in diameter, which forms a downdraft. The downdraft or downburst has a very sharp edge and forms a ring vortex upon contact with the ground, and spreads out causing gust fronts which are particularly hazardous to aircraft during takeoff, approach, and landing. Reaching the ground the burst continues as an expanding outflow.

A *microburst* consists of a small-scale, severe, storm downburst less than two-and-a-half miles across. This flow can be 180° from the prevailing wind, with an average peak intensity of about 45 knots. Microburst winds intensify for about five minutes after ground contact and typically dissipate about 10 to 20 minutes later. Microburst wind speed differences of almost 100 knots have been measured. On August 1, 1983, at Andrews Air Force Base, indicated differences near 200 knots were observed. Some microburst events are beyond the capability of any aircraft and pilot to recover. Although normally midafternoon, midsummer events, microbursts can occur any time, in any season.

The FAA, along with a group of aviation specialists, has developed AC 00-54 *Pilot Windshear Guide*. Although, primarily for the airlines, much of the information can be applied to general aviation. Avoidance is the best defense against a microburst encounter. When the possibility of microbursts exists, the pilot must continually check all clues. Therefore, he or she must learn to recognize situations favorable to this phenomenon.

Wind Shear Recognition

The following discussion is based on AC 00-54, *Pilot Windshear Guide* and a Department of Commerce publication, *Microbursts: A Handbook for Visual Identification*. The latter publication is for sale by the Superintendent of Documents. It contains an in-depth, technical explanation of the phenomena along with numerous color photographs depicting microburst activity. It should be part of every pilot's library.

Microbursts can develop anytime convective activity, such as thunderstorms, rain showers, or virga occur, associated with both heavy and light precipitation. Approximately five percent of all thunderstorms produce microbursts. And, more than one microburst can occur with the same weather system. Therefore, pilots must be alert for additional microbursts—if one has already been encountered or reported—and prepared for turbulence and shear as subsequent microbursts interact. Microbursts are characterized by precipitation or dust curls carried back up toward the cloud base, horizontal bulging near the surface in a rain shaft forming a foot-shaped prominence, an increase in wind speed as the microburst expands over the ground, and abrupt wind gusts.

Microbursts can occur in extremely dry, as well as wet, environments. The lack of low clouds does not guarantee the absence of shear. Microbursts can develop below clouds with bases as high as 15,000 feet. As virga or light rain falls, intense cooling causes the cold air to plunge, resulting in a dry microburst. Evaporative Cooling Turbulence, associated with this phenomena, has already been discussed. Anvils of large dry-line thunderstorms can produce high-level virga and result in dry microbursts. High based thunderstorms with heavy rain should be of particular concern. This was the type that produced intense wind shear in the 1985 Delta accident in Dallas/Fort Worth.

Embedded microbursts are produced by heavy rain from low based clouds in a wet environment. A wet microburst might first appear as a darkened mass of rain within a light rain shaft. As the microburst moves out along the surface a characteristic upward curl appears.

The potential for wind shear and microbursts exists whenever convective activity occurs. Pilots should review forecasts (FAs, FTs, WSTs, and AWWs) for thunderstorms—thunderstorms imply low-level wind shear—or the inclusion of LLWS. Check surface reports and PIREPs for wind shear clues: thunderstorms, rain showers, gusty winds, or blowing dust. Dry microbursts are more difficult to recognize. Check surface reports for convective activity (RWU, CBs, or VIRGA) and low relative humidity (30° to 50° temperature/dew point spread).

The Low-Level Wind Shear Alert System (LLWAS) has been installed at 110 airports in the United States. The system detects differences between wind speed around the airport and a reference center-field station. Differences trigger an alert. Sensors are not necessarily associated with specific runways, therefore descriptions of remote sites are based on the eight points of the compass: "Center field wind three one zero at one five. North boundary wind zero niner zero at three five."

The *Airport/Facility Directory* advertises the availability of LLWAS under Weather Data Sources. The lack of a LLWAS alert does not necessarily indicate the absence of wind shear. LLWAS has limitations. Magnitude of the shear might be underestimated. Surface obstructions can disrupt or limit the airflow near the sensor and due to location of sensors, microburst development might go undetected, especially in the early stages. Sensors are located at the surface, therefore, microburst development that has not yet reached the surface will be undetected and because coverage only exists near the runways, microbursts on approach will not be observed. Even with these limitations, LLWAS can provide useful information about winds near the airport.

Development continues on an automated Terminal Doppler Weather Radar (TDWR) system that is based on the same principle as NEXRAD. TDWR will provide wind shear warnings to controllers and should become operational around 1993.

Airborne radar returns of heavy precipitation indicate the possibility of microbursts. Although potentially hazardous dry microbursts might only produce weak radar returns. Strong wind shear might occur as far as 15 miles from storm echoes. Radar echoes can be misleading by themselves, and it might require a doppler radar to spot the danger of a dry microburst. The southwest edge of an intense storm can appear weak both visually and on radar, however, this area is known to spawn tornadoes and severe wind shear. Convective weather approaching an airport, the downwind side, tends to be more hazardous than activity moving away.

No quantitative means exist for determining the presence or intensity of microburst wind shear. Pilots must exercise extreme caution when determining a course of action. Microburst wind shear probability guidelines have been developed by the FAA, and apply to operations within three miles of the airport, along the intended flight path, and below 1,000 feet AGL. Probabilities are cumulative, therefore when more than one point exists, probability increases.

The following indicate a **high probability of wind shear** with the presence of convective weather near the intended flight path.

1. Localized strong winds reported, or observed blowing dust, rings of dust or tornado-like features.
2. Visual or radar indications of heavy precipitation.
3. PIREPs of airspeed changes 15 knots or greater.
4. LLWAS Alert or wind velocity change of 20 knots or greater.

A pilot must give critical attention to these observations. A decision to avoid, divert, or delay, is wise.

The following indicate a **medium probability of wind shear** with the presence of convective weather near the intended flight path.

1. Rain showers, lightning, virga, or moderate or greater turbulence reported or indicated on radar.
2. A temperature/dew point spread of 30° F to 50° F.
3. PIREPs of airspeed changes less than 15 knots.
4. LLWAS Alert or wind velocity change less than 20 knots.

A pilot should consider avoiding these conditions. Precautions are indicated.

The FAA states: "Pilots are . . . urged to exercise caution when determining a course of action." Probability guidelines ". . . should not replace sound judgment in making avoidance decisions." In aviation weather there are no guarantees. The lack of high or medium probability indicators in no way promises the absence of wind shear when convective weather is present or forecast. *Avoidance is the best precaution.*

Review the following Colorado Springs (COS) SA and UUA for wind shear probability indicators.

```
COS SA 2150 M90 BKN 250 OVC 45TRW– 74/42/3612G24/019/T OVHD MOVG
        E OCNL LTGCG SW AND E
COS UUA /OV COS/TM 2156/ . . . TP PA60/RM AIRSPEED + – 40 KTS, THOUGHT
        I WAS IN THE TWILIGHT ZONE
```

A thunderstorm with rain showers, a 32° temperature/dew point spread, strong, gusty surface winds, and lightning are being reported. Add the PIREP and there are two high and two moderate probability indicators. This is an example of the dry environment. A pilot must be watchful for visual microburst and LLWS clues.

This SA from Chapter 1 illustrates a wet microburst environment.

PHL RS 2250 W6 X 1TRW + F . . . 3618G24/ . . . FQT LTGICCG

A thunderstorm with heavy precipitation, strong, gusty winds, and lightning is being reported. There is certainly a high probability of wind shear and microbursts.

Takeoff, Approach, and Landing Precautions

Select the longest suitable runway for takeoff. Determine at what point the takeoff can be aborted with enough runway to stop the aircraft. Certain manufacturers provide tables for takeoff calculations, otherwise, the pilot will have to base this distance on landing roll tables and experience. Use the recommended flap setting for gusty wind or turbulent conditions, if available. Use maximum-rated takeoff power. This reduces takeoff roll and overrun exposure. Consider increased airspeed at rotation to perhaps improve the ability of the airplane to negotiate wind shear or turbulence after liftoff. Do not use a speed reference flight director. Be alert for airspeed fluctuations that might be the first signs of wind shear. Should shear be encountered with sufficient runway remaining, abort the takeoff. This decision, however, can only be made by the pilot, based on training and experience. After takeoff use maximum rated power and rate of climb to achieve a safe altitude, at least 1,000 feet AGL.

Select the longest suitable runway to land. Consider a recommended approach configuration with a higher than normal approach speed. Turbulent air penetration or maneuvering speed should be considered. Establish a stabilized approach at least 1,000 feet AGL with configuration, power, and trim set to follow the glideslope without additional changes. Any deviation from glideslope or airspeed change will indicate shear. The autopilot, except for autoflight systems, should be disengaged, with the pilot closely monitoring vertical speed, altimeter, and glideslope displacement. Ground speed and airspeed comparisons can provide additional information for wind shear recognition. Increased approach speed, while providing an extra margin for safety, will require longer than normal landing distance.

Wind Shear Recovery Technique

Wind shear recovery technique has not yet been developed for small aircraft. The following wind shear recovery technique, developed for airline aircraft, has been adapted from AC 00-54. It is, however, logical and applicable to most wind shear encounters in practically any aircraft.

Wind shear recognition is crucial to making a timely recovery decision. Encounters occur infrequently with only a few seconds to initiate a successful recovery. The objective is to keep the airplane flying as long as possible in hope of exiting the shear. The first priority must be to maintain airplane control. The following guidelines were developed for the airlines, exact criteria cannot be established. Whenever these parameters are exceeded, recovery and/or abandoning the takeoff or approach should be strongly considered. It must be emphasized that it is the responsibility of the pilot to assess the situation and use sound judgment in determining the safest course of action. It might be necessary to initiate recovery before any of these parameters are reached.

1. Plus or minus 15 knots indicated airspeed.
2. Plus or minus 500 feet per minute vertical speed.
3. Plus or minus one dot glideslope displacement.
4. Unusual throttle position for a significant period of time.

If any condition is encountered, aggressively apply maximum rated power. Avoid engine overboost unless required to avoid ground contact. While on approach, do not attempt to land. Establish maximum rate of climb airspeed. As with any turbulent condition, pitch up in a smooth, steady manner. Should ground contact be imminent, pitch up to best-angle-of-climb airspeed, being careful not to stall the airplane. Controlled contact with the ground is preferable to an uncontrolled encounter. When airplane safety has been ensured, adjust power to maintain specified limits. When the airplane is climbing and ground contact is no longer an immediate concern, cautiously reduce pitch to desired airspeed.

The key to the thunderstorm and LLWS hazard is avoidance. A superior pilot uses superior knowledge to *avoid* having to use superior skill. At the first sign of severe shear reject the takeoff or abandon the approach. It is easier to explain an aborted takeoff or missed approach to passengers rather than explain an accident to the FAA and insurance company—assuming you're still around to do so.

Avoidance is the operative word with thunderstorms, microbursts, and wind shear. A pilot's proper application of many resources—training, experience, visual references, cockpit instruments, weather reports and weather forecasts—make avoidance possible.

10
Air Analysis Charts

CONSIDERABLE MISUNDERSTANDING ARISES BECAUSE MANY AVIATION WEATHER texts fail to adequately describe and explain nonfrontal weather producing systems. A pilot presented with such a situation will commonly ask the briefer, "Where's the front?" Only to be told, "There is no front." Weather occurs at all altitudes within the troposphere; the Surface Analysis Chart often cannot solely explain the weather, even weather occurring at or near the surface.

Surface and upper air analysis charts graphically display a three-dimensional view of the atmosphere based on selected locations at the time of observation. These charts provide a primary source for locating areas of moisture and vertical motion. Products normally available to aviation:

- Surface Analysis
- Weather Depiction
- 850 mb
- 700 mb
- 500 mb
- 300 mb
- 200 mb Constant Pressure Charts

Each provides details on phenomena occurring at that level. The most complete description of the atmosphere can only be obtained from a combined analysis, which should include the Radar Summary Chart.

SURFACE ANALYSIS CHART

The Surface Analysis Chart provides a first look at weather systems. Sea level pressure is the key element. Observed station pressure, converted to sea level, allows analysis from a common reference. The sea level conversion introduces errors, especially in mountainous areas. The data is computer analyzed for a first guess at *isobars*—lines of equal sea level pressure. NWS meteorologists, as seen in FIG. 10-1, manually correct the chart before transmission and annotate the position of fronts based on pressure patterns, wind shifts, the previous chart, and satellite imagery. The chart also contains wind flow, temperature, and moisture patterns, providing a primary source for the synopsis.

Often the exact location, and sometimes even the presence, of fronts is a matter of judgment (a front can be a zone several hundred miles across). Additionally, fronts do not necessarily reach the surface; they might be found within layers aloft. This is especially true in the western United States and the Appalachians where mountain ranges break up fronts. Therefore, there might be differences between the charted position of fronts and their location as described in the FA or TWEBs. In such cases it would be advisable to compare chart, FA, and TWEB analysis, and the time of each product.

Fig. 10-1. *Meteorologists at the National Meteorological Center manually correct computer-generated isobars and annotate fronts on the Surface Analysis Chart before transmission.*

The Surface Analysis Chart is prepared and transmitted every three hours and is available at Flight Service Stations, NWS offices, and through most commercial vendors with graphics capability. Observed data must be plotted and analyzed, so the chart is always old, sometimes several hours, by the time it becomes available. The chart should always be updated with current reports.

An overall perspective of the history of system movements can be obtained by reviewing previous charts. Even though, care must be used with the apparent movement of low pressure centers, fronts, and troughs, especially across the western United States. Their movement is subjectively analyzed by the meteorologist.

Surface Analysis Station Model

Most pilots have forgotten how to read station models. But, with commercial weather vendors and DUAT, pilots might need to brush up on this skill. Flight Watch specialists, trained in their interpretation, use Surface Analysis Chart station models when SAs are not available. Pilots don't need to decode the entire model, just the details significant to aviation.

Figure 10-2 provides an explanation of the station model. Information on the right (in small letters) is primarily for the meteorologists. Above and below the model are cloud types. On the left (in capital letters) is information most significant to aviation. This includes temperature, dew point, present weather, total sky cover, and wind direction and speed.

From TABLE 10-1, total sky cover contains more detail than sequence reports. There is a general correlation, but heights are not provided, and it is the summation of all cloud layers. TABLE 10-1 also decodes cloud-type symbols used with station models. Considerable information can be deduced from reported cloud types. A pilot should have a general

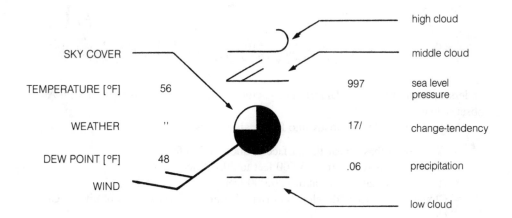

Fig. 10-2. *Surface Analysis Chart station models contain much valuable information. Pilots should be able to decode details significant to aviation.*

Table 10-1. *Station Model Symbols.*

TOTAL SKY COVER:

CLR	LESS THAN 1/10	1/10 – 5/10	6/10 – 9/10	10/10 BINOVC	10/10	X/–X

CLOUDS:

		LOW			MIDDLE			HIGH
1	CU	CUMULUS	1	AS	ALTOSTRATUS	1	CI	CIRRUS
2	CU	CUMULUS	2	AS	ALTOSTRATUS	2	CI	CIRRUS
3	CB	CUMULONIMBUS	3	AC	ALTOCUMULUS	3	CI	CIRRUS
4	SC	STRATOCUMULUS	4	AC	ALTOCUMULUS	4	CI	CIRRUS
5	SC	STRATOCUMULUS	5	AC	ALTOCUMULUS	5	CS	CIRROSTRATUS
6	ST	STRATUS	6	AC	ALTOCUMULUS	6	CS	CIRROSTRATUS
7	FC	FRACTOSTRATUS	7	AC	ALTOCUMULUS	7	CS	CIRROSTRATUS
8	CU/SC	CUMULUS AND STRATOCUMULUS	8	AC	ALTOCUMULUS	8	CS	CIRROSTRATUS
9	CB	CUMULONIMBUS	9	AC	ALTOCUMULUS	9	CC	CIRROCUMULUS

PRESENT WEATHER:

F		BD/BN		RW		SG		T
K		BS		S		ZL		T+
H		L		IP		ZR		TORNADO FUNNEL CLOUD WATER SPOUT
D		R		SP		A		

understanding of the codes. Unfortunately, cloud-type codes might disappear with AWOS observations.

Meteorologists divide clouds into four main groups:

- Low clouds (bases near the surface to about 6,500 feet)
- Middle clouds (bases from 6,500 feet to 20,000 feet)
- High clouds (based at or above 20,000 feet)
- Clouds with vertical development (based near the surface, tops of cirrus; Cu and Cb)

Notice that in TABLE 10-1 Cu and Cb are listed with low clouds, associated with their bases.

The following discussion, based on the cloud types in TABLE 10-1, might refer to a code number (1 through 9) to the left of the contraction and symbol.

The code starts with low clouds with vertical development. *Cumulus* (1) describes fair weather Cu, seemingly flattened, with little vertical development: no significant weather, turbulent below the bases and smooth on top. Cumulus (2) contains considerable vertical development, generally towering. This type precedes the development of cumulonimbus and thunderstorms. SAs often contain the remark TCU (towering cumulus). This refers to growing cumulus that resembles a cauliflower, but with tops that have not yet reached the cirrus level. *Cumulonimbus* (3) exhibit great vertical development with tops composed, at least in part, of ice crystals. Tops no longer contain the well-defined cauliflower shape. Cumulonimbus (9) have clearly fibrous (cirroform) tops, often anvil shaped. Regardless of vertical development, a cloud is classified as cumulonimbus only when all or part of the top is transformed, or in the process of transformation, into a cirrus mass. Any cumulonimbus cloud should be considered a thunderstorm with all the ominous implications.

Stratocumulus (4) and (5), and cumulus and stratocumulus (8) represent a moist layer with some convection. Stratocumulus (4) forms from the spreading of Cu, which indicates decreasing convection. Stratus indicates low-level stability. *Fractostratus* and *fractocumulus* (scud) are normally associated with bad weather.

Middle clouds fall into two general types: *altostratus* and *altocumulus*. Altostratus indicate a stable atmosphere at mid levels. Altostratus (1) is thin, semitransparent, while altostratus (2) is thick enough to hide the sun or moon. Rain or snow, even heavy snow, can fall from altostratus. When the cloud layer thickens and lowers it becomes *nimbostratus* (Ns).

Altocumulus indicate vertical motion at mid levels. Altocumulus (3) is thin, mostly semitransparent. Altocumulus numbers (5), (6), and (7) describe cloud thickness, development, and altocumulus associated with other cloud forms.

High clouds are known as *cirrus*, *cirrostratus*, and *cirrocumulus*. Cirrus (1) consists of filaments, commonly known as mares' tails. Cirrus (2) and (3) are often associated with cumulonimbus clouds. Cirrus (4) usually indicates a thickening layer, which might be associated with the approach of a front. Cirrostratus (5 through 8) describe sheets or layers of cirrus. Sun or moon halos often appear in these layers. Cirrocumulus indicate vertical motion at high levels and might indicate high altitude turbulence.

Cirrus, of itself, has no significance to low-level flights. However, cirrus is often associated with the jet stream and high altitude turbulence. Cirrus that forms as transverse lines or cloud trails perpendicular to the jet stream indicates moderate or greater turbulence. These clouds might be reported as cirrocumulus. Cirrus streaks, parallel to the jet, are long narrow streaks of cirrus frequently seen with jet streams. Jet stream cirrus and cloud trails are easily identified from satellite imagery. Unfortunately, usually the only access to satellite pictures is through an FSS or Flight Watch.

Selected present-weather symbols, and their SA contraction equivalents, are contained in TABLE 10-1. Up to four drizzle, rain, or snow symbols can indicate intensity and trend; the station model in FIG. 10-2 shows two drizzle symbols. Symbols can be combined to indicate more than one phenomena occurring. Precipitation representations will appear above the thunderstorm symbol to indicate type and intensity of precipitation accompanying the "thunder bumper." An inverted, elongated triangle indicates showers. The type of showers (rain, snow, etc.) appears above the triangle. Present-weather symbols can be interpreted in the same way as their SA counterparts.

Temperature and dew point, in degrees Fahrenheit, appear to the left of the station model. Wind is indicated as the direction (true) from which the wind is blowing, with barbs, half barbs, and flags representing speed in knots.

Information to the right of the station model is less significant to the pilot. Sea level pressure, in millibars, is decoded the same as SAs; FIG. 10-2 shows 997, therefore, the sea level pressure is 999.7 millibars. (Refer to Chapter 1 for additional explanation.) The pressure change, during the past three hours, in 10ths of millibars, and its tendency—increasing, decreasing, steady—appear below sea level pressure. Any precipitation during the past six hours, to the nearest hundredth of an inch, appears in the lower right.

Let's decode, translate, and interpret the station model in FIG. 10-2; refer to TABLE 10-1. Total sky cover is broken ($^6/_{10}$ to $^9/_{10}$). Cloud bases are not provided, but they can be inferred from cloud type. The low clouds consist of fractostratus, or scud. Thick altostratus and cirrus are also being reported, so the scud can't be too extensive. The higher cloud types might indicate an approaching front. Wind is out of the southwest at 15 knots. Visibility, which does not directly appear, is probably good in spite of a relatively close temperature/dew point spread (8° F). Moisture is being added by drizzle, however. If the wind remains constant, additional moisture could increase the amount of fractostratus. But if the wind subsides, fog and reduced visibility might result. Except for low-level mechanical turbulence due to wind, the atmosphere appears stable from the cloud types reported. Therefore, mostly smooth flying conditions and light icing in clouds and precipitation above the freezing level are indicated.

TABLE 10-2 contains front symbols, provides a description of the front, and defines hues used for color displays. Frontogenesis, the initial formation of a front or frontal zone, is depicted by a broken line with the appropriate front-type symbol. Frontolysis, the dissipation of a front or frontal zone, is represented by a broken line with the appropriate front-type symbol on every other line. As previously mentioned, frontal zones can occur in layers aloft. Hollow bumps and triangles indicate a frontal boundary aloft.

Surface Chart Analysis

Refer to FIG. 10-3, which is a redrawing of the 0900Z, December 29, 1986, chart; only selected station models appear.

Pressure patterns indicate areas at the surface that are under the influence of high or low pressure, troughs, or ridges. The terms high and low are relative. A *high* is defined as an area completely surrounded by lower pressure. Conversely, a *low* is an area surrounded by higher pressure. Lines known as *isobars* connect areas of equal sea level pressure. Beginning with 1000 mbs (labeled 00 on the chart), lines are drawn at four millibar intervals. Weak pressure gradient may be drawn at two-mb intervals using dashed isobars. Pressures at each pressure center are indicated by a two-digit underlined number. For example, the high center over the Rockies has a central pressure of 1036 mbs, the low near the Great Lakes, 1014 mbs.

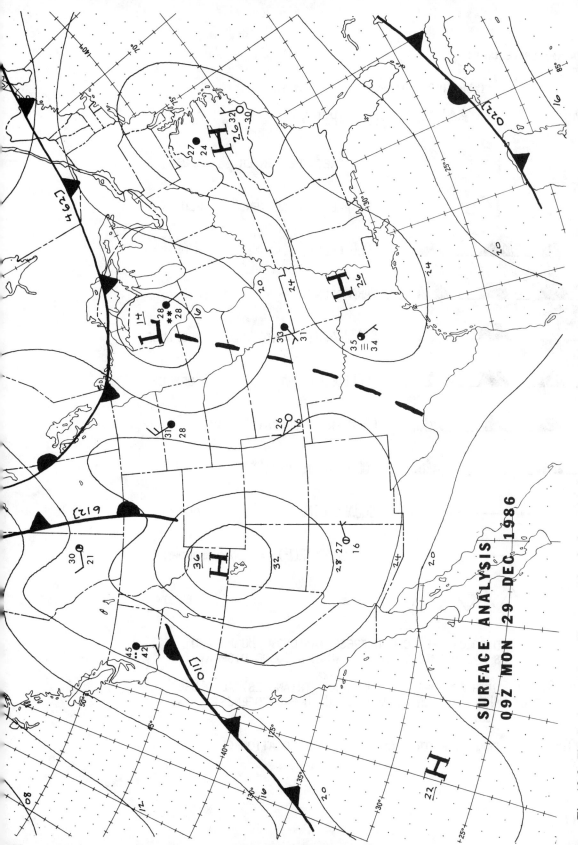

Fig. 10-3. *The Surface Analysis Chart provides the location of moisture and lifting mechanisms at the surface and in the lower atmosphere.*

Table 10-2. *Surface Analysis Chart Symbols.*

SYMBOL	DESCRIPTION	COLOR*
H	HIGH PRESSURE CENTER	BLUE
L	LOW PRESSURE CENTER	RED
▲▲▲	COLD FRONT	BLUE
●●●	WARM FRONT	RED
▼ ● ▼	STATIONARY FRONT	RED/BLUE
▲ ● ▲	OCCLUDED FRONT	PURPLE
▲ ▲ ▲	COLD FRONTOGENESIS**	
▲ ▲	COLD FRONTOLYSIS**	
—‥—‥—	SQUALL LINE	PURPLE
— — —	TROUGH (TROF)	BROWN
∨∨∨∨	RIDGE	YELLOW

* SUGGESTED COLORS FOR COLOR PRESENTATIONS. BUMPS AND TRIANGLES ARE NORMALLY OMITTED WITH A COLOR DISPLAY.

** SYMBOL, WITH APPROPRIATE BUMPS AND TRIANGLES, ALSO USED TO DEPICT WARM, STATIONARY AND OCCLUDED FRONTOGENESIS, AND FRONTOLYSIS.

NOTE: OPEN BUMPS AND TRIANGLES INDICATE LOCATION OF FRONT ALOFT.

A *trough* consists of an elongated area of low pressure. Figure 10-3 shows that a trough extends from the low center near the Great Lakes through central Texas. A *ridge*, the opposite of a trough, is an elongated area of high pressure, almost always associated with anticyclonic (clockwise in the northern hemisphere) wind flow. Figure 10-3 shows that a ridge extends from the high center over the Rockies into western Canada.

Wind blows across isobars, due to friction between the wind and surface causing *convergence* and *divergence*; convergence—upward vertical motion—destabilizes the atmosphere, which increases relative humidity, clouds, and precipitation. Divergence —downward vertical motion—stabilizes the atmosphere, which decreases relative humidity and clouds. Convergence of itself does not necessarily produce poor weather, nor does divergence produce good weather. Other factors, such as moisture, must be considered. Surface convergence and divergence only affect the atmosphere below about 10,000 feet, but they are a major factor in the "weather machine"—vertical motion.

Convergence occurs along curved isobars surrounding a low or trough. Maximum convergence takes place at the low center or along the trough line. Troughs sometimes appear on the surface analysis as a dashed line. Figure 10-3 shows surface winds blowing into the low and converging along the trough. Note that the station model next to the low shows snow falling.

Troughs are not fronts, although fronts normally lie in troughs. A front is the boundary between air masses of different temperatures, whereas, a trough is simply a line of low pressure. Both phenomena produce upward vertical motion.

Note the anticyclonic, outward flow from both high centers in FIG. 10-3. Maximum divergence takes place at the high center or along the ridge line. The symbol for a ridge is a continuous zigzag line, normally not depicted on the surface analysis. A high or ridge implies surface divergence.

There is a misconception that high pressure always means good flying weather. Although good weather often occurs, there are exceptions. Strong pressure gradients at the edge of high cells can cause vigorous winds and severe turbulence. Near the center of a high, or with weak gradients, moisture and pollutants can be trapped at lower levels causing reduced visibilities and even producing zero-zero conditions in fog for days or even weeks.

A three-digit code entered along the front specifies type, intensity, and character (TABLE 10-3). For example, the type, intensity, and character of the front in western Canada is 612. The type is 6 (occlusion), intensity 1 (weak and decreasing), and character 2 (frontal area activity has little change). Two short lines crossing a front indicate a change in classification.

Frontal intensity is based on frontal speed. That is the temperature gradient in the cold sector, the region of colder air at a frontal zone. A front with waves indicates weak low pressure centers or portions of the front moving at different speeds. A front with waves needs to be watched. The weak low pressure areas can intensify and cause significant weather.

The position of the isobars represents pressure patterns or gradient that determine wind flow. Surface wind blows at an angle to the isobars from high to low pressure. Station models show this flow for moderate or strong gradients. However, in mountainous areas, and with weak gradients, the pattern might be confused by terrain or local surface temperature differences.

The isobar pattern represents the relative strength of the wind. Closer spacing of the isobars means stronger pressure gradient force, therefore, the stronger wind. Wider spacing of the isobars means weaker wind. Figure 10-3 shows a weak gradient in Arizona accompanied by light winds and a stronger gradient in South Dakota with stronger winds.

The Surface Analysis Chart can be used to determine vertical motion at and near the surface. Convergence and divergence have been discussed. Fronts also produce vertical motion. TABLES 10-2 and 10-3 describe how this phenomenon is depicted on the Surface Analysis Chart.

A front is generally the zone between two air masses of different density. Temperature is the most important density factor, therefore fronts almost invariably separate air masses of different temperatures. Other factors can distinguish a front, such as a pressure trough, change in wind direction, moisture differences, and cloud and precipitation forms.

Norwegian meteorologist Vilhelm Bjerknes, and his son Jakob, developed the polar front theory at the beginning of the 20th century. World War I had begun and it was popu-

Table 10-3. *Front Type, Intensity, and Character.*

Code	Type (first digit)	Intensity (second digit)	Character (third digit)
0	Quasi-stationary surface	No specification	No specification
1	Quasi-stationary aloft	Weak, decreasing	Frontal area activity, decreasing
2	Warm front surface	Weak, little or no change	Frontal area activity little change
3	Warm front aloft	Weak, increasing	Frontal area activity increasing
4	Cold front surface	Moderate, decreasing	Intertropical
5	Cold front aloft	Moderate, little/no change	Forming or existance expected
6	Occlusion	Moderate, increasing	Quasi-stationary
7	Instability line	Strong, decreasing	With waves
8	Intertropical front	Strong, little/no change	Diffuse
9	Convergence line	Strong, increasing	Position doubtful

Example: 427] would decode:
(4) Cold front at the surface;
(2) weak with little or no change;
(7) with waves.

lar to use the language of the conflict. Thus, weather was described using words like fronts, advances, and retreats. The weather did resemble a war between air masses.

The earth's atmosphere is a giant heat exchanger, moving cold air down from the arctic and warm air up from the tropics. Typically in the northern hemisphere the cold air pushes down from the northwest, lifts, and replaces the warm air. The boundary where this action takes place is known as a *cold front*. However, to accomplish this, at some point, warm tropical air must replace the colder air. This typically takes place ahead of the cold front as the warm air, moving from the south, rises above and replaces the colder, retreating air; this boundary is known as a *warm front*. Cold fronts move faster than warm fronts; sometimes the cold front will overtake the warm front and an *occlusion* occurs and the front is known as an *occluded front*. When frontal speed decreases to five knots or less it is labeled *stationary*. This action is more or less continuous around the world at middle latitudes. Fronts produce vertical motion from the surface to about the middle troposphere.

The intensity and movement of fronts is affected by many factors, such as, temperature, moisture, stability, terrain, and upper level systems. Another factor is *slope*; the average cold front slope is one mile vertically for every 100 miles horizontally. The closer the front is to the jet stream the steeper the slope, and typically the stronger the front.

Fronts run the spectrum from a complete lack of weather, to benign clouds that can be conquered by the novice instrument pilot, to fronts that spawn lies of severe thunderstorms that no pilot or aircraft can negotiate. Each front—for that matter any weather system— must be evaluated separately then a flight decision can be made based on the latest weather reports and forecast, and the pilot's and airplane's capabilities and limitations.

Upslope and downslope flow causes vertical motion. This can be determined from the chart when familiar with the terrain. Upslope produces the same characteristics as convergence and downslope divergence. Strong downslope flows are sometimes given local names, such as the Chinook that develops along the eastern slopes of the Rockies and the Santa Ana of Southern California. The Chinook has been known to raise temperatures as much as 20° F in 15 minutes, and melt and evaporate a foot of snow in a few hours. The strong winds can exceed 85 knots, causing extreme damage. A Santa Ana caused the destruction of a blimp at the Ontario, CA, Airport in January 1989.

Forecast synopses often include "upslope" and might contain "Chinook" or "Santa Ana" when these conditions occur. Figure 10-3 shows upslope flow over southeastern Texas from the Gulf of Mexico and downslope flow from the eastern Rockies into the Great Plains.

Onshore and offshore flows of moderate or greater intensity can be determined from the chart. An onshore flow can translate into advection fog, upslope, or convection with the development of thunderstorms depending on conditions, and an offshore flow clear skies. An onshore flow can be seen in FIG. 10-3 along the Texas Gulf Coast and a weak offshore flow is in Southern California.

Temperature and moisture patterns are determined by analyzing station model temperatures and dew points. Considerable moisture at the surface exists in eastern Texas with light surface winds that have caused fog to develop. Refer to the station models in FIG. 10-3. Because 0900Z is 3 a.m. central standard time, what kind of weather can be expected during the morning? Dry surface conditions with a moderate downslope flow prevail in southwestern Kansas. What kind of weather can be expected in this area? Answers are under Weather Depiction Chart.

WEATHER DEPICTION CHART

The Weather Depiction Chart is computer generated, analyzed, and transmitted every three hours, as a record of observed surface data. Frontal positions are obtained from the previous Surface Analysis. The information is hours old by the time the chart becomes available: data should always be updated with current reports. The chart is analyzed into three categories—IFR, MVFR, and VFR—the same as the Area Forecast outlook.

The chart is computer analyzed, so it cannot consider terrain; nor is it intended to represent conditions between reporting locations. Gross errors between depicted categories and actual weather can occur. Compare FIG. 10-4 and FIG. 10-5; both represent approximately the same period in time. Figure 10-4 indicates extensive IFR and MVFR conditions in Central California and western Oregon; compare that depiction with the visual satellite image in FIG. 10-5. The fog that has created the conditions, has almost dissipated in Central California, and in Oregon is restricted to the Willamette Valley. The rather significant difference between the coverages in FIG. 10-4 and FIG. 10-5 is due to the limitations of the Weather Depiction Chart. The chart is computer analyzed, and unable to consider conditions between reporting locations or terrain. It is several hours old by the time it becomes available. And, conditions could improve, as they did in the example, or deteriorate. The Weather Depiction Chart is not a substitute for current observations.

Weather Depiction Station Model

Station models on the Weather Depiction Chart plot cloud height in hundreds of feet AGL and indicate that beneath the model. When total sky cover has few or scattered clouds (less than $1/10$), the base of the lowest layer appears. Visibilities of six miles or less, and present weather, are entered to the left of the station. Sky cover and present weather symbols are the same as used on the Surface Analysis, as illustrated in TABLE 10-1, with one exception. The symbol contained in the inset of FIG. 10-6 represents mountain obscurement. (AWOS observations might eliminate much useful information.)

The station model in southwestern Texas (FIG. 10-6) (at A) shows the sky overcast (solid station circle), cloud base at 5,000 feet AGL (50, underneath station circle). Visibility is reduced by fog to five miles (5, left of fog symbol). Because the number of stations analyzed exceeds the number plotted, contoured areas might appear without station models: the area of VFR in eastern New York (at B); a station has been analyzed, but not plotted.

Weather Depiction Chart Analysis

The Weather Depiction Chart provides a big, simplified, picture of surface conditions. It alerts pilots and briefers to areas of potentially hazardous low ceilings and visibilities. The chart is a good place to begin looking for an IFR alternate.

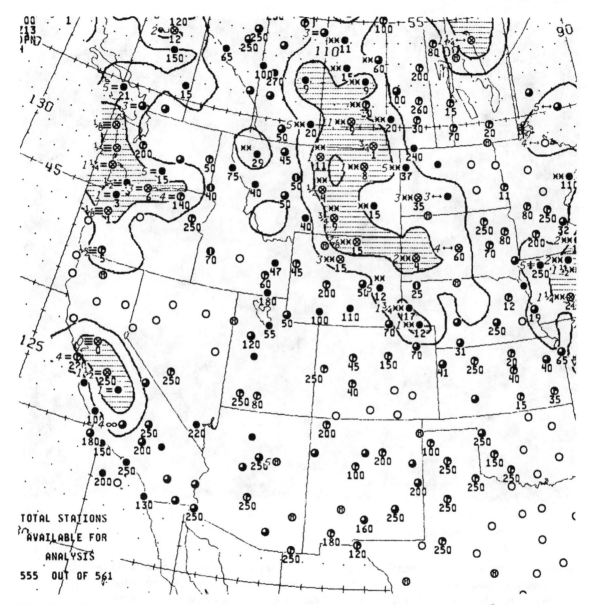

Fig. 10-4. *The computer program that generates the Weather Depiction Chart cannot consider terrain. The chart is not intended to represent conditions between reporting locations.*

Figure 10-6 contains 1300Z data for December 29, 1986, four hours after the Surface Analysis in FIG. 10-3. Widespread IFR conditions exist in California's Central Valley, typical for the time of year (radiation fog). Under the exact conditions depicted, a pilot called flight service and could not understand why IFR conditions existed under a high pressure

Fig. 10-5. *Comparing this satellite image with the excerpt from the Weather Depiction Chart in Fig. 10-4, gross errors between depicted categories and actual weather can be seen.*

system. This emphasizes the point that the presence of high pressure does not necessarily guarantee good weather. And the computer program does not necessarily represent actual conditions, the chart shows MVFR that does not exist over the Sierra Nevada and coastal mountains. Satellite pictures are often helpful determining the actual extent of stratus and fog.

The chart could be used to determine likely locations for a suitable alternate for an IFR flight into eastern Oklahoma. An alternate to the West, the Oklahoma or Texas panhandles, would be indicated. Extensive fog (radiation and upslope) has formed over the southeastern states and clear skies (reduced moisture, moderate winds, and downslope) prevail over western Kansas.

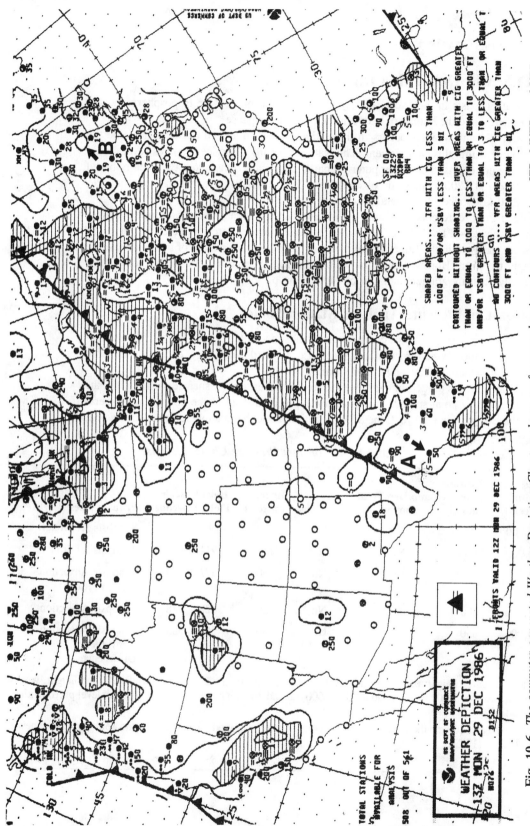

Fig. 10-6. *The computer-generated Weather Depiction Chart analyzes surface weather into three categories—IFR, MVFR, and VFR.*

UPPER AIR ANALYSIS CHARTS

Weather exists in the two lower layers of the atmosphere—the troposphere and the stratosphere—and the boundary between them, the tropopause.

Pilots fly and weather occurs in three dimensions, so a need exists to describe the atmosphere within this environment. The National Weather Service prepares several constant pressure charts. These computer-prepared charts are transmitted twice daily based on 0000Z and 1200Z upper air observations. Each level has a particular significance; TABLE 10-4 describes the general features of each level.

Each chart represents a constant pressure level, so it is analyzed for altitude or height in meters above sea level. Lines, known as *contours*, connect areas of equal height. Contours are analyzed in the same way as isobars, the closer the spacing of the contours, the stronger the wind. However, wind blows parallel to the contours, due to the lack of friction; only pressure gradient and Coriolis forces are present.

Constant Pressure Analysis Station Model

Constant pressure analysis charts depict radiosonde data. Figure 10-7 illustrates standard station plots. Wind direction and speed use standard symbology, except for the contraction LV, which indicates *light and variable*.

Temperature is plotted in degrees Celsius. However, unlike surface station plots the temperature/dew point spread, or *depression*, appears instead of the dew point temperature. For example, in FIG. 10-7, the 850 mb station model has a temperature of minus one,

Table 10-4. *Constant Pressure Chart Analysis.*

Pressure Altitude (feet)	Pressure Level (mb)	Temp/Dew Point Spread	Isotachs	Contour Interval (meters)	Height Meters Plotted/Decode	Primary Uses
39,000	200	Yes	Yes	120	192/11,920	Synopsis Jet Stream
30,000	300	Yes	Yes	120	911/9,110	Synopsis Jet Stream
18,000	500	Yes	No	60	572/5,720	Synopsis Advection Troughs/Ridges
10,000	700	Yes	No	30	928/2,928	Synopsis Advection
5,000	850	Yes	No	30	585/1,585	Synopsis Advection Convergence Divergence

To decode station height: prefix 850 mb level with a "1;" prefix a "2" or a "3" to the 700 mb height, whichever brings it closer to 3,000 meters; add a "0" to 500 mb and 300 mb heights; and, for 200 mb level prefix with a "1" and add a "0."

For 300 mb and 200 mb the temperature/dew point spread is omitted when the air is too cold to measure dew point (less than $-41°$ C).

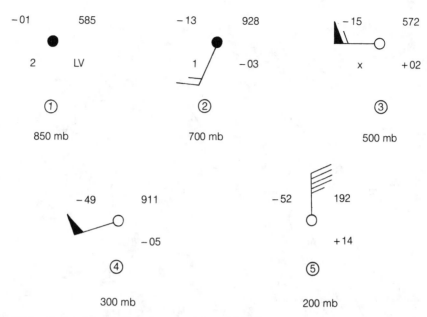

Fig. 10-7. *Constant pressure chart station models depict radiosonde data. They provide height, wind, temperature, and moisture for the constant pressure surface.*

and a dew point depression of two, therefore, the dew point temperature is minus three. Darkened station circles, plotted with a temperature/dew point spread of five degrees or less, indicate a moist atmosphere. This alerts pilots and forecasters to potential clouds, precipitation, and icing depending on temperature. An X indicates a temperature/dew point spread greater than 29 degrees, for example in FIG. 10-7, the 500 mb plot. With temperatures less than −41 air is too dry to measure dew point, and dew point depression is omitted in the 300 mb and 200 mb plots in FIG. 10-7.

The upper right corner of the plot contains the height of the constant pressure level. TABLE 10-4 decodes these values. The number in the lower right corner represents height change during the past 12 hours, in 10s of meters. For example, in FIG. 10-7, the height of the 700 mb surface has lowered 30 meters (−03). In general, lowering heights indicate deteriorating weather and rising heights indicate improving weather. The greater the fall or rise, the more rapid the change. And, systems tend to move in the direction of greatest height change.

850 mb and 700 mb Constant Pressure Charts

TABLE 10-4 shows that the 850 mb and 700 mb charts represent the lower portion of the troposphere, approximately 5,000 and 10,000 feet, providing a synopsis for these levels. The 850 mb chart might be more representative of surface conditions west of the Rockies than the surface analysis. In the west, areas of frictional convergence/divergence can be located. For example, from the 850 mb chart in FIG. 10-8, divergence can be seen

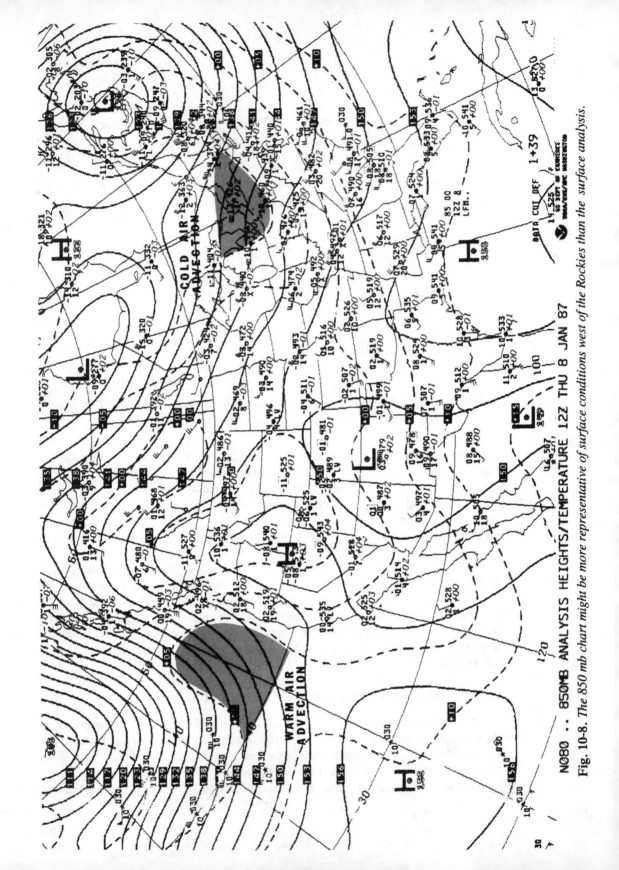

Fig. 10-8. The 850 mb chart might be more representative of surface conditions west of the Rockies than the surface analysis.

in the ridge over western Canada. Additionally, a downslope condition exists in eastern Montana and the Dakotas.

These charts are particularly useful in monitoring cold and warm air advection. When *isotherms*—dashed lines of equal temperature—cross contours at right angles the temperature properties of the air mass are advected (moved) in the direction of the winds. At the 850 mb and 700 mb levels, warm air advection produces upward motion and cold air advection downward motion. Therefore, warm air advection destabilizes conditions, whereas, cold air advection tends to stabilize the weather. Figure 10-8 shows warm air advection in western Canada from a tongue of warm air. And, in the northeast United States a tongue of cold air advances toward the East Coast. Warm air advection might be all that's needed to trigger thunderstorms.

Areas of moisture can be determined by examining station models for temperature/dew point spread. Icing is implied in areas of visible moisture with temperatures between 0° C and −10° C. The 700 mb chart, FIG. 10-9 shows temperatures within this range, at this level, over the entire United States. The air is dry along the West Coast, implying little potential for icing, however, over Kansas and Oklahoma there is considerable moisture present for an increased icing potential.

These charts can be used to determine the potential for turbulence and mountain wave activity. The 700 mb chart is usually the reference level for mountain waves. Winds in excess of 40 knots imply moderate or greater mechanical turbulence. When winds of these speeds blow perpendicular to a mountain range, accompanied by cold-air advection (a stabilizing condition), a strong potential for mountain waves and associated turbulence exists.

Air mass thunderstorms tend to move with the 700 mb winds. And, in mid latitudes a 700 mb temperature of 14° C or greater tends to inhibit convection at this level. If convection occurs below, clouds tend to stop rising and spread out at about the 700 mb height.

500 mb Constant Pressure Chart

Probably the most important and useful chart—maybe even more important to meteorologists than the surface analysis—the 500 mb chart describes the atmosphere in the middle troposphere, which is an altitude of approximately 18,000 feet. This chart provides important pressure, wind flow, temperature, and moisture patterns, and can be used to determine areas of vertical motion at this level.

Troughs and ridges are easily seen in FIG. 10-10. Unlike the Surface Analysis Chart where upward vertical motion takes place along a trough line, upward vertical motion at the 500 mb level takes place between the trough and ridge line (off the west coast and to a lesser degree ahead of the trough moving through Arizona). Troughs transport cold air down from the north and warm air up from the south. Warm air rides northward on the east side of the trough—trough to ridge flow—so the air is lifted as it moves northward, producing upward vertical motion. When moisture is present, such as the area outlined in gray over western Canada, clouds and precipitation in the mid troposphere develop. Conversely, in the ridge-to-trough flow over California, cold air sinks southward, producing downward vertical motion with clear, dry conditions in the mid troposphere. Clouds and

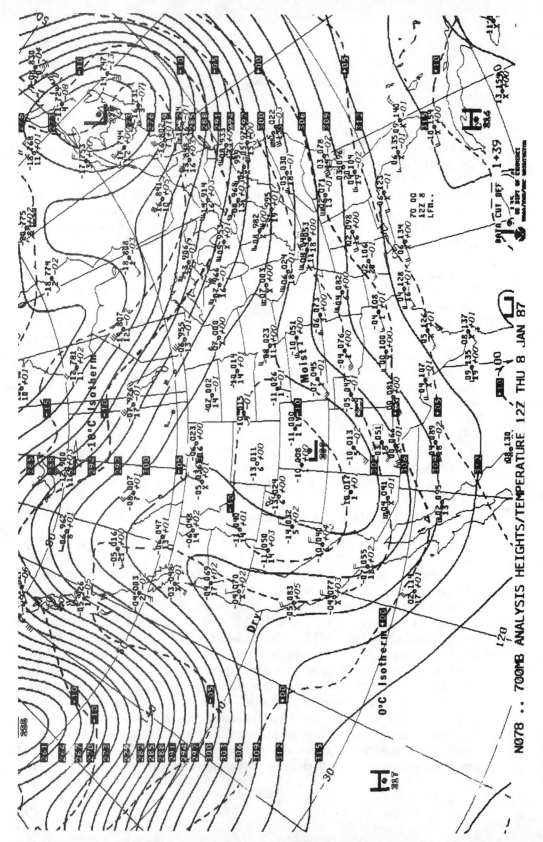

Fig. 10-9. *The 700 mb chart is usually the reference level for mountain waves. Along with the 850 mb chart, it describes the atmosphere in the lower troposphere.*

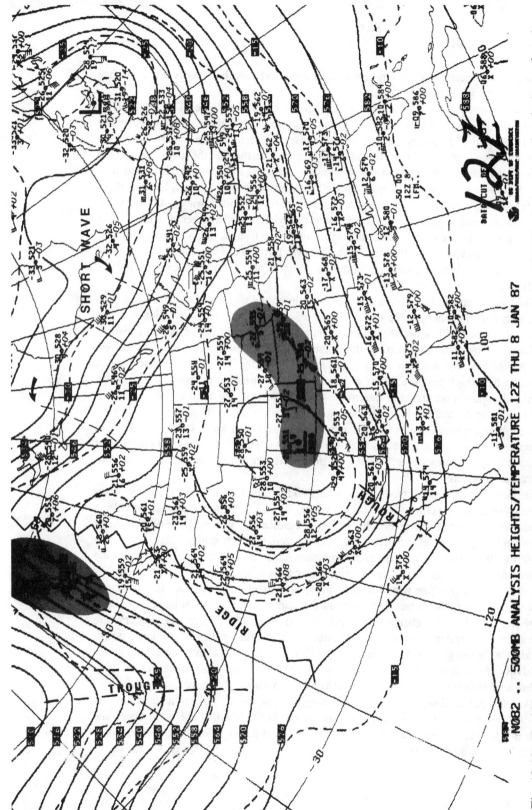

Fig. 10-10. *The 500 mb chart describes the atmosphere in the middle troposphere. The 500 mb chart might be more important to meteorologists than the surface analysis.*

NGB2 .. 500MB ANALYSIS HEIGHTS/TEMPERATURE 12Z THU 8 JAN 87

precipitation frequently accompany upper level lows and troughs, even without surface frontal or storm systems.

Three to seven major waves in each hemisphere circle the globe. These global, or *long-wave*, ridges and troughs extend for thousands of miles. Long-waves move generally eastward at up to 15 knots, but can remain stationary for days or even retreat.

Short waves, embedded in the overall flow, tend to pass through the long-wave pattern at speeds of 20 to 40 knots. Most surface lows and frontal systems are associated with upper level short-wave troughs. Figure 10-10 illustrates two short wave troughs in southern Canada. Although usually best seen on the 700 mb chart, significant waves usually extend to the 500 mb level. Upper troughs are a key to the evolution of weather systems.

When a short wave trough moves through a long wave trough, upward vertical motion is amplified, even upward vertical motion as it moves through a ridge. Short waves can be strong vertical-motion producers. Information on short waves often appears in FA and TWEB synopses.

Cold air advection destabilizes at the 500 mb level and warm air advection stabilizes the atmosphere. This is opposite to the effects of cold and warm air advection near the surface. Rising air will be warmer than surrounding air, so cold air advection enhances thunderstorms by promoting vertical development, sometimes referred to as a *cold low aloft*. A cold low aloft tends to be slow and move erratically. Warm air advection at this level strengthens high pressure ridges and diminishes low pressure troughs. In FIG. 10-10, cold air advection is occurring in the trough-to-ridge flow off the West Coast.

Moisture at the 500 mb level can be determined by darkened station models. In FIG. 10-10, the gray areas of western Canada and over Colorado and Kansas show areas where the temperature/dew point spread is five degrees or less. This chart is a good indicator of high level icing in summer months and with storms that are either well developed or contain tropical moisture.

Surface weather systems tend to follow the 500 mb flow and organized thunderstorms tend to move in the direction of the 500 mb winds. The 12-hour height change provides a general trend for system movement. Rising heights indicate a building ridge or weakening trough, and lowering heights indicate a deepening trough or weakening ridge.

At the 500 mb level, the shape of the contours rather than wind speed determines the potential for turbulence. At this level, wind shear turbulence occurs as an airplane flies through an area of changing wind direction or speed. Therefore, the greater the curvature, or direction change, the greater the potential for, and intensity of, turbulence. The horizontal distance where this change occurs is critical (FIG. 10-10). The greater the curvature of contours, the greater the probability of turbulence. Therefore, more turbulence potential exists in the trough over the western Pacific than over the Southwest United States. The probability of turbulence also exists in the sharp ridge over western Canada. Developing low pressure troughs moving from the northwest are particularly dangerous.

Areas of potential turbulence occur in merging flows or the neck of a cutoff low. In FIG. 10-10, a merging flow exists east of the trough in the Southwest United States and northern Mexico. Turbulence could also be expected in the neck of the cutoff low over eastern Montana and the Dakotas.

FSS specialists have been criticized for not appreciating the importance of, or providing information from, the 500 mb chart, and even discarding the product. I know of no FSS with access to charts that doesn't post the 500 mb. However, like pilots, some specialists are better schooled than others. Translation and interpretation of the chart over the phone is difficult. The best answer is direct access, which should be available through DUAT, unfortunately there will be a fee for graphics.

300 mb and 200 mb Constant Pressure Charts

The 300 mb and 200 mb charts provide details of pressure, wind flow, and temperature patterns at the top of the troposphere and occasionally into the lower stratosphere. The charts indicate the strength of features in the lower atmosphere. Strong storm systems on the surface are reflected in the 300 mb and 200 mb patterns, whereas weaker systems lose their identity at these levels. The 500 mb low over the Rockies in FIG. 10-10 is reflected in FIG. 10-11 at the 300 mb level, but has lost its identity in FIG. 10-12 at the 200 mb level. Rather than a closed low—surrounded by a closed contour—it has weakened into a trough.

At mid latitudes, such as the United States, the jet stream can usually be found on the 300 mb and 200 mb charts. Wind speeds and curvature of contours provide a clue to Clear Air Turbulence. Because wind speed and direction is of primary importance, areas with observed wind speeds of 70 to 110 knots are indicated by hatching. A clear area within the hatching identifies speeds of 110 to 150 knots. If speeds exceed 150 knots, a second hatched area appears. Areas of potential turbulence occur in:

1. Sharp troughs (FIG. 10-11 off the United States-Canadian West Coast and over New England).
2. In the neck of cutoff lows (FIG. 10-11, over the north central United States).
3. In a divergent flow (FIG. 10-12), over southern Canada).

Turbulence in these areas can exist despite relatively low wind speeds.

Jet Stream

The jet stream was virtually unknown until World War II when pilots flying at high altitudes reported turbulence and tremendously strong winds. These winds blew from west to east near the top of the troposphere. Not until 1946 was the jet stream fully recognized as a meteorological phenomenon.

Sharp horizontal temperature differences cause the jet stream; across strong temperature gradients, temperature changes rapidly with height. In such zones, the slope of constant pressure surfaces increases with height. The 500 mb slope is greater than that at 700 mb, and the 300 mb slope is greater than that at 500 mb. The slope of the pressure surface determines approximate wind speed. When pressure surface slope increases with height, wind speed increases with height. This is the general case in the troposphere. Winds are light or calm in areas of little or no horizontal temperature difference. And, in some cases,

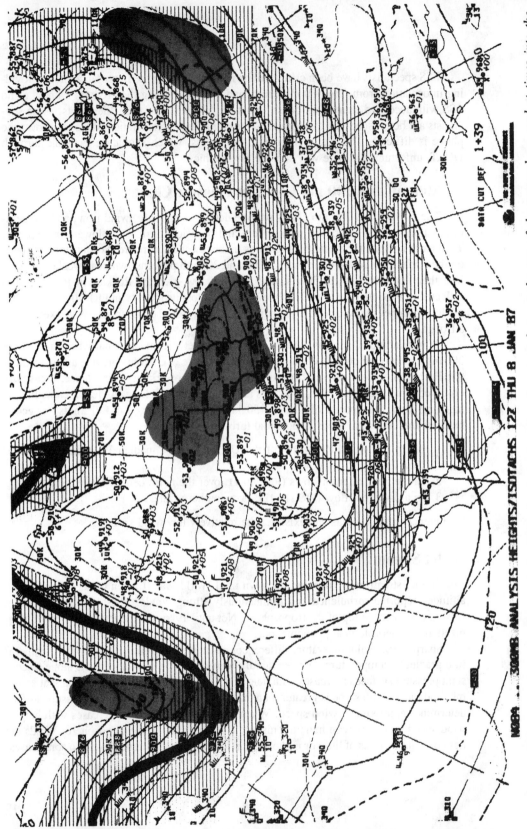

Fig. 10-11. *The 300 mb chart, along with the 200 mb chart, describes the atmosphere at the top of the troposphere, and at times into the lower stratosphere.*

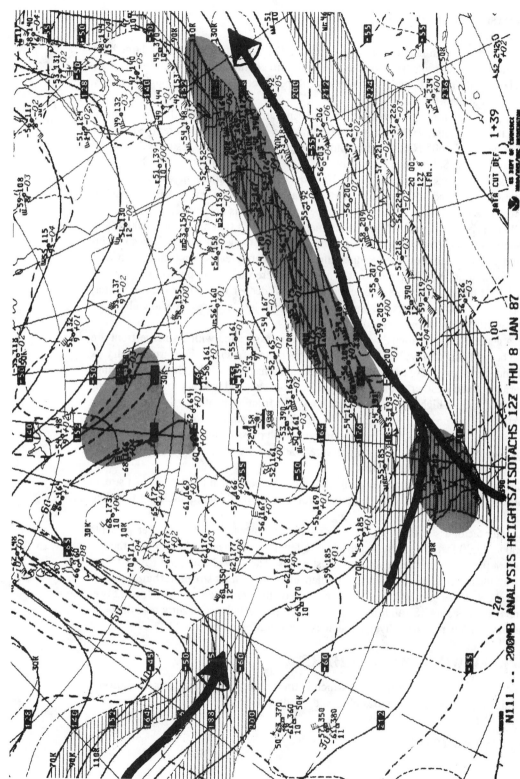

N111 .. 200MB ANALYSIS HEIGHTS/ISOTACHS 12Z THU 8 JAN 87

Fig. 10-12. *The 200 mb chart often depicts the location and speed of the jet stream.*

winds can decrease with height in the troposphere. This tends to occur within large high pressure areas. Since fronts lie in zones of temperature contrast, the jet is closely linked, or associated with frontal boundaries. When wind speed becomes strong enough, the flow is termed a jet stream.

A *jet stream* is a narrow, shallow, meandering area of strong winds embedded in breaks in the tropopause. Two such breaks occur in the northern hemisphere; the Polar Jet located around 30°−60° N at an approximate height of 30,000 feet, associated with the polar front, and the Subtropical Jet around 20°−30° N at approximately 39,000 feet. To be classified a jet stream, winds must be 50 knots or greater; although, winds generally range between 100 and 150 knots; winds can reach 200 knots along the East Coast of North America and Asia in winter when temperature contrasts are greatest.

A "jet" is most frequently found in segments 1,000 to 3,000 miles long, 100 to 400 miles wide, and 3,000 to 7,000 feet deep. The strength of the jet stream increases in winter in mid and high latitudes when temperature contrasts are greatest, and shift south with the seasonal migration of the polar front. The troposphere varies in depth from an average 55,000 feet at the equator to 28,000 feet at the poles, deeper in summer than in winter. The 300 mb and 200 mb charts are ideal for locating the jet. Jet cores are shown by thick black lines in FIG. 10-11 and FIG. 10-12.

As a general rule, locations north of a jet stream associated with a surface front are likely to be cold and stormy; locations south of this boundary tend to be warm and dry. A jet embedded in a long wave can remain relatively stationary for weeks; this usually brings long periods of bad weather to the north of its location and good weather to the south. The movement of surface high and low pressure areas and fronts is related to the movement of the jet stream. Low pressure areas tend to move with the jet stream flow. As the wave with the jet passes, a ridge builds aloft usually bringing high pressure and good weather. However, as high pressure builds, surface pressure gradients are often steep, causing strong, sometimes destructive, surface winds.

The presence of jet streams has significant aircraft operational impact. The jet stream can cause a significant head wind component for westbound flights, increasing fuel consumption and requiring additional landings.

Another factor associated with the jet is wind shear turbulence. With an average depth of 3,000 to 7,000 feet, a change in altitude of a few thousand feet will often take the aircraft out of the worst turbulence and strongest winds. The gray shading in FIG. 10-11 and FIG. 10-12 illustrates areas of potential turbulence. Maximum jet stream turbulence tends to occur above the jet core and just below the core on the north side, as in FIG. 10-12 over the central and eastern U.S. Additional areas of probable turbulence occur where the polar and subtropical jets merge or diverge, such as western Mexico in FIG. 10-12.

OBSERVED WINDS ALOFT CHART

The Observed Winds Aloft Chart, which is transmitted twice daily, plots radiosonde data. This four-panel chart provides observed winds at four levels:

- Second Standard Level
- 14,000 feet (600 mb)

- 24,000 feet (400 mb)
- 34,000 feet (250 mb).

The Second Standard Level (lower left panel FIG. 10-13) occurs between 1,000 and 2,000 feet AGL. The chart provides observed winds above the surface, but within the frictional layer. This chart supplements the constant pressure charts by providing observed wind and temperatures between constant pressure levels. Observed winds are, therefore, available for the following heights:

- 5,000*
- 10,000*
- 14,000
- 18,000*
- 24,000
- 30,000*
- 34,000
- 39,000*
* Obtained from Constant Pressure Charts.

The chart portrays the state of the atmosphere in the past; like constant pressure charts, about two-and-a-half hours old by the time it becomes available. Observed winds *should not be substituted for winds aloft forecasts*. However, should gross differences occur between observed and FD forecasts an FSS or Flight Watch can be consulted. Both have direct access to NWS forecasters.

VORTICITY

Any nonmeteorologist pilot who wishes to better understand atmospheric phenomena will require a basic knowledge of vorticity. Although some pilot-meteorologists feel this subject far too technical for pilots, I disagree. At the very least, pilots, especially those using DUAT, will come across this term in synopses, Convective Sigmets, and the Convective Outlook. Vorticity is mentioned in Chapter 4 with the discussion of WSTs and Chapter 5 with the synopsis. An understanding of vorticity will help relate the fact that not all weather occurrences can be attributed to pressure and frontal systems alone, as displayed on weather charts. However, for those "bottom-liners" that only wish to know the implications of vorticity, skip to the last few paragraphs of this section of the chapter.

Anything that spins has vorticity, which includes the earth. *Vorticity* is a mathematical term that refers to the tendency of the air to spin; the faster air spins, the greater its vorticity. A parcel of air that spins counterclockwise—cyclonically—has positive vorticity; a parcel that spins clockwise—anticyclonically—has negative vorticity.

The earth's vorticity is always positive in the northern hemisphere because the earth spins counterclockwise about its axis. An observer, standing on the north pole, will have maximum vertical spin, one revolution per day. An observer's vertical spin will decrease when moving toward the equator, becoming zero at the equator. (Coriolis force is maxi-

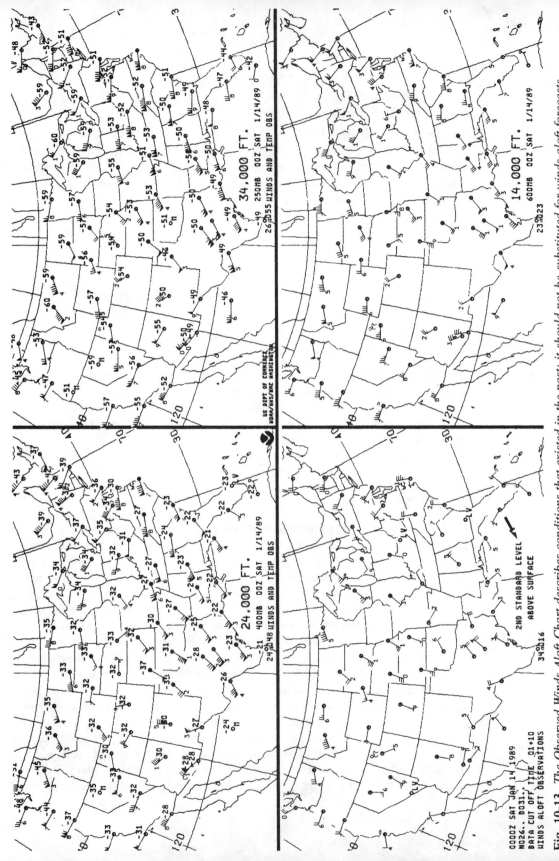

Fig. 10-13. *The Observed Winds Aloft Chart describes conditions that existed in the past; it should not be substituted for winds aloft forecasts.*

mum at the poles and zero at the equator). The rate, or value, of the vorticity produced by the earth's rotation is, not surprisingly, known as the earth's vorticity.

Now consider the atmosphere, which is almost always in motion, and generally will have its own vorticity relative to the earth, or relative vorticity. The sum of the earth's vorticity plus relative vorticity equals absolute vorticity. The value of absolute vorticity at mid latitudes almost always remains positive because of the earth's rotation.

Air moving through a ridge, spinning clockwise, gains anticyclonic relative vorticity. Air moving through a trough, spinning counterclockwise, gains cyclonic relative vorticity. Therefore, there tends to be downward vertical motion in ridge to trough flow, and upward vertical motion in trough to ridge flow.

Absolute vorticity is analyzed at 500 mbs. Although normally not available to the pilot, 500 mb heights/vorticity charts are routinely transmitted over facsimile circuits. High values of absolute vorticity (greater than 16) have strong cyclonic rotation, indicating strong upward vertical motion, and low values (less than 6) have anticyclonic rotation, indicating strong downward vertical motion.

Vorticity is advected like other atmospheric properties. Therefore, the pilot can expect to see the terms *Positive Vorticity Advection* (PVA) and *Negative Vorticity Advection* (NVA) (referring to relative vorticity).

Positive Vorticity Advection indicates:
1. A trough or low moving into an area.
2. A ridge or high moving out of an area.
3. Upward vertical motion probably occurring.
4. Increasing cloud cover and precipitation.

Negative Vorticity Advection indicates:
1. A ridge or high moving into an area.
2. A low or trough moving out of an area.
3. Downward vertical motion probably occurring.
4. Decreasing cloud cover.

Regions of PVA are swept along within the overall flow. They represent micro-systems that can rotate around synoptic scale highs and lows. These areas can be referred to as A VORT MAX or VORT LOBE. If an area of PVA moves over a stationary surface front, a wave can form and a storm can develop. An area of PVA might be all that's required (a lifting mechanism) to trigger thunderstorms when moisture and instability are available. On the other hand, NVA might prevent thunderstorm development.

UPPER LEVEL WEATHER SYSTEMS

This chapter's introduction mentions the fact that many aviation weather texts fail to adequately describe nonfrontal weather producing systems. We've looked at warm and cold air advection in the lower troposphere and aloft, orographic lift (upslope/downslope), and convergence and divergence. We discussed the 500 mb wave and its significance. Shortwaves, vorticity, and the jet stream were described along with their effects on surface and high altitude weather.

Upper level weather systems tend to modify and direct surface weather. They can intensify or stabilize conditions at the surface, cause thunderstorms to occur, and enhance or retard the intensity of frontal zones.

Difluence, divergence aloft, develops when contours diverge or move apart as seen on the 300 mb chart to cause surface convergence and increased cyclonic vorticity. Surface lows can develop in this way. A perfect example occurred one afternoon with scattered thunderstorms forecast for northern California, northern Nevada, and eastern Oregon. No weather systems were depicted on either the surface analysis or 500 mb chart. However, thunderstorms did occur, right along a line of difluence. The difluence caused just enough surface convergence to trigger thunderstorms.

Figure 10-14 illustrates the effects of an upper level weather system. The 0900Z Surface Analysis Chart shows weak surface high pressure over the western United States. However, the 1000Z Weather Depiction Chart discloses extensive areas of IFR and marginal VFR (gray shaded area), with rain and snow occurring throughout New Mexico, Texas, and Oklahoma. The weather closed airports for days, and was blamed for the deaths of dozens of people. The 500 mb analysis reveals the culprit. A deep upper level low along the southern Arizona-New Mexico border, and associated downstream trough produced devastating surface conditions. The synopsis read:

STRONG UPPER LOW OVER SOUTHWESTERN NEW MEXICO WILL MOVE TO NORTH CENTRAL TEXAS BY 22Z.

Lifting mechanisms have a cumulative effect. Upper level troughs parallel to and behind a front intensify the storm. These fronts tend to be fast moving. Figure 10-15 shows a strong cold front moving through Southern California. The satellite picture reveals a trough and low off the Central California coast. These lows occur when cold air at the base of the trough is cut off from the cold air to the north. This closed circulation can lead to a circular jet stream. The weather in Central California remains moist and unstable even though the surface front has passed.

With the approach of an upper level trough, a period of eight to 12 hours of poor weather can be expected. The surface front will precede the trough, usually bringing IFR weather. However, without a front, the upper trough or low might only bring marginal VFR conditions with localized areas of IFR. Under these conditions, VFR flight might be possible, except in mountainous areas that remain obscured in clouds and precipitation.

Figure 10-16, an enhanced infrared satellite picture, shows an upper level low off Southern California. The Area Forecast for February 22, 1987, read:

SRN CA
CSTL SXNS . . . 20 – 30 BKN/SCT 80 BKN LYRD 200 WITH WDLY SCT RW – /ISOLD
TRW – . CB TOPS TO 300. MTNS OBSCD.
INTR SXNS . . . 80 – 100 SCT/BKN 120 BKN 200. ISOLD RW – .

These systems tend to form bands of weather, as can be seen in FIG. 10-16. The weather deteriorates as a band moves through, then improves, only to deteriorate with the

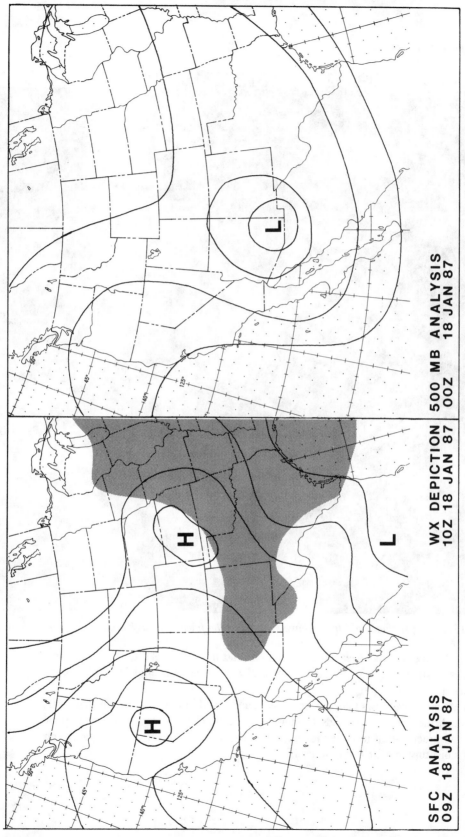

SFC ANALYSIS
09Z 18 JAN 87

WX DEPICTION
10Z 18 JAN 87

500 MB ANALYSIS
00Z 18 JAN 87

Fig. 10-14. *Upper level weather systems can cause devastating surface weather, often without a clue to the cause on the Surface Analysis Chart.*

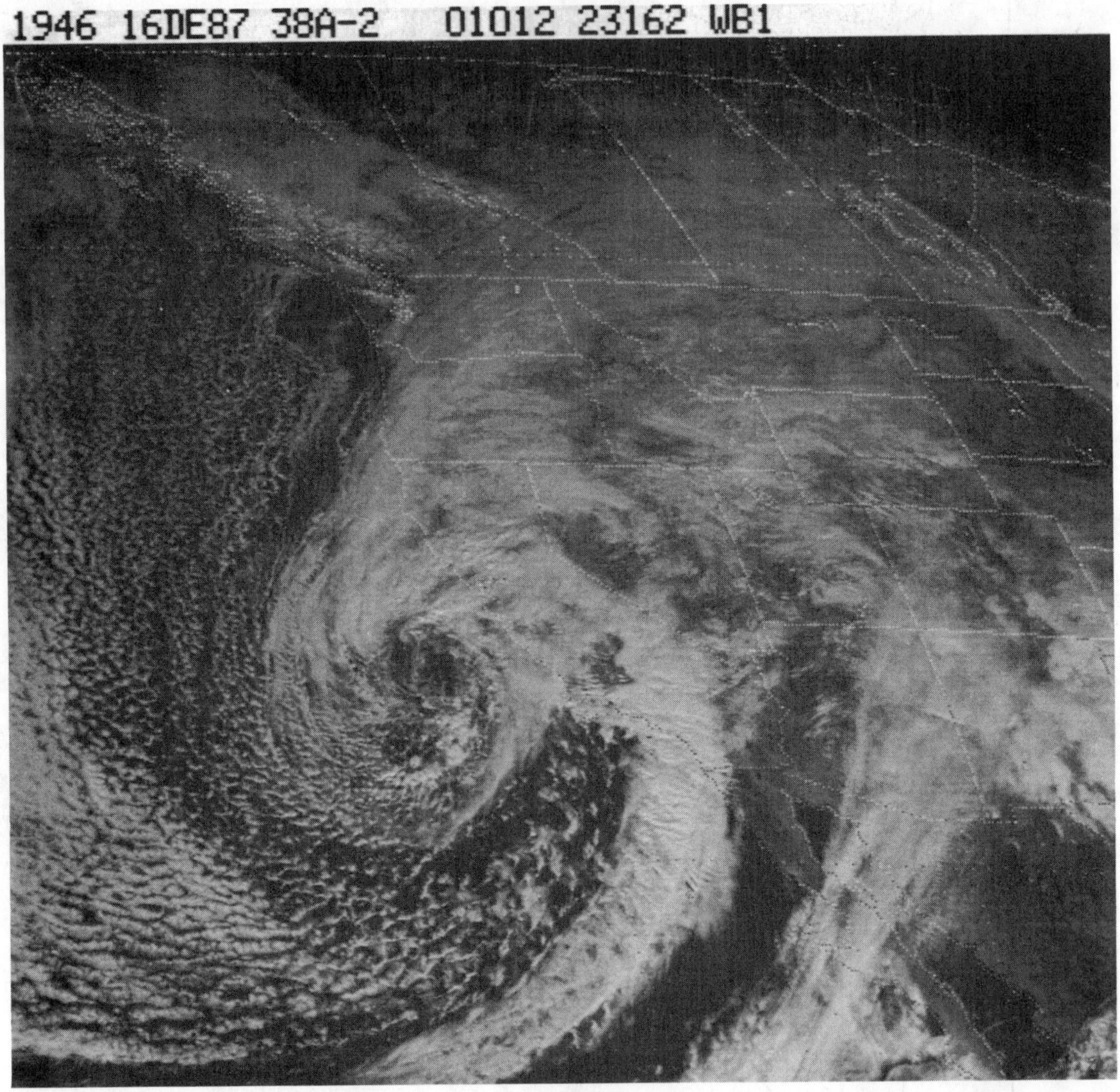

1946 16DE87 38A-2   01012 23162 WB1

Fig. 10-15. *Strong surface cold fronts have support in the form of troughs parallel to and behind the front.*

next band. Notice that the Area Forecast cannot, and does not, take this into account. Under these conditions, a pilot must be careful not to get suckered by a temporary improvement.

Closed upper level lows tend to remain stationary. And, a closed low reflected vertically through the atmosphere tends to move erratically. These systems can cause poor weather and precipitation to linger for days. Off the West Coast the systems can bring bands of moist unstable air from the Pacific.

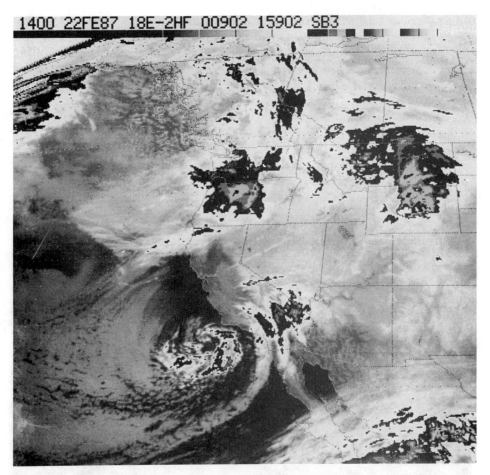

1400 22FE87 18E-2HF 00902 15902 SB3

Fig. 10-16. *Upper level lows produce bands of weather. The weather deteriorates as a band moves through, then improves, only to deteriorate with the next band.*

During one episode an upper low meandered over Red Bluff, CA, for five days. Pilots would call day after day wanting to know when the weather would clear. After awhile, the common response became, "The low is forecast to move east out of the area tomorrow, but that's what they said yesterday."

During winter months, upper lows can form over the Great Basin of Nevada and Utah. Known as the Ely Low, they can persist for days bringing snow and IFR conditions over extensive areas. Over the Midwest and eastern United States, deep upper lows can form over surface frontal systems. When this occurs, surface fronts tend to move slowly, bringing days or even weeks of snow and poor weather, closing airports for hours, or even days, at a time. During summer months, closed lows aloft support the development of thunderstorms, once surface lifting begins.

On the other hand, the absence of an upper level trough will tend to weaken and slow a front's progress. A ridge aloft even with a surface front will not tend to produce thunderstorms or severe weather because the ridge prevents the vertical development required. Figure 10-17 shows a weak surface front moving into Idaho and Nevada. Notice the almost complete absence of clouds in California, even though these fronts often appear on the Surface Analysis Chart. This front has minimal upper air support. A temperature difference marks the boundary, with insufficient moisture and lifting to produce clouds. It is not all that unusual to have cloud tops below 10,000 feet with weak fronts.

The examples provided illustrate how upper level weather systems can cause severe conditions at the surface, or dampen or cancel out the vertical motion required to produce weather. The point that not all weather is caused by frontal systems has been a theme of

Fig. 10-17. *Weak surface fronts have little upper level support. Cloud tops are often below 10,000 feet. With insufficient moisture there might be a complete absence of clouds.*

Fig. 10-18. *The hurricane is the ultimate example of a nonfrontal weather producing system.*

this chapter. In fact, nonfrontal weather producing systems have considerable influence on surface conditions. The hurricane is the ultimate example.

Hurricanes produce just about every kind of nasty weather extending over thousands of square miles. Figure 10-18 is an infrared satellite photo of hurricane Gilbert on September 13, 1988, when winds were reported to 140 knots, pressure in the eye was 26.66 inches, tropical storm-force winds extended over a diameter of 450 miles, and squalls with rainfall of five to 10 inches accompanied the storm. The NWS Hurricane Advisory: "Gilbert may still increase a little more in strength."

11
Pilot Briefings

LITTLE NEED EXISTED FOR METEOROLOGICAL INFORMATION IN THE early days of aviation because all flights were local. Nor was aeronautical information, Notices to Airmen (NOTAMs), necessary because pilots departed and landed at the same field, assuming the engine didn't quit. By the spring of 1918, the U.S. Post Office Department began working on a transcontinental airmail route. A combination rail/air route between New York and Chicago was established by July and a month later extended to San Francisco. Authorization was granted in August 1920 for the establishment of 17 Airmail Radio Stations. Personnel originally were to load and unload mail. However, as traffic increased, the need for weather information became apparent. Airmail radio personnel soon began taking weather observations and developing forecasts. The information was relayed via radio telegraph to adjacent stations. In-flight weather reports were heavily relied upon for the weather briefing.

Postal personnel soon became involved in air traffic as well as postal services and in July 1927 were transferred to the Department of Commerce, Bureau of Lighthouses, along with their facilities, now known as Airway Radio Stations. The stations were transferred in August 1938 to the Civil Aeronautics Authority and they became Airway Communication Stations. Finally, these facilities became Flight Service Stations (FSSs) with the establishment of the Federal Aviation Agency in 1958. The Weather Bureau became increasingly responsible for the collection and distribution of aviation weather and forecasts. Pilots obtained briefings from the Weather Bureau and filed flight plans and acquired aeronautical information from the Flight Service Station.

Due to the increase in air commerce, and other factors, in 1961 the Weather Bureau began the certification of FSS personnel as pilot weather briefers. The Federal Aviation Agency and the Weather Bureau mutually signed a Memorandum of Agreement in 1965 delegating responsibility for pilot weather briefing to the FAA. FSS briefers had little in the way of guidelines during this period regarding the structure of the briefing; They basically read weather reports and forecasts verbatim as requested by the pilot.

A Field FSS Pilot Briefing Deficiency Analysis group began a special evaluation of pilot briefing services in 1975. The group sighted deficiencies in the use of a standardized briefing format. (The standardized format had been taught at the FAA Academy for some time, however, it had yet to be incorporated in the FSS handbook.) Other areas identified were the reading of weather reports and forecasts verbatim as opposed to interpreting, translating, and summarizing data. A poor level of proficiency in reading, understanding, and employing facsimile charts was noted. Briefers failed to obtain sufficient background information to tailor the briefing to the type of flight planned.

From this study came the Agency's emphasis on an extremely rigid briefing format and an ambitious refresher training program. Unfortunately, the Agency did little to inform pilots or other offices within the Agency of this change in policy. This led to a good deal of friction between briefers and pilots.

Over the years, however, through mostly local efforts, pilots have become acquainted with the standard briefing format. The refresher training was to be a continuing program conducted at least every five years. However, with few exceptions, this program has been abandoned presumably due to fiscal constraints.

The National Transportation Safety Board also conducted a special investigation into Flight Service Station weather briefing inadequacies. In six of 72 accidents involving fatalities, the Safety Board determined that pertinent meteorological information was not passed to the pilot during the weather briefing. Basically these deficiencies consisted of failure to pass weather advisories and icing forecasts, and down playing forecasts of hazardous weather. The result of which has led to what many pilots consider overdoing dissemination of these advisories.

A major change occurred in 1983 when the extremely rigid format was relaxed somewhat. Three types of briefings emerged:

- Standard briefing
- Abbreviated briefing
- Outlook briefing
- (Requirements for in-flight briefings were also specified).

Almost from the time the FAA took over pilot briefing responsibility in 1965, the Service A (weather) teletype system was obsolete. Since that time, proposal after proposal was made to update weather distribution. Even by the early 1980s, most Flight Service Stations still used the 100 word per minute electromechanical teletype equipment. Briefers had to sift through mountains of paper to provide a briefing with weather reports as much as one-and-a-half hours old by the time they were relayed and available. Figure 11-1 shows a typical teletype era briefing position.

Fig. 11-1. *In the teletype era, briefers had to sift through mountains of paper, and weather reports were often one-and-a-half hours old.*

The FAA approved what was termed the interim Service A system in November 1978 that had been tested at the Chicago FSS. It has since incorporated the Service B teletype system for the transmission of flight plans and other messages. Referred to as the Leased A and B System (LABS), it is in use at FSSs that do not have the Model 1 computer system. LABS was designed to update FSS Service A until a complete computer system could be developed and installed. The equipment does not include graphics. LABS eliminates the need for the briefer to sort and post SPs, PIREPs, NOTAMs, and most amended forecasts. These housekeeping chores, which took considerable time, have been eliminated. With this system, most weather reports are available within five to 15 minutes of observation. Figure 11-2 shows a LABS briefing position.

Development of Model 1, a so-called completely computerized system, began in 1982 and came on line in 1985. Most AFSSs use this equipment. Figure 11-3 shows a typical Model 1 briefing display. Some Model 1 facilities have computer graphics while others use facsimile and closed-circuit television. As of August 1988, 37 AFSSs were using Model 1, others operated with LABS, and an additional 186 FSSs were still to be consolidated. The program of 61 AFSSs to be completed by 1993 had slipped to 1995. The future

Fig. 11-2. *LABS special reports and amendments are more timely and weather reports are only five to 20 minutes old.*

of Model 1, which was to have been installed at all AFSSs, is in serious question. Some facilities will be moving into new buildings with LABS, facsimile, and closed circuit television.

According to the FAA, "The primary benefit of the (FSS automation) program is improved productivity through automation of specialist's access to detailed briefing information and flight plan filing. To some extent the improved quality of pilot briefings reduces the need for multiple briefings as in the past." Model 1 is in the same evolutionary category as ARTCC flight data processing was in the early 1970s. It takes care of many of the data processing functions, such as flight plan transmission and tracking.

From a weather briefing point of view however, it presents the same information as was available from teletype, and now LABS. Model 1 amendments are more timely, but

Fig. 11-3. *At Model 1 facilities much of the flight data processing has been automated, but weather briefing remains essentially the same.*

this won't be directly obvious to the pilot. Model 1 does not improve pilot briefing productivity, in fact productivity might even be reduced. Model 1 presents information in much the same way as commercial briefing services, which will be discussed at the end of this chapter.

Federal Aviation Regulation 91.103, Preflight action, states:

> Each pilot in command shall, before beginning a flight, become familiar with all available information concerning that flight. This information must include—For a flight under IFR or a flight not in the vicinity of an airport, weather reports and forecasts . . . and any known traffic delays of which the pilot has been advised by ATC.

Additional regulations specify fuel and alternate airport requirements. The regulations do not, however, require that meteorological and aeronautical information be obtained from the FAA. A number of sources satisfy this requirement.

STANDARD BRIEFING

The *standard briefing*, previously known as a complete briefing, is designed for a pilot's initial weather rundown prior to departure. Standard briefings are not normally provided when the departure time is beyond six hours, nor current weather beyond two hours. It is to the pilot's advantage to obtain a standard briefing, or update the briefing as close to departure time as possible.

Background Information

Before beginning a briefing, the specialist must obtain background information that is pertinent and not evident or already known. The amount of information varies with the training and experience of the briefer, weather conditions, and the pilot's request. Pilots can assist the briefer and reduce delays by volunteering the following information.

1. The Aircraft Number or Pilot's Name. This is evidence that a briefing was obtained, as well as an indicator of FSS activity. In the absence of an aircraft number, the pilot's name is sufficient. Some pilots object to providing either a number or name. One briefer requested the pilot's aircraft number: "I don't have one." When asked for his name, the pilot again replied, "I don't have one." Most briefings are recorded and reviewed in case of incident or accident, so the briefer can't get in trouble on that one. It's in the pilot's interest to get "on the record" as having received a briefing.

2. The Aircraft Type. Low, middle, and high altitude flights present different briefing problems. This information allows briefers to tailor the briefing to a pilot's specific needs. For example, the briefer would not brief a Learjet pilot like a student pilot in a Piper Cherokee. By knowing the aircraft type, the briefer, many times, can estimate general performance characteristics such as altitude, range, and time en route.

3. The Type of Flight Planned. Always advise the briefer if the flight can only be conducted VFR, or that an IFR flight is planned, or can be conducted IFR, if necessary. Normally, the briefer will assume a pilot is planning VFR, unless stated otherwise. Student pilots should always state this fact to help the briefer provide a briefing tailored for a student's needs. Also, new low-time pilots and pilots unfamiliar with the area will receive better service if they advise the briefer. This alerts the briefer to proceed more slowly, with greater detail.

4. The Departure Airport. For some reason, some pilots are reluctant to specify their departure airport. They use generalities such as Los Angeles when their actual departure airport is Oxnard, more than 50 miles away. And, of course, there is always the ever popular departure point "Here." Pilots must be specific, they know the airport, but the briefer usually doesn't. This is becoming more important with FSS consolidation, "800" phone numbers, and in metropolitan areas.

5. The Route of Flight. The briefer will assume a pilot is planning a direct flight, unless otherwise stated. If not, a pilot must provide the exact route or preferred route, and any planned stops. The increased use of loran navigational systems has quite logically increased the capability of direct flights. However, if the planned flight is more than 200 miles, the pilot should specify intermediate points. This will assist the briefer in providing weather for the planned route. It is often difficult to visualize reporting locations for a direct flight without studying a map. A pilot will receive a faster, more accurate briefing by specifying intermediate points; rather than Oakland direct El Paso, the pilot could specify Oakland, Las Vegas, Prescott, El Paso. Computerized systems, such as Model 1, will help, but not all locations can be programmed.

6. The Destination Airport. Again, pilots must be specific. If not, a pilot might not receive all available weather and NOTAM information. A Piper Cub pilot on one occasion requested a briefing to Los Angeles. The briefer asked if his intended destination was Los Angeles International. It was! Another pilot obtained a briefing from Chino, CA, to his stated destination Stockton, CA, and was told there were no NOTAMs for the route. At the end of the briefing he matter-of-factly said he was actually going to an airport about 20 miles east of Stockton, Columbia. Now there were a few NOTAMs!—the airport would be closed during certain hours, a temporary tower was in operation, and acrobatic flight and parachute jumping were being conducted.

7. The Estimated Time of Departure and Estimated Time En Route. The estimated time of departure is essential, even if general, such as morning or afternoon. Many briefers can estimate time en route based on aircraft type. This information is needed to provide en route and destination forecasts. Total time en route is essential when stops or anything other than a direct flight are planned; for IFR flights, the estimated time of arrival is required to determine alternate requirements. Briefer: "When are you planning on departing?" Pilot: "Well, that depends on the weather." This response tells the briefer nothing. In such a situation a pilot could respond, "I'd like to go this afternoon, but I can put the flight off until tomorrow."

8. The Proposed Altitude or Altitude Range. This information is needed to provide winds and temperatures aloft forecasts. If an altitude range is specified, for example 8,000 to 12,000 feet, the briefer can provide the most efficient altitude for direction of flight.

This might seem like a lot of information, but it really isn't. The briefer must obtain this information before or during the briefing. Providing background information will allow briefers to do their job better, which is provide the pilot with a clear, concise, well organized briefing, tailored to his or her specific needs.

Briefing Format

All right, the background information has been provided; what can a pilot expect in return? The briefer is required, using all available weather and aeronautical information, to provide a briefing in the following order. Pilots should be as familiar with this format as the mnemonic C-I-G-A-R (Controls, Instruments, Gas, Attitude, Runup), or the IFR clearance format.

1. Adverse Conditions. Any information, aeronautical or meteorological, that might influence the pilot to cancel, alter, or postpone the flight will be provided at this time. Items will consist of FA flight precautions, weather advisories, major NAVAID outages, runway or airport closures, or any other hazardous conditions. The idea is to present the bad news first. Keep in mind that even though such phenomena as moderate turbulence, mountain obscurement, or IFR conditions might not necessarily be hazardous to an individual pilot or flight operation, the briefer is required to provide this information at this time.

The adverse conditions provided should only be those pertinent to the intended flight. This is one reason why the pilot must provide the briefer with accurate and specific background information. The briefer should then only furnish those conditions that affect the flight. There is, unfortunately, some paranoia among briefers where they provide anything within 200 miles of the flight.

2. VFR Flight is not Recommended (VNR). Undoubtedly the VNR statement is the most controversial element of the briefing, nevertheless, the FAA requires the briefer to:

> Include this recommendation when VFR flight is proposed and sky conditions or visibilities are present or forecast, surface or aloft, that in (the judgment of the specialist), would make flight under visual flight rules doubtful.

This leaves considerable leeway for the briefer; some use this statement more than others. The inclusion of this statement should not necessarily be interpreted by the pilot as an automatic cancellation, nor its absence as a go-for-it day. Notice that VNR applies to sky condition and visibility only. Such phenomena as turbulence, icing, winds, and thunderstorms, of themselves, do not warrant the issuance of this statement. And it is important to remember that this is a recommendation. Why then such a statement? It's simple, every year pilots insist on killing themselves and their passengers at an alarming and relatively constant rate by flying into weather where they have no business. This statement was instituted in 1974, presumably because the last person a pilot would talk to was usually the briefer. A logical, although alarming, result of this statement is the increasing number of pilots who, in the absence of VNR, ask, "Is VFR recommended?" So far, the answer remains that the decisions as to whether the flight can be safely conducted rests solely with the pilot.

According to the *Flight Services* handbook the reason for VNR must be provided. For example, "VFR is not recommended into the Monterey area because of ceilings 200 feet and visibilities one-half mile, conditions are not expected to improve until around noon." Briefers have been known to use some exceeding poor technique in this area. A briefer told a pilot "The San Fernando Valley is still VNR." Oh well.

3. Synopsis. The synopsis is extracted and summarized from FA and TWEB route synopses, weather advisories, and surface and upper level weather charts. This element might be combined with adverse conditions and the VNR statement, in any order, when it would help to more clearly describe conditions. The synopsis should indicate the reason for any adverse conditions, and tie in with current and forecast weather.

4. Current Conditions. Current weather will be summarized: point of departure, en route, and destination. Current and relevant PIREPs and RAREPs will be included. Weather reports will not normally be read verbatim, and might be omitted if proposed departure time is beyond two hours, unless specifically requested by the pilot. The briefer might provide NOTAMs during this portion of the briefing. Because the SA data base is normally reloaded between three and six minutes past the hour, to obtain the latest reports avoid, if possible, calling just prior to or after the hour.

5. En Route Forecast. The en route forecast will be summarized in a logical order (climb out, en route, and destination) from appropriate forecasts (FAs, TWEBs, weather advisories, and prognosis charts). The briefer will interpret, translate, and summarize expected conditions along the route.

6. Destination Forecast. Using the terminal forecast where available, or appropriate portions of an FA or TWEB forecast, the briefer will provide a destination forecast, along with significant changes from one hour before until one hour after ETA. This contradicts a notion held in some circles that without an FT there is no destination forecast. A destination forecast is always available, although maybe not as detailed as one might like.

7. Winds Aloft Forecast. The briefer will summarize forecast winds aloft for the proposed route. Normally, temperatures will only be provided on request. Large differences between altitudes or flight levels will be brought to the pilot's attention. On request, the briefer will provide the most favorable altitude for the proposed flight.

8. Notices to Airmen (NOTAMs). The briefer will review and provide applicable NOTAMs that are on hand, for the proposed flight and not already carried in the Class II NOTAMs publication. This information consists of NAVAID status, airport conditions, temporary flight restrictions, changes to instrument approach procedures, and flow control information. In the briefing, the term NOTAMs is all-inclusive. I briefed a student one day, and as is my practice, informed him there were no NOTAMs for the route. There was a pause. I asked him if he knew what NOTAMs were, he didn't.

The United States Notam System (USNS) is computerized and occasionally fails. When this occurs, briefers will include the statement: "Due to temporary NOTAM system outage, en route and destination NOTAM information may not be current. Pilots should contact FSSs en route and at destination to ensure current NOTAM information." (Chapter 13, The Notice to Airmen System, contains a detailed explanation of NOTAMs.)

9. Other Services and Items Provided on Request. At this point in the briefing, briefers will normally inform the pilot of the availability of flight plan, traffic advisory, and Flight Watch services, and request pilot reports. Upon request, the specialist will provide information on military training route (MTR) and military operation area (MOA) activity within 100 miles of the FSS, review the *Notices to Airmen* publication, check LORAN NOTAMs, and provide other information requested.

It's not necessary to copy all the information provided because much is supplementary and provides a background for other portions of the briefing. Pertinent information should be noted and it's often advantageous to copy this data. The Weather Log in FIG. 11-4 is specifically designed to organize information in the FAA's briefing format. This form also serves as a checklist to ensure all necessary areas have been covered.

ABBREVIATED BRIEFING

Briefers provide abbreviated briefings when a pilot requests specific data, information to update a previous briefing, or supplement an FAA mass dissemination system (Transcribed Weather Broadcast, Transcribed Information Broadcast System, Pilot's Automatic Telephone Weather Answering Service, Interim Voice Response System, or locally prepared recording).

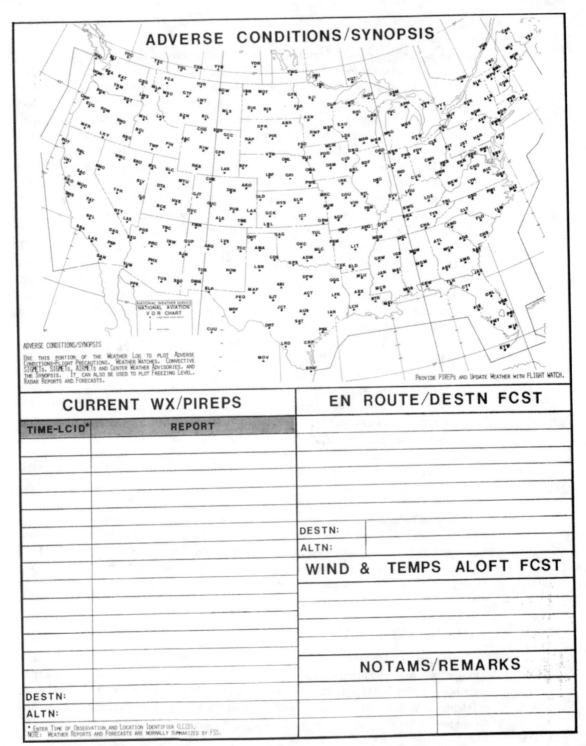

Fig. 11-4. *It is often helpful to note significant items on a form, such as the Weather Log.*

Requests for Specific Information

When all that's required is specific information, a pilot should state this fact and request an abbreviated briefing. Because the briefer must normally make a request for each individual item, it's extremely helpful to request all items at the beginning of the briefing, thus reducing delays. The briefer will then provide the information requested. When using this procedure, the responsibility for obtaining all necessary and available information rests with the pilot, not the briefer. Pilots must realize that the briefer is still required to offer adverse conditions. Pilots sometimes become irate when the briefer mentions flight precautions, however, this is a *Flight Services* handbook requirement.

Requests to Update a Previous Briefing

Pilots requesting an update to a previous briefing must provide the time the briefing was received and necessary background information. The briefer will then, to the extent possible, limit the briefing to appreciable changes. An alarming number of pilots when asked the time of their previous briefing respond, "I got the weather last night." Needless to say this practice does not comply with FARs. These individuals should be requesting a standard briefing.

Requests for Information to Supplement FAA Mass Dissemination Systems

Again, the briefer must have enough background information and the time the recording was obtained to provide appropriate supplemental data. The extent of the briefing will depend on the type of recording and the time received.

OUTLOOK BRIEFING

With a proposed departure time beyond six hours, an outlook briefing will normally be provided. The briefing will contain available information applicable to the proposed flight. The detail will depend on the proposed time of departure. The farther in the future, the less specific. As a minimum the outlook will consist of a synopsis and route/destination forecast.

Significant Weather Prognosis Charts

Outlooks beyond FA, TWEB, and FT valid times are available using Significant Weather Prognosis Charts (Sig Wx Progs). Two charts, manually prepared at the National Meteorological Center, provide forecasts up to 42 hours from the time of reception at the FSS. Figure 11-5 shows an NMC meteorologist preparing a significant weather prog. These charts use standard weather symbols.

The 12−24 hour Low-Level Significant Weather Prog is issued four times a day, valid at 0000Z, 0600Z, 1200Z, and 1800Z depending on issuance time. By the time the chart becomes available, however, valid times are only six and 18 hours because it takes approximately six hours to prepare and distribute the chart. If a pilot calls just prior to the next

Fig. 11-5. *The Significant Weather Prog is manually prepared by meteorologists at the National Meteorological Center, outside Washington, D.C.*

issuance, only a 12-hour forecast would be available. The 12−24 hour prog consists of four panels. The two upper panels forecast significant weather from the surface to 400 mb (24,000 feet). Forecast weather categories (VFR, MVFR, and IFR) have similar definitions and limitations to the Weather Depiction Chart. Turbulence is depicted within dashed lines, with turbulence symbols indicating intensity.

In FIG. 11-6, over the Rockies, moderate to severe turbulence is forecast below 14,000 feet MSL. Note the turbulence symbols representing moderate and severe, respectively and, although icing is not directly forecast, it's implied in clouds and precipitation above the freezing level.

Freezing level is represented by short, dashed lines, and the freezing level at the surface is denoted by a continuous line of dots and the contraction SFC. The lower panels are surface progs, frontal and weather symbols are standard. A single weather symbol indicates intermittent precipitation, a double symbol continuous.

Alternating dashes and dots enclose areas of showery precipitation, and a continuous line encloses areas of continuous or intermittent precipitation.

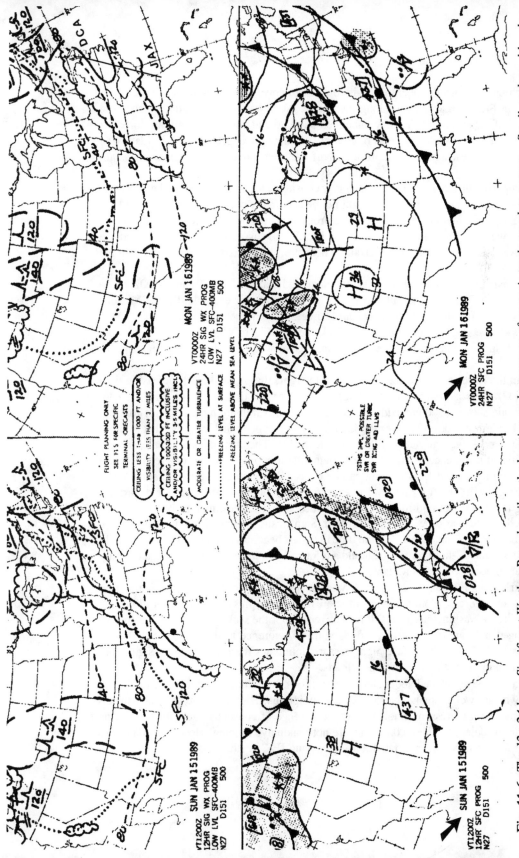

Fig. 11-6. The 12–24 hour Significant Weather Prog describes the location and movement of synoptic-scale weather systems. Small scale and local events cannot be depicted.

Hatching indicates the phenomena is forecast to cover half or more of the area. For example, in FIG. 11-6 at 0000Z, along the Pacific Northwest Coast, scattered (covering less than half the area) rain showers embedded in an area of continuous rain are forecast; east of the Cascades, scattered areas of continuous snow are expected; and, in Idaho and Montana, widespread (covering more than half the area) areas of continuous snow are forecast.

In preparing this chart, forecasters cannot consider mesoscale features; the chart is a synoptic depiction. Local conditions might not be accurately portrayed. The Limited Fine Mesh (LFM) is the main ingredient, so these progs tend to underestimate convective activity in the west, along with the intensity of Pacific storms and the forecaster tends to smooth over local variations due to terrain. Therefore, these charts are most useful in the Midwest and East.

The chart in FIG. 11-6 is valid at 1200Z Sunday, January 15, 1989, and 0000Z Monday, January 16, 1989. Be careful converting to local time, for example, 0000Z Monday translates to 4 p.m. Sunday Pacific Standard Time.

Let's say we're planning a flight from Jacksonville, FL, to Washington, D.C., for the evening of Sunday, January 15. The appropriate panel would be the 0000Z, January 16 forecast.

From the lower panel we see a surface cold front, that is weak, but increasing with waves (437). This is obtained from TABLE 10-1. Over the first two-thirds of the route, scattered rain showers and embedded areas of continuous rain are forecast, with continuous rain becoming widespread over the final third. The upper panel indicates that weather will deteriorate as we proceed—VFR to MVFR to IFR. The chart does not forecast tops. No significant turbulence is expected. But thunderstorms imply severe or greater turbulence, severe icing, and LLWS. Icing can be expected in clouds and precipitation above the freezing level. The freezing level is expected to be about 12,000 feet for departure, lowering to 12,000 feet mid route, and around 8,000 feet for destination.

Strictly a surface prog, the 36−48 hour Significant Weather Prog is issued twice daily, valid at 0000Z and 1200Z. By the time the chart becomes available, valid times only provide a 30- and 42-hour forecast. Should a pilot call just prior to the next issuance, only a 30-hour forecast would be available.

Referring to FIG. 11-7, the 1200Z Monday panel shows the front, scattered rain showers, and overcast clouds moving offshore with high pressure moving in along the Jacksonville-to-Washington route. Pilots must remember the scalloped lines on the 36−48 hour prog denote areas of overcast clouds with no reference to the height of the cloud bases. By 0000Z Tuesday surface high pressure dominates the route, with no significant precipitation or synoptic scale overcast clouds.

What can be concluded about clouds, visibilities, turbulence, and icing? Drawing on our knowledge, we can make the following assumptions. High pressure generally means fair weather. Weak pressure gradients and the absence of convective activity indicate no significant turbulence. These conditions are not conducive to icing. However, conditions are right for extensive areas of radiation fog causing IFR weather.

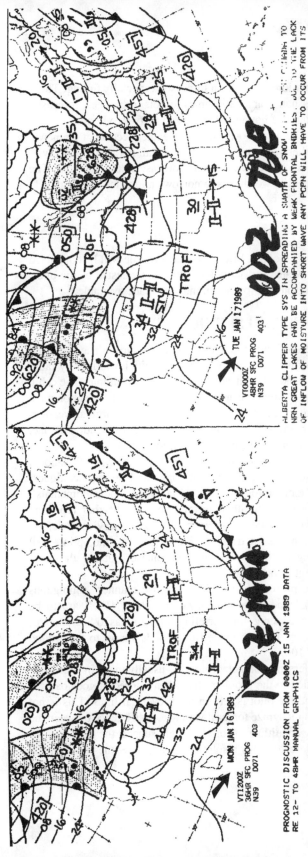

PROGNOSTIC DISCUSSION FROM 0000Z 15 JAN 1989 DATA
RE 12- TO 48HR MANUAL GRAPHICS

STRONG ZONAL FLOW ACROSS NRN PAC IS FCST TO PUSH A SERIES OF RAPIDLY
MOVING SHORT WAVES EAST TO PAC NW COAST. COPIOUS AMTS OF MOISTURE ASSOCIATED
WITH SHORT WAVES SHOULD COMBINE WITH STRONG WRLY FLOW AT ALL LEVELS TO
PRODUCE SIGNIFICANT PCPN ALONG WRN SLOPES OF CASCADES NEXT 48HRS. PCPN IS
FCST TO BE IN THE FORM OF SNOW FROM THE CASCADES EAST UNTIL STRONG WARM
ADVECTION TAKES OVER AND MOVES RAIN-SNOW LINE INTO 1D BY 48HRS. SHORT WAVE
WHICH WAS INITIALLY OVER NRN GULF OF ALASKA IS FCST TO DROP SWIFTLY SEWD
TO UPPER MISS VALLEY NEXT 48HRS. DURING ITS TREK SEWD IT WILL ACT LIKE AN

ALBERTA CLIPPER TYPE SYS IN SPREADING A SWATH OF SNOW (...) ... CANADA TO
NRN GREAT LAKES AND BE ACCOMPANIED BY WEAK FRONTAL BNDRIES. DUE TO THE LACK
OF INFLOW OF MOISTURE INTO SHORT WAVE ANY PCPN WILL HAVE TO OCCUR FROM ITS
OWN UPPER DYNAMICS AND RESIDUAL MOISTURE. MEANWHILE, ONE-TWO PUNCH OF SHORT
WAVES OVER SRN GREAT BASIN AND NRN OH VALLEY WILL PUSH COLD FRONT RAPIDLY
EAST FROM MISS VALLEY AND LOWER PLAINS TO THE ATL NEXT 48HRS. REENFORCING
COLD FRONT WILL DIG SEWD THRU GREAT LAKES TO NEW ENG THEN DISSIPATE WHILE
TRIGGERING MAINLY SCT SNOWSHWRS OVER GREAT LAKES DURING THE FIRST 12-18HRS
BULK OF PCPN WILL ACCOMPANY INVERTED SFC TROF ALONG EAST COAST BEFORE
SHIFTING TO LEADING FRONTAL BNDRY IN 24HRS. ..WOLF

Fig. 11-7. On the 36—48 Hour Significant Weather Prog, scalloped lines enclose areas of overcast clouds with no reference to the height of cloud bases.

227

Using progs, remember the limitations on aviation forecasts, especially timing. Then, when requesting outlooks, review issuance and valid times to obtain the latest forecasts. Keep in mind that these forecast progs are not available beyond forty-two hours.

A last word on outlooks, pilots should not overlook the weather section of the newspaper or local TV programs. Often these sources contain local detail not available in aviation outlook products. Regardless of source, the outlook forecast axiom remains: The weather tomorrow is going to be what the weather is tomorrow, no matter what anybody says.

IN-FLIGHT BRIEFING

Although discouraged, unless unavoidable, briefings once airborne will be conducted in accordance with a standard, abbreviated, or outlook briefing as requested by the pilot. As with any briefing sufficient background information must be made available.

FAA'S PILOT WEATHER BRIEFING SERVICE

Briefings can be obtained in person, over the telephone, or by radio. The preferred methods are to obtain a weather briefing in person or by phone. Initial briefings by radio are discouraged, except where there is no other means. The reasons are simple. The cabin of an aircraft plunging into the wild gray yonder is no place to plan a flight. Attention must be diverted from flying the aircraft to the briefing. And especially with marginal weather, certain pilots have a tendency to push on, regardless of conditions, not to mention the fact that it usually unnecessarily ties up already-congested radio frequencies.

Flight Service Station specialist training begins at the FAA Academy, in Oklahoma City, with the equivalent of a college year in basic meteorology and briefing techniques: the weather portion taught by NWS meteorologists. At field facilities, "developmentals" receive training in Area Knowledge (local weather, terrain features, weather reporting locations) and must be certified by both the FAA and National Weather Service. Briefers, like pilots, at some point must get hands-on training. From time to time, pilots will encounter this situation; the briefing might not be clear or concise, but use the same patience that briefers use with student pilots.

The briefing is supposed to be presented in a clear, concise manner. Ambiguous terms, such as "looks bad, scuzzy," and even generalizations like "VFR," are to be avoided. An FSS friend of mine received a one-liner briefing from Salinas to Sacramento, CA, "It's VFR." What does that mean? It could range from clouds almost to the ground and one mile visibility, to clear and 100.

The point is made that FSS briefers are not meteorologist—usually made by meteorologists. These individuals call attention to the problem that when a forecast goes bad the quality of the briefing falls apart and the pilot is left on the proverbial limb. This is not often the case. Briefers are trained to recognize forecast variance, a difference between the forecast for a given time and existing conditions. A briefer might suggest the pilot wait for a new forecast or coordinate with a forecaster for resolution. In any case, the pilot is made aware of the problem.

Pilots have access to NWS personnel, to a limited degree. The FAA/NWS memorandum of agreement generally assigns responsibility for international flights and flights beyond the time of normal forecast products to the National Weather Service. Telephone numbers are normally only available from an FSS. Pilots will not necessarily talk to a forecaster.

A rather new flight instructor brought his novice student into a National Weather Service (NWS) office collocated with an FSS. The instructor explained that if the student wanted a really good briefing always go to the NWS. Unfortunately, for this young instructor, a rather crusty old met tech (Meteorological Technician) was on duty. The met tech, quite unceremoniously, admonished the instructor, explaining that many NWS specialists are not meteorologists, nor engaged in aviation, that for aviation, the FSS was the place to go for the weather.

Many FSS specialists are excellent interpreters of the weather, familiar with local weather patterns and terrain, and pass on their knowledge and experience to the pilot.

The biggest complaint about the FAA's pilot briefing service is delays. An Aviation Safety Reporting Service (ASRS) study states: "The inability to reach flight service by telephone was the complaint. . . ." in a number of incidents. "Reporters relate waits as long as 20 to 45 minutes on hold and then being disconnected. Reporters allege that, because of the inability to reach flight service, many pilots in their area depart without preflight weather briefings or take off and contact en route flight advisory service." Flight Watch is not for an initial briefing; pilots who elect to use this procedure must call an FSS on the station's discrete frequency for an initial briefing.

It's no big mystery why delays are so lengthy. Let's take a large FSS with a Flight Plan Area that serves about 30,000 pilots. At any one time there might be from four to eight briefers during peak periods. Guess what happens when more than eight pilots call? The longest delays occur when weather is marginal; during these periods, the average briefing might take five to eight minutes, whereas during good weather briefs only average two or three minutes. Add to this that after initial checkout, the FAA provides little training to help briefers become more productive.

Pilots complain about the deluge of superfluous information provided by certain briefers, and the difficulty of getting information from others. These complaints result from poor briefer training and perceived paranoia about accident investigations.

Pilots are equally guilty of tying up briefing lines. Pilots inhibit the system by not being prepared for the briefing nor prepared to file a flight plan, and some have unrealistic expectations. This begins with the flight instructor who fails to properly prepare a student for the briefing, to pilots—that should know better—who call to file an IFR flight plan, but haven't looked at the charts yet. These are usually the people that complain the loudest about delays. I have had, on many occasions, students call for a briefing and to file a flight plan with zero knowledge of how to accomplish either. Instructors must take the responsibility to prepare their students, and instructors still have students call for practice briefings during peak periods.

Pilots need to be specific about the information they require. Ambiguous statements such as, "is it VFR? I'm looking for some soft IFR. Where is it good? Just tell me what I need to know. Is there anything significant?" have no place in the pilot briefing environment. Is that VFR in controlled or uncontrolled airspace, above or below 10,000 feet, or special VFR? Try finding soft IFR in the Pilot Controller Glossary. "Good" to one briefer could be "1,000-foot ceiling and three miles visibility." "Significant" falls into the same category as "good." Some pilots will still simply ask the briefer, "Are there any AIRMETs and SIGMETs for the route?" These individuals might miss significant information.

In the January 1989 issue of *AOPA Pilot*, Richard Collins wrote "Six Bits . . . of the Right Stuff." Collins discusses six virtues that make a good pilot. These virtues equally apply to a pilot's dealings with Air Traffic Controllers and Flight Service Station Specialists.

Collins says, "Patience is the only virtue and impatience the only sin." That's certainly true when holding on the phone for 20 or 30 minutes. There are very few reasons for departing without a briefing, or requesting an initial briefing en route; there are lots of excuses. The pilot is as cool on the ground as in the air. These pilots realize the problems of other pilots, controllers, briefers, and forecasters. They are patient with training controllers and briefers because they remember when they were student pilots. These pilots would no more lose control with a controller or briefer than control of the aircraft.

A pilot with intuition seldom blunders into situations and occasionally cancels or discontinues trips because of the weather, according to Collins. A pilot with this virtue knows the limitations of weather reports and forecasts, and plans accordingly. Based on their experience and the capabilities of the aircraft, they know when the weather answer is "no-go."

A pilot with the right stuff has his or her act together. The homework is done; routes have been reviewed and a partial flight plan completed. This pilot is ready for the briefing and to file a flight plan; he or she doesn't guess at the route trying to file from memory. The pilot has the virtue of organization.

The decisive pilot uses information to make sound decisions. He or she always has more than one way out. When only one out is left, it's exercised. This might mean cancelling a flight, circumnavigating weather, avoiding hazardous terrain, or an additional landing en route. The 180-degree turn is made before entering clouds. If the situation becomes uncertain, assistance is obtained before an emergency becomes an accident.

This pilot will never be caught on top or run out of fuel. Collins says ". . . coordination deals with what is happening now, what is coming next, and the use of the brain." This pilot combines organization, cool, decisiveness, and coordination to update weather en route, devise a plan based on this information, and coordinate the action before the situation becomes critical.

Perhaps one more virtue: courtesy. A specialist that's been briefing for four to six hours on a marginal weather day is in no mood for pilot sarcasm. Briefers do not have to put up with obnoxious, rude, or profane pilots; that's the purpose of the telephone release button. Courtesy is a two-way street, however. Pilots don't have to put up with obnoxious or rude briefers. If you don't think you're being treated in a courteous, professional manner, talk to the supervisor or facility manager, or call the FAA's Hot Line (800) FAA-SURE.

Using the FAA's Weather Briefing Service

The weather briefing is a cooperative effort between the pilot and FSS specialist. Preliminary planning should be complete, including a general idea of route, terrain, minimum altitudes, and possible alternates. Where available, obtain preliminary weather from one of the recorded broadcasts. From the broadcast, determine the type of briefing required—standard, abbreviated, or outlook.

During the briefing, try not to interrupt, unless the briefer is going too fast. Often pilots interrupt with a question that was just about to be answered. This can cause the briefer to lose his or her train of thought, resulting in the inadvertent omission of information.

Finally, from the "things that bug briefers the most" category; some pilots unintentionally engage in a form of Chinese water torture—after every word the briefer says, they interject "ah ha." This is terribly annoying and distracting.

I briefed a student one day and about 15 minutes later he called back. I recognized the aircraft and said, "Didn't I just brief you?" "Well, I couldn't make heads or tails of my notes. This time I'm recording it." An outstanding idea. More students and instructors should adopt this practice. This has the added advantage that the pilot can listen without taking his or her attention from the briefing to write, or requesting the briefer to repeat information.

Briefers make mistakes and many are not pilots. At the end of the briefing, don't hesitate to ask for clarification or additional information on any point you do not understand. If conditions are right for turbulence or icing and these phenomena were not mentioned, ask the briefer to verify that there are no flight precautions or advisories. Remember that forecasts for light to locally moderate icing do not warrant a flight precaution, nor locally severe turbulence a SIGMET. Forecasts for these conditions can be overlooked. On the other hand, don't expect the freezing level on a clear day.

"Based on the relative stability of the number of student pilots for the last few years and the strong demand for airline transport pilots," FAA forecasts, "the downward trend in the pilot populations are expected to turn around in 1989. Slow growth is anticipated . . ." through the turn of the century. FAA forecasts through the year 2000 also predict a slow but steady increase in the demand for briefings and flight plan services.

With this as a background and FSS staffing being further reduced, the question becomes how can a pilot best use the services available? First, become familiar with the weather services in your area. Don't overlook newspaper weather sections or TV, perhaps "A.M. Weather," a 15-minute weather program available Monday through Friday mornings on many public television stations; consider recording the show for later viewing.

Become familiar with recorded weather information in your area: TWEB, TIBS, PATWAS, and IVRS. Figure 11-8 shows a typical FSS broadcast position. These programs have been established to help reduce delays. They provide a general weather picture, with usually enough information to determine if further checking is warranted. If the weather is IFR or beyond a pilot's limits, there's no need to tie up a briefer. Additionally, pilots can determine if, on a particular day, a flight to the coast, the desert, or the mountains would be best. Briefers can be on the line for 10 minutes or more with pilots looking for a place

Fig. 11-8. *Recorded broadcasts in the form of TWEB, TIBS, and PATWAS provide a first look at the weather. They can often be used to determine if further checking is warranted.*

to fly. This could be eliminated if these individuals would use the recordings. This also applies to student pilots looking for suitable cross-country routes.

Broadcasts are available over low frequency radio beacons, VORs, and by phone. TWEB and TIBS provide much of the information in a standard briefing. Some areas are served by another recorded service called PATWAS. Although summarized to a greater degree than TWEB, PATWAS contains basically the same information. The *Airport/Facility Directory* contains frequencies and phone numbers. Normally these services contain the synopsis, adverse conditions, route, and winds aloft forecasts through 12,000 feet, and selected surface weather reports. Forecasts are normally available 24 hours, although, surface weather reports are normally suspended between 10 p.m. and 5 a.m. Depending on the broadcast, other information, such as terminal forecasts, NOTAMs, and military training activity are not available. These broadcasts do not meet FAR requirements for IFR. However, often the information will be sufficient for a VFR flight. If any clarification or additional information is required, the FSS should be consulted.

IVRS is currently available in 24 cities around the country. This service has advantages and disadvantages over TWEB, TIBS, and PATWAS. IVRS allows access to most reporting locations. The system provides Severe Weather Forecast Alerts (Alert Weather Watches—AWW), convective SIGMETs, non-convective SIGMETs, AIRMETs, surface observations, TWEB route forecasts, terminal forecasts, and winds and temperatures aloft forecasts.

Note that the FA, including the flight precautions section, and NOTAMs are not yet available from this service. IVRS does require some fancy finger work with the touch-tone phone.

The main drawback to IVRS is the complexity of using the system and the requirement for a touch-tone phone. Certain pilots say the system is too complex. I find it hard to believe that anyone who can earn a pilot certificate finds IVRS too complex. On the other hand, many pilots use IVRS almost exclusively. As far as touch-tone phones go, there are commercially available tone-producing units for use with rotary phones. In fact, some pilots have a programmable unit already set to the locations for their routine flights. A booklet called *A Pilot's Guide to IVRS* is available through most Flight Service Stations and Flight Standards District Offices.

When using TWEB, TIBS, PATWAS, IVRS, or other FSS-recorded services the Weather Log, illustrated in FIG. 11-4, is ideal for jotting down information because it is organized in the same order as the broadcast.

There are additional uses of the FAA's weather broadcast systems. Knowing when the broadcasts are updated, pilots can obtain an outlook for the following day. Broadcast updates usually coincide with FA and TWEB forecast issuance times. Pilots can check with their FSS for broadcast update times; most publish these times in Letters to Airmen or Pilot Bulletins. Student and low-time pilots can use broadcast systems to learn aviation weather terminology. I always recommended this to students. In this way, they can become familiar with the terms and phrases used in weather briefings. Anything they don't understand can be discussed with their instructor.

Pilots have a say in the content of these services. Although the FAA prescribes the general content and format, the exact items of information, such as individual weather reports, is left to the discretion of the facility. Facility managers are supposed to solicit comments from users—pilots—about their content. If pilots want a particular item on the broadcast, they should contact the facility.

Finally, pilots should know where to complain. As far as broadcasts go, this usually means it was intelligible or read too fast. If there's a problem, contact the supervisor or manager, or use the FAA's Hot Line (800) FAA-SURE. If pilots don't make the FAA aware of a problem, who's fault is it if it doesn't get fixed?

COMMERCIAL WEATHER BRIEFING SERVICES/DUAT

The FAA authorized Data Transformation and Contel in February 1990 to provide Direct User Access Terminal (DUAT) service to pilots within the contiguous United States. This computerized system, available at airports and through personal computers, allows direct access to weather briefing and flight plan services. DUAT, and virtually all other commercial services use National Weather Service products, which contradicts the misconception that computer briefings somehow provide a different product than available through an FSS.

When using these services, it's essential to know what information is available. Pilots using a commercial system must check with the vendor to determine how their system handles aviation products. Certain advisories, for example CWAs, might not be available on some systems, none provide local NOTAMs. Know your service, and check with an FSS for any additional information required, or to clarify anything you don't understand—remember the disclaimer.

Let's review a DUAT aviation briefing, planning a flight in a Cessna 182 from Livermore, CA (LVK), to Salt Lake City, UT (SLC). The briefing filled seven complete pages and the weather was good. Only significant portions of the briefing, for discussion purposes, are included. Once on-line with access code and password verified, the pilot receives prompts through a series of menus to the desired service. The briefing begins with:

```
    ADVERSE CONDITIONS
        HAZARDS – FLIGHT PRECAUTIONS
    SFOH FA 251045
    WA OR CA AND CSTL WTRS
    FLT PRCTNS . . . IFR . . . WA OR AND CSTL WTRS
            . . . MTN OBSCN . . . WA OR CA
            . . . ICING . . . WA OR CA AND CSTL WTRS
            . . . TURBC . . . WA OR CA AND CSTL WTRS
    SLCH FA 251045
    ID MT WY NV UT CO AZ NM
    FLT PRCTNS . . . IFR . . . WY CO
            . . . MTN OBSCN . . . ID MT UT WY CO AZ NM
            . . . ICING . . . ID MT UT WY CO AZ NM
            . . . TURBC . . . ID MT NV UT WY CO AZ NM
```

The pilot is now asked if he or she wishes details on the hazards. If so, the icing, turbulence, and significant clouds and weather sections are displayed.

```
        TURBULENCE – LOW LEVEL WIND SHEAR
    SFOT FA 251045
    WA OR CA
    FROM YDC TO LKV TO EED . . . TO SAN TO 40W SBA TO FOT TO TOU TO YDC
    MDT TURBC BLO 150 . . . .
        SIGNIFICANT CLOUDS AND WEATHER
    SFOC FA 251045
    CNTRL CA
    CLR. OTLK . . . VFR.
    SLCC FA 251045
    NV
    CLR OR SCT CI. OCNL 140 SCT/BKN XTRM NRN PTN AFT 18Z . . . .
    UT
    NWRN PTN . . . 100 SCT . . .
    ERN AND SRN PTNS . . . 100 BKN 150 BKN. WDLY SCT RW. MTNS OCNLY
```

```
OBSCD. ISOLD TRW AFT 18Z . . .
        SEVERE WEATHER WARNINGS . . . NONE
        TROPICAL DEPRESSION/HURRICANE ADVISORIES . . . NONE
        CONVECTIVE SIGMETS
MKCW WST 251455
CONVECTIVE SIGMET . . . NONE
        CENTER WEATHER ADVISORY . . . NONE
        SYNOPSIS
SFOS FA 251045
SYNOPSIS VALID UNTIL 260500
UPR LVL TROF MOVG SLOWLY EWD ACRS RCKYS WILL CONT WLY FLOW ALF . . .
        CURRENT CONDITIONS
LVK SA 1455 150 – BKN 20 0000/012
```

(Twenty-six weather reports followed.)

```
SLC SA 1452 55 SCT 70 SCT 100 SCT 40 142/51/35/0211/001/ACSL SE – W
        PILOT REPORTS
SCK UA /OV ECA/TM 1353/FL075/TP BE55/WV 360035 – 40/TB LGT
SLC UA /OV SLC – FFU/TM 1451/FL160/TP G2/SK SCT 090 – 100/TB LGT/RM
SMTH DURGC
        RADAR WEATHER REPORTS
SAC 1425 PPINE =
        TERMINAL FORECASTS
```

(Fifteen FTs followed.)

```
SLC FT 250909 . . . 18Z 60 SCT 3515G20 SLGT CHC C55 BKN RW – . . .
        WINDS ALOFT
```

(Winds for the route through 12,000 followed.)

NOTICE TO AIRMEN (NOTAMS)

(Eleven NOTAMs followed, none affecting a VFR flight for our route.)

FLIGHT DATA CENTER (FDC) NOTAMS . . . NONE

The pilot is now asked if he or she would like FDC NOTAMs not associated with a facility identifier. These would generally be airway changes.

Adverse conditions are derived from weather advisories, the FA, and NOTAMs. Each product must be checked, much will not apply. The FAs cover the western half of the United States, each FA is displayed in its entirety. For our flight, HAZARDS advertises mountain obscurement, turbulence, and icing for California, Nevada, and Utah. The only condition that applies, however, is the forecast for moderate turbulence for the California portion of the route.

The synopsis indicates an upper level trough moving eastward across the Rockies. Current weather is presented along the route using standard LCIDs and contractions.

Reporting locations might or might not be applicable to the flight. PIREPs and RAREPs are included in a separate section. Forecast conditions are obtained from weather advisories, FA, and terminal forecasts. Winds aloft are provided; NOTAMs follow.

The pilot is presented with the same products—except charts and local NOTAMs—available at the Flight Service Station. He or she must then decode, translate, and interpret the information to determine which reports and forecasts apply. This briefing took about 15 minutes to obtain and print, and an additional 10 minutes to analyze and apply. After a little practice you should be able to scan the material as it is displayed and only print significant portions for further review.

An FSS briefing would go something like this:

> There are flight precautions for moderate turbulence over California. There is a strong northerly flow aloft over California, with an upper level trough over the Rockies moving eastward. Livermore's reporting 15,000 thin broken, visibility two zero, wind calm. Over Stockton at 7,500 a Baron reports light turbulence with northerly winds 35 to 40 knots. En route, broken to overcast cirroform clouds and unrestricted visibilities becoming, by the Elko, Salt Lake City portion of the route, scattered clouds based around 6,000 to 7,000. Salt Lake surface winds zero two zero at one one, with standing lenticular altocumulus southeast through west. A Gulfstream two during climb out of Salt Lake southbound reports smooth, tops of scattered clouds 9,000 to 10,000. Conditions forecast to remain the same en route, with Salt Lake 6,000 scattered, a slight chance of ceilings 5,500 broken in light rain showers, surface winds three five zero at one five peak gusts two zero. Winds aloft forecast at 11,500, northwesterly at two five knots. There are no NOTAMs for the route.

The advantages of computer briefings are the relatively prompt access and the capability of a personal copy. With these advantages come the responsibility to decode, translate, interpret, and apply information to a flight. The pilot will have to sift through the mountains of written data, formally reserved for the FSS specialist, to determine if a particular flight is feasible under existing and forecast conditions, and aircraft/pilot capability.

The sheer amount of information might be overwhelming, especially for long distance flights. A pilot might have to study several pages for a single sentence that applies. Flight instructors and pilot examiners might wish to save briefings for training and flight tests. Finally, if you have a problem with one of these services you'll have to contact the vendor.

When obtaining a briefing from an FSS or other source keep in mind that they are in "sales," not "production."

12
Updating Information

APILOT'S RESPONSIBILITY DOES NOT END WITH AN UNDERSTANDING OF forecast products and limitations, and the means of collecting meteorological and aeronautical information. Due to the dynamic character of the atmosphere, data must be continually updated. Surprisingly, many pilots have not been taught, or learned, the importance of updating weather reports, forecasts, and NOTAMs en route. Failure to exercise this pilot-in-command perogative can have disastrous results.

The importance of updating weather and NOTAMs en route cannot be overemphasized. The focal points for these services are the FAA's Flight Service Stations, through FSS communication and broadcast, and Flight Watch.

FLIGHT SERVICE STATION COMMUNICATIONS

With FSS consolidation, correct, concise, and accurate communications becomes more important. FSS frequencies will be busier than ever, with specialists required to provide communications over larger areas. Correct communications technique, a seemingly simple task, will take on a greater significance. Towers, approach controls, and centers have specific frequencies for specific purposes (ground control, local control, clearance delivery, ATIS, etc.). Flight Service Stations also have different frequencies for specific services. Normally available are the common FSS, airport advisory, facility discrete, and emergency frequencies. FSSs also have voice capability over many VORs. A pilot's first task is to select the appropriate frequency for the service desired.

FSS Common Frequency

The FSS common frequency is 122.2 MHz simplex (transmit and receive on the same channel) and is available at virtually every FSS. It is normally not published on aeronautical charts, unless available at a remote site. When unsure of the appropriate frequency 122.2 MHz can be used; although, it is likely to be congested, especially over flat terrain or when used at high altitudes. If at all possible, the FSS common frequency should never be used to obtain an initial weather briefing or file a flight plan.

Airport Advisory Frequency

The Airport Advisory Service (AAS) frequency is 123.6 MHz (123.62 or 123.65 MHz at some locations). Used at nontower airports this service provides wind, altimeter setting, favored or designated runway, and known traffic. Local weather conditions can also be included. At airports where part-time towers are collocated with an FSS, Airport Advisory Service will be provided on the tower local control frequency when the tower is closed. VFR flights should monitor the frequency when within 10 miles of the airport. IFR flights will be instructed to contact the advisory frequency by the control facility.

The FAA's position remains that Automated Flight Service Stations will not provide AAS. This seems to be a waste of a valuable resource. And, an FAA group has proposed a similar service for AFSSs. AAS for local or remote airports would be considered on an individual bases. Wind and altimeter would be provided either from direct-reading instruments or the local SA. If the local SA is used, the time of observation would be included. The inclusion of time will alert the pilot that wind direction is true, rather than magnetic, as reported from direct-reading instruments.

Discrete Frequency

Routine communications (weather information, flight plan services, position reports, etc.) should be accomplished on the station's discrete frequency. These frequencies are unique to individual facilities. Their use will usually avoid frequency congestion with aircraft calling adjacent stations.

FSS frequencies can be found on aeronautical charts (FIG. 12-1) and in the *Airport/ Facility Directory*. A heavy line box indicates standard FSS frequencies, 122.2 MHz and the emergency frequency 121.5 MHz. Other frequencies, such as the station discrete and airport advisory, are printed above the box. If a frequency is followed by the letter R (122.15R), the FSS has receiver-capability-only on that frequency. The pilot must receive transmissions from the FSS on another frequency, usually the associated VOR; this *duplex communications* requires the pilot to ensure the volume is turned up on the VOR receiver.

For example, refer to the Limited Remote Communications Outlet/NAVAID portion of FIG. 12-1. Fresno FSS, noted below the box, has a remote receiver at the VOR site on 122.1 MHz, noted above the box. A pilot wishing to communicate through the VOR would tune his or her transmitter to 122.1 MHz, and select Friant, 115.6 MHz, on the VOR receiver. The pilot must remember to turn up the volume on the VOR receiver because Fresno FSS will transmit on that frequency. A thin-line box indicates a Remote

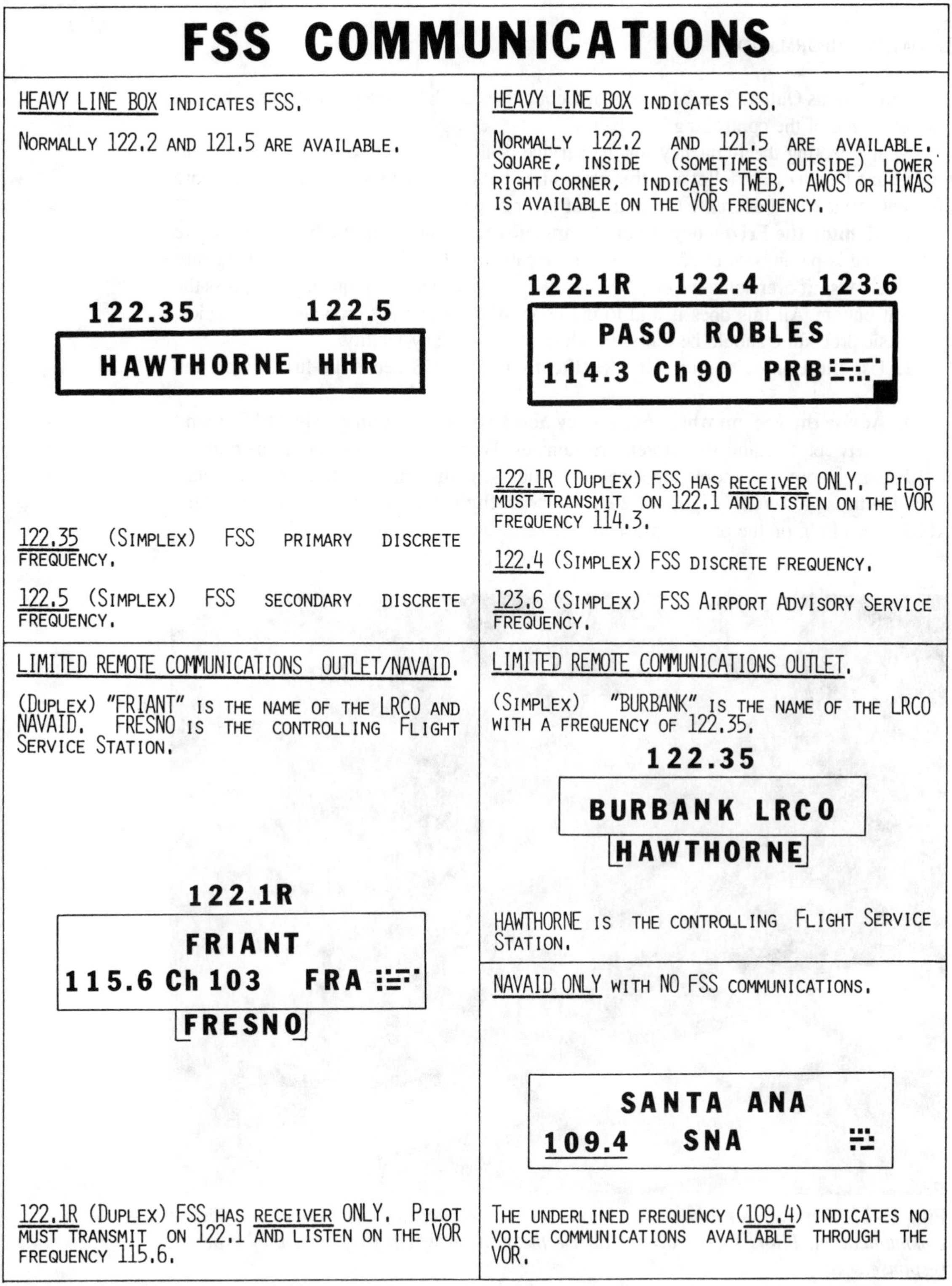

FSS COMMUNICATIONS

HEAVY LINE BOX INDICATES FSS.

NORMALLY 122.2 AND 121.5 ARE AVAILABLE.

122.35   122.5

HAWTHORNE HHR

122.35 (SIMPLEX) FSS PRIMARY DISCRETE FREQUENCY.

122.5 (SIMPLEX) FSS SECONDARY DISCRETE FREQUENCY.

HEAVY LINE BOX INDICATES FSS.

NORMALLY 122.2 AND 121.5 ARE AVAILABLE. SQUARE, INSIDE (SOMETIMES OUTSIDE) LOWER RIGHT CORNER, INDICATES TWEB, AWOS OR HIWAS IS AVAILABLE ON THE VOR FREQUENCY.

122.1R   122.4   123.6

PASO ROBLES
114.3 Ch 90   PRB

122.1R (DUPLEX) FSS HAS RECEIVER ONLY. PILOT MUST TRANSMIT ON 122.1 AND LISTEN ON THE VOR FREQUENCY 114.3.

122.4 (SIMPLEX) FSS DISCRETE FREQUENCY.

123.6 (SIMPLEX) FSS AIRPORT ADVISORY SERVICE FREQUENCY.

LIMITED REMOTE COMMUNICATIONS OUTLET/NAVAID.

(DUPLEX) "FRIANT" IS THE NAME OF THE LRCO AND NAVAID. FRESNO IS THE CONTROLLING FLIGHT SERVICE STATION.

122.1R

FRIANT
115.6 Ch 103   FRA
FRESNO

122.1R (DUPLEX) FSS HAS RECEIVER ONLY. PILOT MUST TRANSMIT ON 122.1 AND LISTEN ON THE VOR FREQUENCY 115.6.

LIMITED REMOTE COMMUNICATIONS OUTLET.

(SIMPLEX) "BURBANK" IS THE NAME OF THE LRCO WITH A FREQUENCY OF 122.35.

122.35

BURBANK LRCO
HAWTHORNE

HAWTHORNE IS THE CONTROLLING FLIGHT SERVICE STATION.

NAVAID ONLY WITH NO FSS COMMUNICATIONS.

SANTA ANA
109.4   SNA

THE UNDERLINED FREQUENCY (109.4) INDICATES NO VOICE COMMUNICATIONS AVAILABLE THROUGH THE VOR.

Fig. 12-1. *FSS communication frequencies are depicted on aeronautical charts. Pilots should select the appropriate frequency for the service desired.*

Communications Outlet. The frequency or frequencies available are printed above the box with the name of the controlling FSS below.

After selecting the frequency for the service desired, correct communications technique must be used. By following the procedures below, pilots will realize faster, more efficient service, and decrease the chance of error or delay.

1. Monitor the Frequency Before Transmitting. Monitoring the frequency before transmitting is paramount to effective communications. How many times have we heard someone transmit over someone else? We've all done it; select the frequency and press the transmit button. All this does is add to the congestion of already crowded frequencies. This basic procedure should be followed when contacting any facility.

2. Use the Complete Aircraft Identification. The FSS needs the full aircraft call sign.

3. Advise the FSS on which Frequency You Expect a Response. Most FSSs monitor from between five and 10 different frequencies. With FSS consolidation, this practice will become more and more important for efficient communications, especially when receiving through a VOR. Figure 12-2 shows the in-flight console at the McAlester, OK, AFSS. Each light on the panel represents one receiver.

Fig. 12-2. *With FSS consolidation, correct technique becomes imperative for effective communication. Pilots should always advise the FSS on which frequency they expect a response.*

4. Establish Communications Before Proceeding with Your Message. The specialist might be busy with other aircraft on other frequencies or other duties, when positions are combined. Then, listen to what the specialist says. A classic failure occurs when a pilot calls to file a flight plan. The specialist, busy with another aircraft on another frequency, advises the pilot to stand by. The pilot proceeds with the flight plan. The specialist has no option, but to mute the receiver and conclude the contact with the other aircraft. The pilot wishing to file is somewhat miffed when the specialist says, "Go ahead with your flight plan."

5. AFSS Procedures. When requesting weather from an AFSS always provide the point of departure, destination, and complete aircraft identification regardless of the type of briefing desired. This information is required by the automated data processing system (Model 1) used at many of these locations.

EN ROUTE FLIGHT ADVISORY SERVICE (FLIGHT WATCH)

The objective and purpose of Flight Watch is to enhance aviation safety by providing en route aircraft with timely and meaningful weather advisories. This objective is met by providing complete and accurate information on weather as it exists along a route pertinent to a specific flight, provided in sufficient time to prevent unnecessary changes to a flight plan, but when necessary, to permit the pilot to make a decision to terminate the flight, or alter course before adverse conditions are encountered.

Flight Watch is not intended for flight plan services, position reports, initial, or outlook briefings, nor is it to be used for aeronautical information, such as NOTAMs, center or navigational frequencies, or for single or random weather reports and forecasts. The altimeter setting will only be provided on request. Pilots requesting services not within the scope of Flight Watch will be advised to contact an FSS.

Using all sources, Flight Watch provides en route flight advisories, which include any hazardous weather, presented as a narrative summary of existing flight conditions—real time weather—along the proposed route of flight, tailored to the type of flight being conducted.

The purpose of Flight Watch is to provide meteorological information for that phase of flight that begins after climb out and ends with descent to land, therefore the specialist can concentrate on weather trends, forecast variance, and hazards. Flight Watch is specifically intended to update information previously received, and, serve as focal point for system feedback in the form of PIREPs. Air Traffic Controllers do accept PIREPs, but weather is a secondary duty and, unfortunately, PIREPs aren't always passed along; if at all possible, PIREPs should be reported directly to Flight Watch. The effectiveness of Flight Watch is to a large degree dependent on this two-way exchange of information.

A Bonanza pilot approached an area of thunderstorms in California's Central Valley. The pilot received the latest weather radar and satellite information, as well as PIREPs and surface observations from Flight Watch. He safely traversed the area with minimum diversion or delay.

This is not a very exciting story, but that's the purpose of Flight Watch, to assist pilots in conducting uneventful flights. En Route Flight Advisory Service has been around for almost 20 years. In spite of this, its function, and the best way to use this important service, is misunderstood by many pilots.

En Route Flight Advisory Service (EFAS), originally En Route Weather Advisory Service (radio call Eee'waas, which no one could pronounce), began on the West Coast in 1972 originally as a 24-hour service; Flight Watch now normally operates from 6 a.m. until 10 p.m. local time. Flight Watch is not available at all altitudes in all areas. The service provides communications generally at and above 5,000 feet AGL. Although, in areas of low terrain and closer to communication outlets, service will be available at lower altitudes. Figure 12-3 shows the Los Angeles Flight Watch position in the mid 1970s.

The system expanded in 1976 and a network of 44 Flight Watch Control Stations became operational in 1979. The common frequency 122.0 MHz immediately became congested, especially from aircraft at high altitudes. A discrete high altitude frequency was assigned Flight Watch stations in the Southwest in 1980, to help resolve the problem. With Flight Service Station consolidation Flight Watch responsibility has been assigned

Fig. 12-3. *Flight Watch began on the West Coast in 1972. Originally specialist only had teletype reports and forecasts. Then and now, pilot reports are the mainstay of this service.*

Fig. 12-4. *Today's Flight Watch specialists have at their command a vast network of information, which includes real time weather radar and satellite imagery.*

the FSSs associated with the Air Route Traffic Control Centers (Oakland FSS—Oakland Center, Hawthorne FSS—Los Angeles Center, etc.). Figure 12-4 shows the Columbia, MO, AFSS Flight Watch console. A discrete high altitude frequency, for use at and above Flight Level 180, will be assigned each Flight Watch Control Station to cover the associated center's area.

Flight Watch Procedures

Establishing communications is the first step. Because only one frequency is available for low altitudes, pilots must exercise frequency discipline. In addition to the basic communications technique already discussed, the following procedures should be used when contacting Flight Watch.

1. Use the name of the Flight Watch Control Station and the radio call "Flight Watch."

   When known, the name of the Flight Watch Control Station (Hawthorne Flight Watch) should be used. If not, simply calling Flight Watch is sufficient.

2. State the aircraft position in relation to a major topographical feature or navigation aid (in the vicinity of Fresno, over the Clovis VOR, etc.).

   Exact positions are not necessary, but the general aircraft location is needed. Flight Watch facilities cover basically the same areas as Air Route Traffic Control Centers. With numerous outlets, on a single frequency, the specialist needs to know which transmitter serves the pilot's area. This will eliminate interference with aircraft calling other facilities, garbled communications, and repeated transmissions. Failure to state the aircraft position on initial contact is the biggest single complaint from Flight Watch specialists.

3. When requesting weather or an en route flight advisory, provide the specialist with cruising altitude, route, destination, and IFR capability, if appropriate.

   The specialist needs sufficient background information to provide the service requested.

Flight Watch specialists are required to continually solicit reports of turbulence, icing, temperature, wind shear, and upper winds regardless of weather conditions. This information, along with PIREPs of other phenomena, is immediately relayed to other pilots, briefers, and forecasters. Together with all sources of information the specialist has access to the most complete weather picture possible.

ARTCC controllers are helpful relaying reports of turbulence and icing, and providing advice on the location of convective activity, but the information is limited by equipment, and usually limited to immediate and surrounding sectors. Their primary responsibility is the separation of aircraft. On the other hand, Flight Watch has only one responsibility, weather. Flight Watch—with live National Weather Service weather radar displays (east of the Rockies), satellite pictures, and the latest weather and pilot reports—provides specific real time conditions, as well as the big picture. And, Flight Watch specialists have direct communications with Center Weather Service Unit personnel and NWS aviation forecasters.

Getting a hold of Flight Watch is usually a simple matter, even for single-pilot IFR operations. ATC will almost always approve a request to leave the frequency for a few minutes, but don't wait until the last minute. Trying to find an alternate airport in congested approach airspace is no fun for anyone. I routinely use this procedure and have never been denied the request from en route controllers.

The early days of airline flying were plagued by thunderstorms as well as icing, turbulence, widespread low ceilings and visibilities, and the limited range of the aircraft. Today's jets have virtually overcome these obstacles. More and more pilots of general aviation aircraft, equipped with turbochargers and oxygen or pressurization, are encountering the same problems as yesterday's airline captains. The only difference is a vastly improved air traffic and communication system. And, among one of the FAA's best kept secrets is the implementation of high altitude Flight Watch.

Continually updating the weather picture is the key to managing a flight, especially at high altitude in aircraft without ice protection and storm avoidance equipment, and with relatively limited range. Winds aloft can be a welcome friend eastbound or a terrible foe westbound. With limited range even a small change in winds at altitude can have a disastrous result. At the first sign of unexpected winds, Flight Watch should be consulted, if for no other reason than to provide a pilot report. A significant change in wind direction or speed is often the first sign of a forecast gone sour. A revised flight plan might be required. Flight Watch can provide needed additional information on current weather, PIREPs, and updated forecasts upon which to base an intelligent decision.

A primary reason for high altitude flying is to avoid mechanical, frontal, and mountain wave turbulence; however, the flight levels have their own problems—wind shear or Clear Air Turbulence. When problems are encountered, Flight Watch can help find a smooth altitude or alternate route. If the pilot elects to change altitude, an update of actual or forecast winds aloft is often a necessity.

Icing is normally not a significant factor in the flight levels, except around convective activity or in the summer when temperatures can range between $0°$ C and $-10°$ C. However, icing can be significant during descent, especially when destination temperature is at or below freezing. Flight Watch can provide information on tops, temperatures aloft, reported and forecast icing, and current surface conditions.

Many aircraft are equipped with airborne weather radar and Stormscopes. However, these systems are plagued by low power, attenuation, and limited range. A pilot might pick his or her way through a convective area only to find additional activity beyond. With RRWDS or radar facsimile, Flight Watch has the latest NWS weather radar information. Well before engaging any convective activity, a pilot should consult Flight Watch to determine the extent of the system, its movement, intensity, and intensity trend. Armed with this information, he or she can determine whether to attempt to penetrate the system or select a suitable alternate. ATC prefers issuing alternate clearances compared to handling emergencies in congested airspace and severe weather.

Finally, destination and alternate weather. The preflight briefing provided current and forecast conditions at the time of the briefing. This information should be routinely updated en route; airlines do it, often through Flight Watch. Are updated reports consistent with the forecast? If not, why? Flight Watch specialists through their training are in an excellent position to detect forecast variance. Whether the forecast was incorrect or conditions are changing faster or slower than forecast, the pilot needs to know and plan accordingly. A knowledge of forecast issuance times is often helpful. Forecasts might not be amended if the next issuance time is close. Flight Watch is in the best position to provide the latest information and suggest possible alternatives.

Updates must be obtained far enough in advance to be acted upon effectively. This must be done before critical weather is encountered or fuel runs low. Hoping a stronger-than-forecast head wind will abate, or arriving over a destination that has not improved as forecast, is folly. At the first sign of unforecast conditions, Flight Watch should be consulted and, if necessary, an alternate plan developed. This might mean an additional routine landing en route, which is eminently preferable to, at best a terrifying flight, or at worst an aircraft accident.

High altitude Flight Watch frequencies for individual ARTCCs are provided in FIG. 12-5. Frequencies and outlets can also be found on the inside back cover of the *Airport/*

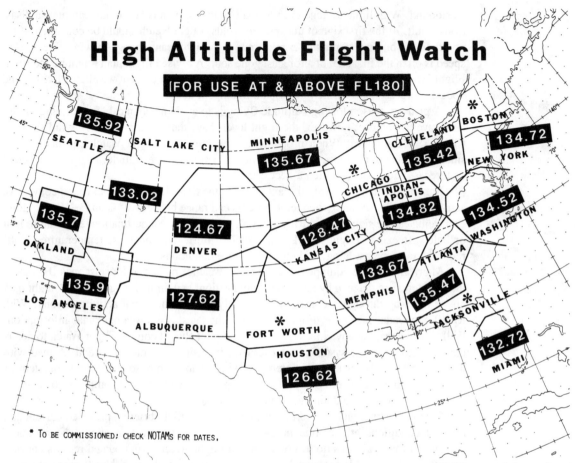

Fig. 12-5. *Discrete high altitude Flight Watch frequencies are being commissioned. The use of these channels will eliminate much frequency congestion for aircraft at low altitudes.*

Facility Directory. And, although not easy to find, Jeppesen high altitude charts carry the frequencies (SEA WX −*135.92). Standard frequency 122.0 MHz can be used when a pilot is unsure of the discrete frequency.

13
Notices to Airmen
(NOTAMs)

FAILURE TO CHECK NOTICES TO AIRMEN HAS LEAD MANY A PILOT INTO AN embarrassing and potentially hazardous situation. Increased use of Direct User Access Terminals and other commercially available briefing systems means that interpreting and understanding NOTAMs will take on a greater significance.

The Federal Aviation Administration advertises the status of components or hazards in the National Airspace System (NAS) through aeronautical charts, the *Airport/Facility Directory*, other publications, and the National Notice to Airmen System. Changes are normally published on charts, in the Directory, or appear in the *Notices to Airmen*, Class II publication. Class II refers to NOTAMs that appear in printed form for mail distribution. The need for current charts and publications cannot be overemphasized. A pilot called flight service and requested a briefing from Bishop to Santa Cruz, CA. The briefer explained that the airport was closed. "Oh, I must be using an old chart," said the pilot. Indeed, the airport had been closed for two years.

Aeronautical information not received in time for publication is distributed on the FAA's telecommunications systems, including unanticipated or temporary changes, or hazards when the duration is for a short period or until published. Unpublished NOTAMs are not necessarily given during abbreviated or outlook briefings, but routinely provided as part of an FSS standard briefing. Briefings from the National Weather Service do not contain NOTAMs.

NOTAMs are issued for the commissioning, decommissioning of facilities, or restrictions to landing areas (runways and waterways), including closures, braking action, and problems due to snow, ice, slush, or water. Lighting aids that affect landing areas, or are part of an instrument approach procedure, along with pilot-controlled lighting (PCL), receive NOTAM distribution, as well as other lighting aids (airport beacons, VASIs, wind-T lights, obstruction lights, etc.). NAVAID status, together with hours of operation for air traffic control facilities, control zones, and services (EFAS, HIWAS, AWOS, etc.) receive NOTAM distribution. Unpublished NOTAMs are divided into three groups:

- NOTAM (D)
- NOTAM (L)
- FDC NOTAMs

FSS specialists are responsible for classification, format, and transmission of NOTAM (D)s and NOTAM (L)s. The country is divided into Flight Plan Areas. NOTAM responsibility for airports and NAVAIDs within the Flight Plan Areas belongs to a designated FSS. The tie-in FSS that is responsible for a facility can be determined from the *Airport/Facility Directory*.

TERMINOLOGY

Times used on NOTAMs are UTC, except control zone effective times, which use local (LCL). The day begins at 0000Z and ends at 2359Z. To allow automated NOTAM processing, one of the following terms will be used: EFF (effective), TIL (until), or THRU (through); followed by time, or date time group, describing the effective period. Runways are identified by magnetic bearing (12-30, 12, or 30). If magnetic bearing has not been established, the runway is identified by the nearest eight points of the compass (NE-SW, N 200 N-S RY).

NOTAM (D)

NOTAM (D)s contain information that might influence a pilot's decision to make a flight, or require alternate routes, approaches, or airports. They are considered "need-to-know" and issued for certain landing area restrictions, lighting aids, special data, and air nagivation aids that are part of the National Airspace System. The exception is LORAN-C NOTAMs; not distributed as a true NOTAM (D), they are available from the FSS, but only on request. TABLE 13-1 contains NOTAM (D) issuance criteria.

NOTAM (D) information is given distant dissemination on the FAA's Service A (weather) telecommunications system, appended to a station's weather report in the same manner as PIREPs. However, as with PIREPs, NOTAM (D)s can be separated from the associated SA. DUAT or other commercial service users must check the vendor to determine how their system handles NOTAMs. It will be the pilot's responsibility to obtain, decode, and understand the information. NOTAM (D)s are prepared and transmitted using standard contractions and abbreviations contained in Appendix A, Abbreviations.

OAK SA 1245 250 – SCT 10 56/52/3105/989
!OAK 03/005 OAK VORTAC OTS TIL 2200

Table 13-1. *NOTAM Criteria.*

NOTAM (D)	NOTAM (L)
Landing Area	
Commissioning or decommissioning all or a portion of a landing area	Runway information that does not restrict or preclude the use of a runway
Conditions that restrict or preclude the use of any portion of a runway or waterway	Conditions pertaining to taxiways and ramps
Airport closure	Men and equipment on or adjacent to runway
Lighting Aids	
Runway lights	Taxiway lights
Approach lighting system	Airport beacon
Pilot controlled lighting	VASI/REIL/Obstruction lights

Note: Landing area and lighting aid NOTAMs will only be issued as NOTAM (D)s for airports that are annotated with the section symbol in the *Airport/Facility Directory*. All NOTAMs for airports that are NOT annotated will be issued as NOTAM (L)s.

NOTAM (D)	NOTAM (L)
NAVAID/Communication/Service	
NAVAID which is part of NAS	NAVAID that is not part of NAS
Communication outlet or service	ATIS/TWEB
Special Data	
Withdrawal of weather reporting service	MTRs/MOAs/Aerial refueling
Restricted areas	In-flight bird activity
Air show, high speed aircraft	Air shows, parachute jumping

This Oakland (OAK) NOTAM was issued in the third month of the year and is the fifth NOTAM (D) issued during the month for the OAK NOTAM file (03/005). The Oakland VORTAC is scheduled to be out of service until 2200Z (OAK VORTAC OTS TIL 2200).

NOTAM (D)s are issued for those airports annotated by the section symbol—a reference mark—in the *Airport/Facility Directory*. These include relatively busy airports, and those with published instrument approaches. Note in FIG. 13-1 that Nevada County Airpark, Visalia Municipal, and Watsonville Municipal airports receive NOTAM (D) distribution, indicated by the section symbol in the left margin. Depending on system, the pilot might have to determine the NOTAM file for a particular facility. This is becoming more

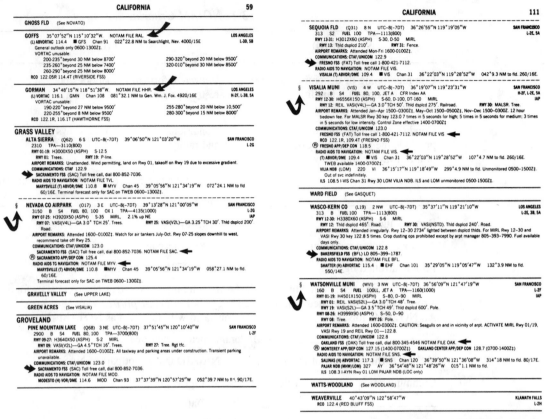

Fig. 13-1. *The* Airport/Facility Directory *can be used to determine if an airport receives NOTAM D distribution, the tie-in FSS, and airport and NAVAID NOTAM files.*

and more complex with FSS consolidation. The appropriate *Airport/Facility Directory* contains this information. For the following discussion, refer to FIG. 13-1. Note that the NOTAM files for the Goffs and Gorman VORTACs are Riverside (RAL) and Hawthorne (HHR) respectively (GOFFS—NOTAM FILE RAL; GORMAN—NOTAM FILE HHR). Therefore, information on the status of these NAVAIDs would be found in the respective NOTAM files (RAL and HHR).

The Directory indicates that the Visalia Municipal airport has both airport (listed under COMMUNICATIONS-FRESNO FSS) and NAVAID (listed under RADIO AIDS TO NAVIGATION) NOTAMs assigned to the Visalia (VIS) NOTAM file. Pilots planning either a VFR or IFR flight to Visalia would need to check VIS for both airport and NAVAID NOTAMs. For the Nevada County Airpark, airport NOTAMs are contained in the Sacramento NOTAM file (SAC); however, NAVAID NOTAMs appear in the Marysville NOTAM file (MYV). This is because the tie-in FSS for Nevada County is the Sacramento FSS. The NAVAID serving the airport is Marysville and its NOTAM file is MYV.

A pilot planning a VFR flight to Nevada County must check SAC for destination NOTAMs. An IFR pilot would be required to check both SAC and MYV. Airport NOTAMs for Watsonville Municipal appear in the Oakland NOTAM file (OAK), RADIO AIDS TO NAVIGATION NOTAMs in the Salinas NOTAM file (SNS). Again, when two NOTAM files are listed, it's always best to check both.

```
SAC 12/005 SAC PRIRA 30 NMR MYV045005 OTS TIL 03092359
TVL 01/035 SWR TACAN AZM OTS
```

The SAC NOTAM was the fifth NOTAM issued for the SAC NOTAM file during the 12th month of the year (12/005). The Sacramento primary radar (SAC PRIRA) within a 30 nm radius of the Marysville VOR 045 radial at five miles (30 NMR MYV045005) will be out of service until March 9 at 2359Z (03092359). This alerts pilots that radar services to aircraft not equipped with transponders will be unavailable. This might be significant for a non transponder aircraft, if an approach existed that required radar to execute the procedure.

The second NOTAM advertises the fact that the Squaw Valley (SWR) TACAN azimuth is out of service. This would normally only affect military aircraft.

Below are a few NOTAM (D)s that illustrate common usage.

```
SFO 10L – 28R CLSD EFF 170700 – 1500
```

San Francisco runway 10 Left/28 Right will be closed on the 17th between 0700Z and 1500Z: UTC dates and times. The runway is scheduled to be closed between 11 p.m. on the 16th until 7 a.m. on the 17th, Pacific Standard Time. Pilots must use care converting UTC to local times.

```
SJC 12R – 30L CLSD 0800 – 1400 DLY TIL 271400
```

This San Jose runway closure will occur daily (DLY) from 0800Z through 1400Z until the 27th at 1400Z, which is daily from midnight local through 6 a.m., until the 27th at 6 a.m.

```
BUR 7 – 25 CLSD TKOF 12500/OVR
BUR 7 – 25 E 254 CLSD
```

Burbank Runway 7-25 is closed for takeoffs to aircraft with gross weights of 12,500 pounds and over, probably because, as the second NOTAM reveals, the eastern 254 feet of the runway is closed.

```
PAE PTCHY THN IR
CLM 8 – 26 THN SNW
```

There is patchy thin ice on the runway at Paine, WA. Port Angeles' Runway 8-26 is covered with thin snow. Often the depth of ice, snow, and slush will be indicated (3/4 SLR, three-quarters of an inch of slush on the runway).

```
MIT 12 – 30 RY LGTS PCL CMSND/MED INTST CONT UNTIL 0800 OTRW KEY
122.8 FIVE TIMES WI 5 SEC MED INTST
```

Notices to Airmen (NOTAMs)

At Minter Field, Shafter, CA, pilot-controlled lighting (PCL) has been commissioned for Runway 12-30. Lights are on medium intensity continuously until 0800Z, then must be activated by keying 122.8 five times within five seconds for medium intensity.

UKI LOC DME 15 OTS

The Ukiah localizer DME for Runway 15 is out of service. Be careful, only the DME, not the localizer, is out, but, this approach cannot be conducted without the DME.

SBA ILS DME UNMON 0700 – 1400 DLY

The Santa Barbara ILS DME is not monitored (UNMON) between the hours of 0700Z and 1400Z daily. This does not mean the DME is off or out of service, only that if the facility fails, a NOTAM would not be issued immediately; a pilot report would probably be the first indication of an outage. Most NAVAIDs within NAS are monitored, usually by a tower or FSS.

MQO VOR 290 – 090 UNUSBL BYD 7 BLO 7000

The Morro Bay VOR is unusable between the 290 and 090 radials beyond seven nm below 7,000 feet MSL. If an airway, approach segment, or fix be within the specified area, it could not be used for navigation.

DAG VORTAC UNMON/VOICE OTS

The Daggett VORTAC is in a unmonitored status, but not out of service. Most likely the monitor line is down, because voice communications through the VOR are also out of service. Weather advisory broadcasts will not be available.

PDT A/C 1330 – 0630 DLY

Pendelton, OR, approach control services operate daily between 1330Z and 0630Z.

ONP CTLZ HRS 0800 – 1700 LCL

The Newport, OR, control zone is effective daily between 8 a.m. and 5 p.m. local time.

NOTAM (L)

Only distributed locally, NOTAM (L)s advertise conditions or hazards that do not meet the criteria for a NOTAM (D). Landing area information that does not restrict or preclude the use of the runway is issued as a NOTAM (L): cracks and soft edges, men and equipment on or adjacent to the runway, braking action reports of good or fair, nonstandard runway markings, and bird activity.

They include landing area restrictions and lighting aids for airports not identified by the section symbol in the *Airport/Facility Directory*. Alta Sierra, Pine Mountain Lake, Sequoia Field, and Wasco-Kern County airports are NOTAM (L) airports as indicated by the absence of a section symbol in FIG. 13-1.

NOTAM (L)s also pertain to less critical items such as ATIS, TWEB, and UNICOM. Or, a single frequency outage when there is more than one frequency available. For example, if a tower's ground control frequency was out of service the information would be issued as a NOTAM (L), because the local control frequency was normal. TABLE 13-1 describes conditions issued as NOTAM (L)s.

The FAA defines local dissemination as the area affected by the aid, service, or hazard being advertised. That is, within the issuing FSS, and the appropriate towers or centers when necessary. For example, if parachute jumping was to occur at the Sequoia Field Airport, Fresno FSS, the tie-in facility, would issue a NOTAM (L). The NOTAM would also be given to Fresno approach control and Oakland center because the jump would occur in their airspace. The NOTAM, however, would not be forwarded to any other facilities.

Selected NOTAM (L)s are transmitted to adjacent Flight Service Stations. These NOTAM (L)s contain conditions that restrict or preclude the use of an airport (airport closures or runway restrictions, or airport runway lights). If the Sequoia Field airport were closed, Fresno FSS would issue a NOTAM (L) and transmit it to adjacent FSSs. However, briefings from other than adjacent FSSs will not contain this NOTAM, nor, would a briefing from DUAT or other commercial briefing services. NOTAM (L)s are a hole in the system that pilots need to avoid. When flying to a non NOTAM (D) airport it's important to check with the destination's tie-in FSS before landing for local NOTAMs. This is best accomplished by contacting the facility by radio before descent.

Notice on TABLE 13-1 that military activity is advertised as a NOTAM (L); recall that Flight Service Stations only retain MTR and MOA activity within 100 miles of the facility. Pilots should not expect the status of routes or areas beyond this limit. FSSs only have a listing of active MTRs by route number, therefore pilots requesting MTR status should provide the briefer with the route numbers.

FDC NOTAMs

FDC NOTAMs contain regulatory information (chart amendments, changes to instrument approach procedures, and temporary flight restrictions). FDC NOTAMs are transmitted over the FAA's Service A telecommunications system. FSSs normally only retain those FDC NOTAMs that pertain to their Flight Service Area (an area within 400 miles of the facility). During a standard briefing, FDC NOTAMs that are pertinent, on hand, and not yet published are provided. When published in the *Notice to Airmen*, Class II publication, they are only available on request. This is extremely important to National Ocean Service (NOS) chart users because NOS charts are not updated as often as other commercially available charts. NOS users should routinely check Class IIs.

FDC 9/1769 SMO FI/T SANTA MONICA, SANTA MONICA, CA.
NDB – B ORIG PROC NA.

This FDC was issued in 1989 (FDC "9"/1769). It was the 1,769th FDC issued during that year (FDC 9/"1769"), and pertains to the Santa Monica airport (SMO). The information contained in the NOTAM is temporary (FI/T flight information of a temporary nature).

The SMO NDB-B original issuance approach procedure is not authorized.

FDC 9/4047 STS FI/T SONOMA COUNTY, SANTA ROSA, CA.
ILS RWY 32 AMDT 15 . . . VOR RWY 32 AMDT 18 . . . VOR/DME RWY 14 AMDT
1 . . . CHANGE NOTE TO READ: WHEN CTLZ NOT IN EFFECT, EXCEPT
OPERATORS WITH APPROVED WEATHER REPORTING SERVICE, USE TRAVIS AFB
/SUU/ ALTIMETER SETTING AND INCREASE ALL DH'S AND MDA'S BY 390
FEET.

This FDC changes a note on the three approaches listed to increase the decision heights and minimum descent altitudes by 390 feet when the control zone is not in effect, unless the pilot has access to an approved weather reporting service. When the control zone is not in effect (the tower is closed) the altimeter setting is not available. Pilots without approved weather reporting service must use the Travis AFB (SUU) altimeter. The use of a remote altimeter setting, requires an increase in minimums. (AWOS will solve this limitation.)

CLASS II NOTICES TO AIRMEN

Published every 14 days, the *Notices to Airmen*, Class II booklet, shown in FIG. 13-2, is divided into two sections. Section one contains information of a general nature, such as airways, flight restrictions, airports, facilities, and procedural NOTAMs. Section two contains special notices too long for section one that concern a wide or unspecified geographical area, or items that do not meet section one criteria. Information in section two varies widely, but is included because of its impact on flight safety. From FIG. 13-2, the February 26, 1987, issue includes in section two: Airport Radar Service Areas, Terminal Area Graphics, LORAN-C Status Information, Fly-ins, etc.

Figure 13-3 contains an example of section one. Most are FDC NOTAMs, such as Santa Ynez where the NDB Runway 8 approach procedure is NA (not authorized). Other entries, such as South Lake Tahoe, advertise a change in VOR name and identification. The vertical bar in the margin indicates information new with this issuance (Santa Monica). A letter to the editor of a national publication requested assistance in translating FDC NOTAM SANTA MONICA VOR – A. DME REQUIRED. The intersections (for the approach) can be determined by either the SMO DME or radials off the LAX VOR. This FDC NOTAM was issued during the time that the LAX VOR was out of service for an extended period, thus DME was required to make the approach. This emphasizes the point that pilots need to become familiar reading and interpreting information of this nature.

USING THE NOTAM SYSTEM

Let's say we're planning a flight from Hayward, CA, in the San Francisco Bay Area to Agua Dulce Airpark north of the Los Angeles Basin. As part of the standard briefing we receive any pertinent NOTAMs that are on hand. We can expect to receive NOTAMs on

FEBRUARY 26, 1987
Next Issue
March 12, 1987

Notices to Airmen

U.S. Department
of Transportation

**Federal Aviation
Administration**

```
CLASS TWO NOTAMS
```

HAZARDOUS INFLIGHT WEATHER ADVISORY
SERVICE (HIWAS)
See page S-1

AIRPORT RADAR SERVICE AREAS (ARSA)
See page S-3

TERMINAL AREA GRAPHIC NOTICE
SOUTH LAKE TAHOE, CALIFORNIA
LAKE TAHOE AIRPORT
See page S-10

HIGH ALTITUDE / EN ROUTE
FLIGHT ADVISORY SERVICE
(HA / EFAS) (CORRECTED)
See page S-13

LORAN-C STATUS INFORMATION
See page S-14

COLORADO SKI COUNTRY AIRPORTS
SPECIAL AIR TRAFFIC MANAGEMENT
PROGRAMS
(November 14, 1986 thru April 13, 1987)
See page S-15

FAA HOTLINES
See page S-18

THE EAA SUN 'N FUN FLY-IN
LAKELAND MUNICIPAL AIRPORT, FLORIDA
(March 15 thru 21, 1987)
See page S-19

DANIEL BOONE TEMPORARY MILITARY
OPERATIONS AREA
KENTUCKY
(March 2 thru 6, 1987)
See page S-25

EXERCISE GOLDEN EAGLE 1987
KENTUCKY/TENNESSEE
(February 17 thru March 11, 1987)
See page S-27

CHANGE TO CLASS II CONTENTS CRITERIA
Section One of the Class II Notices to Airmen
contains FDC and NOTAM-D information only.
(NOTAM-D data for Alaska and Hawaii is also
included).

Fig. 13-2. *Pilots are responsible for information contained in the* Notices to Airmen, *Class II publication. Information in this document will only be provided on request during FSS weather briefings.*

NOTICES TO AIRMEN (NOTAMs)

CALIFORNIA

RIVERSIDE

Riverside Muni

FDC 8/574 /RAL/ FI/T RIVERSIDE MUNI, RIVERSIDE, CA.
VOR-A AMDT 4...VOR RWY 9 AMDT 9. PROCS NA.

SACRAMENTO

Sacramento Executive ATCT

ATCT HRS 0600-2100 LCL. (2/88)

Sacramento Metropolitan

RY 16R ALSF2 OTS INDEFLY.(03/88)

SAN FRANCISCO

San Francisco Intl

FDC 8/796 /SFO/ FI/T SAN FRANCISCO INTL. SAN
FRANCISCO, CA. ILS RWY 19L AMDT 17 GLIDE SLOPE
UNUSABLE BELOW 140 FEET MSL.

SAN LUIS OBISPO

San Luis Obispo EFAS

HIGH ALT EFAS FREQ 135.9 CMSND. MONITORED BY HHR
FSS. (3/88)

San Luis Obispo County ATCT

ATCT HRS 0700-1900 LCL. (3/88)

SANTA ANA

John Wayne Arpt-Orange County

FDC 8/714 /SNA/ FI/T JOHN WAYNE AIRPORT-ORANGE
COUNTY, SANTA ANA, CA. ILS RWY 19R AMDT 11...DYERS
FIX MINIMUMS...LOC BC RWY 1L AMDT 10...NDB RWY 19R
ORIG... CIRCLING MDA 680/HAA 626 ALL CATS. NDB RWY
19R ORIG...CIRCLING CAT C VIS 1 3/4. TMPRY 375 FT MSL
CRANE 3/4 MI NE RWY 19R THR.

SANTA BARBARA

Santa Barbara Muni ILS/DME RY 7

(I-SBA) ILS UNMONITORED WHEN FSS CLSD. (2/88)

Santa Barbara Muni

FDC 7/1079 /SBA/ FI/T SANTA BARBARA MUNI, SANTA
BARBARA CA. ILS RWY 7 AMDT 1...VOR RWY 25 AMDT
4...ALTERNATE MINIMUMS NA 0700Z-1230Z.

SANTA MONICA

Santa Monica NDB

FDC 8/977 CA FI/P CORRECT US GOVT VFR TERMINAL AREA
CHART & AREA CHARTS -US LOS ANGELES CA 16TH
EDITION DATED 10 MAR 88. SANTA MONICA NDB (SQQ) IS
STILL A NON-OPERATIONAL FACILITY. DISREGARD SIGNALS
FROM NAVAID UFN. COORDINATES ARE LAT 34-00-50N
LONG 118-27-20W.

SANTA ROSA

Sonoma County

FDC 7/220 /STS/FI/T SONOMA COUNTY, SANTA ROSA CA.
IFR DEPARTURE PROCEDURE: RWY 1 TURN LEFT, RWY 14
TURN RIGHT, RWY 19 CLIMB STRAIGHT AHEAD, RWY 32
CLIMB STRAIGHT AHEAD TO 1800, THEN CLIMBING LEFT
TURN, DIRECT STS VOR. INTERCEPT AND CLIMB
SOUTHBOUND ON STS R-202 WITHIN 15 MILES, TO

CALIFORNIA

RECROSS STS VOR AT OR ABOVE MEA FOR DIRECTION OF
FLIGHT, OR COMPLY WITH SONOMA COUNTY SIDS.

FDC 7/11 /STS/FI/T SONOMA COUNTY..SANTA ROSA CA. ILS
RWY 32 AMDT 14...VOR RWY 32 AMDT 18. CHANGE NOTE TO
READ: WHEN CONTROL ZONE NOT IN EFFECT. EXCEPT FOR
OPERATORS WITH APPROVED WEATHER REPORTING
SERVICE: 1. USE TRAVIS AFB ALTIMETER SETTING. 2.
INCREASE ALL DH AND MDAS BY 180 FEET.

SANTA YNEZ

Santa Ynez

FDC 6/1617 /IZA/ FI/T SANTA YNEZ SANTA YNEZ, CA. NDB
RWY 8 ORIG PROC NA.

SOUTH LAKE TAHOE

Lake Tahoe VORTAC

(LTA) EFFECTIVE 5 MAY 88 NAV IDENTIFIER TO BE CHANGED
TO SWR & NAME TO BE CHANGED TO SQUAW VALLEY. (1/
88)

STOCKTON

Stockton Metropolitan

FDC 7/497 /SCK/ FI/T STOCKTON METROPOLITAN,
STOCKTON CA. ILS RWY 29R AMDT 18...VOR RWY 29R AMDT
17...NDB RWY 29R AMDT 14. RAISE CIRCLING MDA CATS A/
B/C TO 580. REASON: 275 MSL CRANE 4900 FT NW APCH
END RWY 11L.

COLORADO

AKRON

Akron FSS

FSS DCMSND. (3/88)

DENVER

Jeffco

RY 29R REJL DCMSND.(2/88)

FDC 8/436 /BJC/ FI/T JEFFCO, DENVER, CO. ILS RWY 29R
AMDT 10. TCH 53 GS OM CROSSING HEIGHT 7195.

Stapleton Intl

FDC 8/115 /DEN/ FI/T STAPLETON INTL, DENVER, CO. ILS/
DME 1 RWY 8R AMDT 4...CONVERGING ILS/DME 2 RWY 8R
AMDT 1. MISSED APCH HOLDING ALT 10000 FT. ILS/DME 1
RWY 17L AMDT 5...CONVERGING ILS/DME 2 RWY 17L AMDT
1. TERMINAL ROUTE DEN 15.0 DME TO DEN 13.0 DME ALT
9000 FT, DEN 13.0 DME TO TARGS INT/DEN 5.6 DME/TOT
NDB ALT 7000 FT. MISSED APCH HOLDING ALT 9000 FT.
LOC/DME RWY 18 AMDT 1. TERMINAL ROUTE WENNY INT
TO CHOSE/I-UGT 12.5 DME ALT 9000 FT, CHOSE INT TO
LAKEE/I-UGT 5.5 DME ALT 7000 FT, NDB RWY 26L AMDT
37...NDB RWY 26R AMDT 7. TERMINAL ROUTE IOC VORTAC
TO WATKI INT ALT 10000 FT. MISSED APCH HOLDING ALT
10000 FT. ILS RWY 26L AMDT 45. MISSED APCH HOLDING
ALT 10000 FT. ILS RWY 35L AMDT 27. TERMINAL ROUTE IOC
VORTAC TO SKIPS INT/I-SPO 17.7 DME ALT 10000 FT, SKIPS
INT TO DEBIT INT/I-SPO 13.4 DME ALT 9000 FT., DEBIT INT
TO LENDI OM/INT/I-SPO 7.7 DME ALT 7500 FT. PROC TURN
NA. ILS RWY 35R AMDT 10...ILS RWY 35R CAT II AMDT
10...ILS RWY 35R CAT III AMDT 10. TERMINAL ROUTE IOC
VORTAC TO SEDAL INT/I-RRV 18.5 DME ALT 10000 FT,
SEDAL INT TO ENGLE INT/I-RRV 14.2 DME ALT 9000 FT,
ENGLE INT TO GANDI OM/INT/I-RRV 8.5 DME ALT 7500 FT.
PROC TURN NA. MISSED APCH HOLDING ALT 10000 FT. LDA/
DME RWY 35R AMDT 1. MISSED APCH HOLDING ALT 10000

9

Fig. 13-3. *Pilots need to become familiar reading and interpreting information in the Class II publication. Anytime doubt exists about an entry, clarification should be obtained from an FSS.*

the status of NAVAIDs, airway changes, and airspace restrictions—NOTAM (D)s and FDC NOTAMs, unless there is a temporary NOTAM system outage. In such a case, we will have to check with FSSs en route and at the destination to ensure receipt of current NOTAMs. Information contained in the Class II publication will only be provided on request.

From the *Airport/Facility Directory* we see that Agua Dulce is not annotated with the section symbol, destination airport NOTAMs will not be available through the departure FSS. This information will normally only be available from the destination airport's tie-in FSS. From the Directory we determine that the Lancaster FSS has tie-in responsibility. When within radio range of Lancaster we request NOTAMs for Agua Dulce. In the unlikely event that we could not land, we could determine a suitable alternate.

Here's the bottom line. Request a standard briefing. NOTAMs are not necessarily provided during abbreviated or outlook briefings. If the specialist doesn't mention NOTAMs, ask. Briefers are human and NOTAMs are easy to overlook. Keep in mind NOTAMs are not available on TWEB, TIBS, PATWAS, or IVRS. A check of the *Airport /Facility Directory* should be a standard part of flight planning; significant information may be published. If the destination is not annotated in the Directory, request NOTAMs from the tie-in FSS prior to descent and landing. Finally, if you don't have access to the Class II publication, ask the briefer to check.

Pilots using DUAT or other commercially available systems will have to decode and translate NOTAMs. The system will usually not provide NOTAM Ls, information contained in the *Airport/Facility Directory*, or the *Notice to Airmen* Class II publication. The contents of these documents will still remain the responsibility of the pilot. Should any doubt exist about the meaning or intent of a NOTAM, consult a Flight Service Station for clarification.

Pilots should be aware that prominent events (major sporting events, parades, ceremonies, etc.), disasters (forest fires, oil spills, train wreck's, etc.), and presidential visits invariably evoke temporary flight restrictions. It remains the pilot's responsibility to obtain these NOTAMs, and a call to the Flight Service Station may be the easiest answer.

The procedures discussed in this chapter apply equally to VFR and IFR flights. Only by understanding the system can pilots ensure they meet their obligation of obtaining all available information.

It's like going to the restroom before a flight: We know we should, but sometimes it's just not convenient. Both oversights can lead to a very uncomfortable flight!

14
VFR Flight Planning

ASK ANY GROUP OF PILOTS WHY THEY FILE VFR FLIGHT PLANS AND YOU'RE guaranteed some interesting answers. "My instructor told me to file a flight plan." "To let my boyfriend know when to pick me up at the airport." "To alert search and rescue in case of an accident." The primary purpose of a VFR flight plan is to alert search and rescue. There are secondary uses, however. For example, requesting customs on international flights, alerting medical personnel on lifeguard missions, requesting special handling from Air Traffic Control, or letting someone know when we'll be arriving—if we know how to use the system.

Most pilots take VFR flight plans for granted. Unfortunately, certain flight instructors were never taught the purpose of flight plans or how to use them and are unable to teach their students. The following classic example is all too often repeated.

The student pilot calls the FSS and says, "I would like to file a flight plan." The specialist responds, "Go ahead." There is silence. The specialist advises the pilot to just read off the information on the flight plan form, to which the student responds, "I don't have a form. My instructor told me to call flight service and file a flight plan." FSS specialists will walk pilots through the flight plan, if necessary. One pilot complained about a lengthy phone delay then told the briefer he did not have a flight plan form; after taking the flight plan, the briefer explained the reason for the delay was the previous pilot didn't have a form either.

It's an appalling fact that many flight plans submitted to Flight Service Stations contain errors or are in some violation of FARs. Most errors are small or technical, and corrected by the FSS specialist. The time required, however, significantly contributes to delays in reaching the FSS. It is to every pilot's advantage to know and understand the FAA's VFR flight plan service.

A few pilots are in for a rude awakening with DUATs. At least at this time, DUAT is not available for DVFR, border crossings, international trips, or flight plans into or out of military bases. Before accepting the flight plan, the computer will check for errors and omissions, with the slightest fault resulting in a reject.

FLIGHT PLAN INFORMATION

OK, let's say we've decided to file VFR, obtain a copy of FAA Form 7233-1 (8-82), illustrated in FIG. 14-1. (The reverse side of the form is for military flight plan use.) Many commercially available flight planning organizers provide a flight plan form. The Preflight Planner in FIG. 14-2 is the other side of the Weather Log used in previous chapters and contains a flight plan form. This facilitates the transfer of information from the Navigation Log to the flight plan.

Check VFR, then enter the full aircraft identification, including the N, followed by the aircraft type and special equipment code. Pilots pay a lot of money for their airplanes, and are understandably proud. One pilot filed an aircraft type as "a P-A Thirty-Two T slant T slant alpha." Upon inquiry it seemed he had a T-tailed, turbo-charged Lance

Form Approved: OMB No. 2120-0026

U.S. DEPARTMENT OF TRANSPORTATION FEDERAL AVIATION ADMINISTRATION **FLIGHT PLAN**	(FAA USE ONLY) ☐ PILOT BRIEFING ☐ VNR ☐ STOPOVER		TIME STARTED	SPECIALIST INITIALS

1. TYPE	2. AIRCRAFT IDENTIFICATION	3. AIRCRAFT TYPE/ SPECIAL EQUIPMENT	4. TRUE AIRSPEED	5. DEPARTURE POINT	6. DEPARTURE TIME		7. CRUISING ALTITUDE
VFR					PROPOSED (Z)	ACTUAL (Z)	
IFR							
DVFR			KTS				

8. ROUTE OF FLIGHT

9. DESTINATION (Name of airport and city)	10. EST. TIME ENROUTE		11. REMARKS
	HOURS	MINUTES	

12. FUEL ON BOARD		13. ALTERNATE AIRPORT(S)	14. PILOT'S NAME, ADDRESS & TELEPHONE NUMBER & AIRCRAFT HOME BASE	15. NUMBER ABOARD
HOURS	MINUTES			
			17. DESTINATION CONTACT/TELEPHONE (OPTIONAL)	

16. COLOR OF AIRCRAFT	CIVIL AIRCRAFT PILOTS. FAR Part 91 requires you file an IFR flight plan to operate under instrument flight rules in controlled airspace. Failure to file could result in a civil penalty not to exceed $1,000 for each violation (Section 901 of the Federal Aviation Act of 1958, as amended). Filing of a VFR flight plan is recommended as a good operating practice. See also Part 99 for requirements concerning DVFR flight plans.

FAA Form 7233-1 (8-82)   CLOSE VFR FLIGHT PLAN WITH_____ FSS ON ARRIVAL

Fig. 14-1. *Every pilot should keep handy a copy of FAA Form 7233-1 Flight Plan. Forms are available at all FSSs and other locations, and contained on many commercially available flight planning forms.*

PREFLIGHT PLANNER™

© 1988 T. LANKFORD

NAVIGATION LOG

ROUTE	TC	Estimated CAS CRUISE ALT Temp	WIND DIR SPD	TAS	TH	+− VAR	MH	CH	+− DEV	GS	Dist	Time	Fuel	Fuel Consumption ___ GPH/PPH REMARKS
	C									K	nm	:	:	
	C									K	nm	:	:	
	C									K	nm	:	:	
	C									K	nm	:	:	
	C									K	nm	:	:	
	C									K	nm	:	:	
TOTAL											nm	:	:	

WT & BALANCE

ITEM	WT	× ARM =	MOM
1. Aircraft			
2. Pilot & Front Seat			
3. Rear Seat/Cargo			
4.			
5. Fuel ___ gal*/lb			
6. Fuel ___ gal*/lb			
7. Oil (7.5 lbs/gal)			
8. Baggage			
9.			
10. RAMP			
11. [−] Fuel start−runup			
12. TAKE OFF			
13. [−] Fuel to DESTN			
14. LANDING			

* 6 lbs/gal

mom = ___
wt = ___   C G

NAVCOM

LOCATION	CPT* ATIS	DEP** APCH	TWR	GND	VOR NDB	FSS	REMARKS

DEP ATIS:
CODE: ___

DESTN ATIS:
CODE: ___

* CPT−CLEARANCE PRETAXI (CLNC DELIVERY)
** DEP−DEPARTURE CONTROL

COMMON FREQUENCIES/CODES
121.5 EMERGENCY
122.2 COMMON FSS
122.75 FLIGHT WATCH
         AIR TO AIR
1200 VFR
7600 LOST COM
7700 EMERGENCY

CRUISING ALTITUDES
EASTBOUND MAGNETIC COURSE
VFR − Odd Thousands + 500*
VFR − Odd Thousands
WESTBOUND MAGNETIC COURSE
VFR − Even Thousands + 500*
VFR − Even Thousands
* ABOVE 3,000 AGL

SPECIAL EQUIPMENT CODES
N − NONE
X − TRANSPONDER
U − TRANSPONDER/ALTITUDE
D − DME ONLY
B − TRANSPONDER & DME
A − TRANSPONDER & DME
        ENCODING & DME
W − RNAV
C − TRANSPONDER & RNAV
R − TRANSPONDER/ALTITUDE
        ENCODING & RNAV

TIME CONVERSION UTC (Z)
EST +5 = UTC   CDT +4 = UTC
CST +6 = UTC   MDT +5 = UTC
MST +7 = UTC   PDT +6 = UTC
PST +8 = UTC

A − ALPHA   H − HOTEL   O − OSCAR   V − VICTOR
B − BRAVO   I − INDIA   P − PAPA   W − WHISKEY
C − CHARLIE   J − JULIETT   Q − QUEBEC   X − XRAY
D − DELTA   K − KILO   R − ROMEO   Y − YANKEE
E − ECHO   L − LIMA   S − SIERRA   Z − ZULU
F − FOXTROT   M − MIKE   T − TANGO
G − GOLF   N − NOVEMBER   U − UNIFORM

FLIGHT PLAN (FAA USE ONLY) ☐ PILOT BRIEFING ☐ VNR ☐ STOPOVER

U.S. DEPARTMENT OF TRANSPORTATION
FEDERAL AVIATION ADMINISTRATION

| 1 TYPE | 2 AIRCRAFT IDENTIFICATION | 3 AIRCRAFT TYPE / SPECIAL EQUIPMENT | 4 TRUE AIRSPEED | 5 DEPARTURE POINT | 6 DEPARTURE TIME | 7 CRUISING ALTITUDE |
| VFR / IFR / DVFR | | | KTS | | PROPOSED (Z) / ACTUAL (Z) | |

8 ROUTE OF FLIGHT

9 DESTINATION (Name of airport)	10 EST TIME ENROUTE HOURS / MINUTES	11 REMARKS
12 FUEL ON BOARD HOURS / MINUTES	13 ALTERNATE AIRPORT(S)	14 PILOT'S NAME, ADDRESS & TELEPHONE NUMBER & AIRCRAFT HOME BASE	15 NUMBER ABOARD
16 COLOR OF AIRCRAFT	17 DESTINATION CONTACT TELEPHONE (OPTIONAL)		

CIVIL AIRCRAFT PILOTS. FAR Part 91 requires you file an IFR flight plan to operate under instrument flight rules in controlled airspace. Failure to file could result in a civil penalty not to exceed $1,000 for each violation (Section 901 of the Federal Aviation Act of 1958, as amended). Filing of a VFR flight plan is recommended as a good operating practice. See also Part 99 for requirements concerning DVFR flight plans.

CLOSE VFR FLIGHT PLAN WITH ___   FSS ON ARRIVAL

FAA Form 7233-1 (8-82)

Fig. 14-2. *The Preflight Planner organizes a pilot's preflight calculations, contains time conversions, special equipment codes, the international phonetic alphabet, and a copy of the flight plan form. This, or other commercially available forms, lets the pilot transfer preflight data to the flight plan for FSS or DUAT filing.*

(PA32). Selecting correct type designators is required with DUAT. Appendix A contains a listing of FAA civil, general aviation, aircraft type designators. Pilots should become familiar with the designators for the aircraft they routinely fly.

Special equipment codes, as defined in FIG. 14-3, should be included on VFR flight plans. The Preflight Planner, as well as other commercially available forms, contains a listing of special equipment codes. An added advantage of today's Air Traffic Control computerized radar system is helping locate missing aircraft and saving lives. This technique involves the use of recorded radar data that can be played back to determine the point at which an aircraft disappeared. The data retrieved enables rescuers to all but pinpoint a crash site and pick up the surviving pilot.

Continuing across the form, enter true airspeed in knots. Next is departure point and proposed departure time. The proposed departure time should be UTC (Zulu). Forms such as the Preflight Planner contain conversion tables. But, if we aren't sure how to convert local to Z the FSS specialist will assist. It's better to provide local time, letting the FSS specialist do the conversion, than give an incorrect UTC time. And, please don't use the 24 clock for local time, provide a.m. or p.m., as appropriate. The proposed initial cruising altitude is next; because it's the initial altitude, changes en route are not required. If we wish, we can enter VFR to indicate various VFR altitudes.

The proposed route of flight and destination should be as accurate as possible using radio navigation aids, airways, towns, or any prominent geographical landmarks. Remember, if search and rescue becomes necessary, this route will be searched first. The destination city and airport must be complete. Many towns and cities have more than one airport listed under the same general name.

Pilots using DUAT will have to specify appropriate location identifiers. These can be obtained from charts, the *Airport/Facility Directory*, and through the DUAT location encode, decode function. In addition to providing identifiers, DUAT includes weather report types (SA, FT, etc.), tie-in FSS and Center, and latitude-longitude for Loran and other users with coordinate-capable equipment. Pilots filing with an FSS are not required to provide LCIDs; Specialists are normally familiar with LCIDs within their Flight Ser-

X	No transponder; no DME.
T	Transponder, no altitude encoding; no DME.
U	Transponder, with altitude encoding; no DME.
D	DME only.
B	Transponder, no altitude encoding; with DME.
A	Transponder, with altitude encoding; with DME.
W	RNAV (area navigation, including Loran, etc.) only.
C	Transponder, no altitude encoding, with RNAV.
R	Transponder, with altitude encoding, with RNAV.

Fig. 14-3. *Pilots should file special equipment codes on VFR flight plans to assist search and rescue, if a search is necessary.*

FSS FLIGHT PLAN PROCEDURES

The FSS will hold the flight plan in abeyance until a departure report is received, or until one hour after the proposed departure time, when the flight plan is cancelled and filed. Therefore, if a flight will be delayed by more than an hour, the pilot should revise the departure time with the FSS.

The best way to open or activate a flight plan is by radio. A specific request is required. The FSS cannot assume that a radio call or even a departure time is a request to open a flight plan. It's always a good idea to provide the point of departure and destination. The specialist will provide any pertinent updates and ensure appropriate flight precautions have been received. For non-radio aircraft, or in areas with poor or no radio coverage a pilot can request an assumed departure and the FSS will activate the flight plan at the pilot's proposed departure time. However, if the pilot is delayed or decides to cancel, the FSS must be advised. This procedure should only be used when direct radio contact is not possible.

Occasionally a pilot calls to open and is told the FSS cannot find the flight plan. After a number of questions, the FSS determines the pilot filed using a different aircraft identification. If a pilot changes aircraft, he or she must advise the FSS, either before departure or upon activation. Pilots must provide any changes, such as special equipment code or aircraft color. Pilots using DUAT who depart before the FSS has received the flight plan proposal will be required to refile.

With FSS consolidation and toll-free phone numbers, filing with one FSS and opening with another has become routine. However, it takes time to forward the flight plan proposal. The FSS receiving the flight plan forwards the proposal to the departure FSS. This will be automatic and almost instantaneous at AFSSs with Model 1, but that is still in the future for many areas; nonautomated facilities can take 30 minutes or more.

Upon activation, the departure FSS becomes responsible for search and rescue. That FSS transmits a flight notification message consisting of the aircraft identification, type, destination, ETA, and any pertinent remarks to the destination tie-in FSS. When the destination FSS acknowledges receipt, they become responsible for search and rescue. The message is suspended—either written on a flight progress strip or stored electronically in the inbound file of the Model 1 computer—until the flight plan is closed, or search and rescue is initiated.

FAR 91.153 requires that "When a flight plan has been activated, the pilot in command, upon canceling or completing the flight under the flight plan, shall notify an FAA Flight Service Station or ATC facility." It's best to close with the destination's tie-in FSS. If a pilot plans to close with other than the destination's FSS, that intent should be indicated in the remarks of the flight plan, although, a flight plan can be closed with any FSS. Towers and centers are also required to accept VFR flight plan cancellations, however, this should be avoided because ATC is often busy with higher priority duties and closures get lost.

Certain pilots prefer to close their flight plan in the air by radio, while others would rather wait until they are on the ground. It's often convenient to close in the air, before switching to approach or the tower. Sometimes pilots can become so involved with ATC and the completion of the flight that the flight plan is completely forgotten.

Two axioms apply to closing flight plans: There are many excuses, but few reasons; There are those who have forgotten, and those who will.

SEARCH AND RESCUE

An aircraft is considered overdue when it cannot be located and the pilot has not cancelled or revised the flight plan within 30 minutes after the ETA. The FSS will attempt to locate an overdue aircraft by checking the destination and adjacent airports. Please note: The FAA looks for aircraft, not people. A message is sent to the departure FSS, or the FSS holding the flight plan (if filed with other than the departure station), or the DUAT contractor, to obtain complete flight plan information.

When the flight plan has not been closed or the aircraft has not been located within one hour after the ETA, an INREQ (information request) is transmitted. This message is addressed to all FSSs, Flight Watch control stations, and centers along the flight-planned route, as well as the Rescue Coordination Center (RCC) at Scott AFB, Illinois.

When replies to the INREQ are negative and the aircraft has not been located within two hours after the ETA an ALNOT (alert notice) is issued. An ALNOT requires an extended communications search of all airports within 50 miles of the flight-planned route, from the last known position to the destination. This is a primary reason for frequent position reports, which reduce the search area, if a search becomes necessary.

RCC is kept informed and is responsible for the physical search for the aircraft. These procedures are time-consuming and expensive. They often involve dozens of FAA, law enforcement, and military agencies. Pilots must make every effort to close flight plans or revise ETAs when the flight will be late by 30 minutes or more.

It's unfortunate that FSSs must take action on about 10 percent of aircraft on a VFR flight plan. If a pilot fails to close, the FSS can file an incident report with the appropriate Flight Standards District Office, which usually leads to the counseling of the pilot. However, depending on the circumstances—or if there have been prior incidents—stronger measures, such as a letter of warning or certificate suspension can result. Most often, however, the FSS locates the aircraft, and the pilot never hears a word. This, regrettably, leads to pilot complacency when it comes to closing VFR flight plans.

It's the pilot's prerogative to take advantage of the FAA's VFR flight plan service, but the pilot must adhere to certain rules and procedures. Procedures described here will take the maximum advantage of, and the increased safety afforded by, the VFR flight plan.

USING VFR FLIGHT PLAN SERVICE

My first FSS facility was in Lovelock, NV. My wife remained in the Los Angeles area and for about six months I commuted weekly in my Cessna 150. I would normally file VFR from Lovelock to Van Nuys with a landing at Bishop, CA. In those days the only way to contact flight service at Bishop was a long distance phone call or by radio; there were no procedures for separate VFR flight plans. (If the flight was today, I would have to file two separate VFR flight plans at the departure point. One from Lovelock to Bishop, and another from Bishop to Van Nuys. This procedure would be a distinct advantage if search and rescue should become necessary.)

The purpose of the VFR flight plan was to provide search and rescue protection over the sparsely populated sections of California and Nevada. Upon landing at Bishop, I would contact Tonopah radio and advise them that I had landed. This in effect was a position report. I would also advise them of my departure. If search and rescue became necessary, this would have narrowed the search area to the second half of the route. I made additional position reports at approximately one-hour intervals.

My wife would contact Los Angeles FSS, ask for the flight data position, and request the ETA for N1115R, my aircraft. Remember the FAA only has aircraft numbers, not names. If you want someone to be able to check on your flight, you must file and open a VFR flight plan, and give them the aircraft number. If the Van Nuys area was IFR. . . . Please refer to Chapter 15, IFR Flight Plans and Flight Planning.

The decision to use the FAA's VFR flight plan service rests solely with the pilot. It is my opinion that a VFR flight plan for short legs (less than an hour)—except over water, desolate, or unpopulated areas, and except for training purposes—probably isn't necessary. But, it's mighty comforting on long flights, especially over sparsely inhabited regions of the country.

Normally, the FSS will not accept flight plans with en route delays of more than an hour. Pilots have been known to file flight plans with six to 10 hours en route and as many as half a dozen stops. This procedure defeats the purpose of a VFR flight plan because search and rescue would not start until 30 minutes after the ETA at the final destination. If search and rescue becomes necessary, the search area might extend for more than 1,000 miles, thus decreasing the odds of a timely rescue. Additionally, pilots on these flight plans often lose track of time, thus unnecessarily initiating search procedures. A far better idea is to file individual flight plans for each leg. This can be done with the original departure FSS.

Under certain circumstances, such as flying into and out of remote areas, a round-robin flight plan—a landing en route and return to original departure point—is the most practical procedure. However, it should only be used when filing separate legs is not practical and ground time will not exceed an hour. The same points that apply to landings en route, apply to round-robin flight plans. Certain flight instructors have students file round-robin flight plans for all cross-country flights. Unfortunately, this denies the student the practice of filing, opening, and closing flight plans, which should be an essential part of training. Unexpected delays and losing track of time often occur.

Additionally, the closing and filing of separate flight plans assures that the student will obtain the latest weather information. One flight instructor called the FSS and inquired if his student had left Santa Barbara. The student had filed a round-robin flight plan from the L.A. Basin to Porterville to Santa Barbara and back. The FSS informed the instructor of the pilot's ETA, which had not yet expired. The instructor asked again, if the pilot had left Santa Barbara. He was informed that because the pilot had filed a round-robin flight plan this could not be determined and that the FSS would not take any action because the aircraft was not overdue. If the instructor had taught the student to file separate legs, the FSS could have determined the status of the flight.

Revise an ETA with any FSS. Transmit original point of departure, destination, and the revised estimate time of arrival. Model 1 equipment is unable to automatically process extension, therefore, FSSs are required to obtain *revised ETAs only*. If a pilot wishes to revise a flight plan he or she will have to provide the revision in the form of a revised ETA.

En route change of destination can be accomplished without submitting a complete flight plan. The pilot will have to provide the FSS with aircraft identification, type, original departure point, original destination, new destination and new route, and new ETA. The FSS will notify the original destination and new destination and provide search and rescue coverage until the new destination acknowledges receipt.

SPECIAL VFR

Basic VFR weather minimums within controlled airspace are designed to allow pilots to fly visually. This requires a visual horizon or contact with the ground, and enough visibility to see and avoid terrain, obstructions, and other aircraft. Basic VFR weather minimums were developed in the '30s when aircraft speeds averaged between 50 and 150 knots, and the minimums do not take into account the increased speeds of today's aircraft. FAR requirements are, as the regulations state, *minimums*. Minimum does not necessarily equate to safe.

Pilots have been known to become disoriented and lose control of the aircraft in visibilities as much as five miles. The pilot in command is still responsible to determine if the flight can be safely conducted, based on his or her experience and capabilities. I recommend low-time pilots obtain information from a competent instructor in operations under special VFR, and in actual special VFR weather conditions.

Aircraft can be safely flown visually in less than basic VFR conditions required for controlled airspace. Special VFR allows pilots to operate in this environment which is a visual horizon or contact with the ground and enough visibility to avoid terrain and obstructions. Under such conditions someone else, Air Traffic Control, must ensure separation from other aircraft. Although, ATC provides separation from other aircraft, it is still the pilot's responsibility to maintain terrain and obstruction clearance.

These operations must be conducted in accordance with FAR 91.157 Special VFR weather minimums. Special VFR applies only to operations within low density control zones. Special VFR is prohibited within high density control zones, designated by the "T" control zone symbol on aeronautical charts. Weather minimums for an airplane operating under special VFR are clear of clouds and one statute mile visibility. To operate at night under the provisions of special VFR, the pilot and airplane must be equipped and certified for IFR.

Prior to departure, or before entering less than basic VFR weather conditions, the pilot must obtain a clearance from the ATC facility with jurisdiction over the control zone. IFR operations have priority over special VFR.

A rather shaky voice called Van Nuys ground and requested taxi instructions. The visibility was less than basic VFR and the controller asked what type of clearance he would like. The pilot replied, "I don't have one of those," presumably referring to an instrument rating. The controller responded, "That's OK, I've got plenty."

Special VFR must be requested by the pilot. ATC is not allowed to suggest the procedure.

USING SPECIAL VFR

It might seem that special VFR is of little practical use. This is not the case, however, because special VFR has a specific and practical application. Special VFR is intended to allow a pilot to depart or enter a control zone when conditions are less than basic VFR, but safe enough for contact flying.

This often occurs in metropolitan areas where surface visibilities are reduced to less than three miles, but remain above one mile, in haze, smoke, and fog. Usually at a few thousand feet, AGL visibilities improve significantly. This procedure can also be used to allow a pilot to depart controlled airspace into uncontrolled airspace, with its reduced VFR requirements.

Pilots must be careful, special VFR can be a clearance to nowhere. Notice that the provisions of special VFR do not relieve the pilot from maintaining appropriate minimum safe altitudes as required by FAR 91.119. Fresno was reporting ceiling 400 overcast, visibility one mile. A pilot departed special VFR and flew 15 miles before tangling with some high tension wires.

Departing Long Beach, CA, one morning with a surface visibility of $2^1/_2$ miles, we requested and received a special VFR clearance. We were cleared out of the control zone to the north, "climb and maintain VFR conditions. Report VFR on top or leaving the control zone." As soon as we topped the haze, we had almost unrestricted flight visibility, reported on top, and were cleared to leave the frequency. Pilots must report on top or leaving the control zone. ATC is providing separation, so when the pilot fails to report, the airspace must be sterilized until the aircraft is located. This causes extensive, unnecessary delays to all.

Arrivals are conducted the same way. The pilot reports over the airport, or other prominent landmark, in VFR conditions above the visibility restriction, and contacts the control facility for a special VFR clearance.

Special VFR might be more efficient than an IFR approach. Santa Barbara was reporting 500 broken, one zero miles visibility. Even though the ceiling was less than VFR, we could see the runway. We requested special VFR and made a straight-in approach, rather than a 15 mile round trip, which would have been required to execute the ILS approach. On another occasion our destination was Crescent City, CA. The VOR was out of service, eliminating an IFR approach. Weather was ceiling 500 feet, one mile visibility. Finding a hole by the coastline, we requested a special VFR clearance through the Crescent City FSS. Because of the low ceiling and visibility, I slowed the Mooney to approach speed, about 100 knots. There was no sane reason to be blasting along in these conditions at 160 knots. We knew the tops were at 1,500; if the ceiling or visibility dropped, we could have climbed through the clouds to on top. ATC was providing separation, so there shouldn't have been any other aircraft in that airspace.

I was flying from Ontario to my home airport Whitman Airpark in the Los Angeles Basin one rainy afternoon. I had obtained clearance through the Burbank Airport Traffic

Area when the controller advised visibility was $2^1/2$ miles in rain and fog, and requested my intentions. I requested and received a special VFR clearance out of the control zone to the northwest. I reported leaving the control zone and landed at my destination, which was in uncontrolled airspace.

Delays, extensive at times, should be anticipated. A pilot can never count on making it in special VFR; a solid VFR alternate should always be within reach.

FLIGHT ASSISTANCE SERVICE

FAA air traffic controllers and flight service specialists are trained in various techniques to locate disoriented pilots, and assist with navigational or mechanical difficulties. However, none of this training or resources are of use to a pilot unwilling to take advantage of this service. All too often we find ourselves hung up on semantics. What constitutes an emergency? When is a pilot lost?

As a brand new private pilot I was flying from Leeds to Oxford in England. Soon, nothing on the chart looked like anything on the ground. I was not lost. I was in the center of England. I was disoriented. Before things got out of hand I requested assistance and reoriented myself.

Most pilots think an emergency is an engine failure or an in-flight fire. An emergency is simply a situation involving distress, the need to resolve uncertainty, or a means of alerting those who are in a position to help. Distress or uncertainty can result from mechanical failure, pilot incapacitation, insufficient fuel, penetration of IFR conditions by a VFR pilot, or a pilot unable to locate his or her position.

The FAA says an emergency exists when an emergency is declared by the pilot, by FAA facility personnel, or by officials responsible for the operation of aircraft.

FAA facilities use all available resources to assist aircraft in difficulty: radar, direction finders (DF), NAVAIDS, (VOR and NDBs), and landmarks. When an aircraft is "located," the pilot determines the best course of action. This might be nothing more than continuing to destination, or the execution of an emergency DF or radar approach, if the pilot is on top of a cloud deck and unable to proceed to a VFR airport.

Thorough flight planning, understanding weather reports and forecasts, and frequent weather updates should alleviate most problems. Mechanical and electronic systems fail and, being human, we can find ourselves in need of assistance. When a pilot encounters an uncertain situation, the five Cs apply:

- Confess
- Communicate
- Climb
- Comply
- Conserve

Confess and communicate the difficulty; certain pilots compound problems by waiting until they have only a few minutes of fuel. A pilot who requests assistance before the situation becomes critical has many more options. Any time the outcome of a flight situation becomes uncertain, whether due to unknown position, marginal fuel or weather, navigational, or mechanical problem, contact an FAA facility for assistance. Resolve the situation before a simple flight assist becomes an accident.

Climb if possible to improve communications, radar, and DF capability. Comply with instructions. One pilot requested assistance and was instructed to squawk 7700. The pilot replied, "I don't think it is that much of an emergency." After some coaxing, code 7700 was selected. Within 60 seconds the FSS was able to relay her exact position, received from a local radar facility. This pilot proceeded to her destination without further difficulties.

Don't blindly follow instructions that will take you through clouds. Keep in mind that you are still the pilot in command. If penetrating clouds is unavoidable, inform ATC immediately.

Conserve your remaining fuel, if possible, by reducing to a maximum endurance power setting. Pilots should be familiar with this setting for each aircraft they fly.

Most parts of the country are covered by some kind of air-ground communications: might be military or FAA. Pilots already in contact with a facility when a problem arises should use that frequency. The facility might change the frequency if they feel better handling will result. Otherwise, 121.5 MHz, the international VHF emergency frequency can be used. Some pilots believe that the only time this frequency should be used is when the aircraft is going down in flames. That's not true. Frequency 121.5 is simply a clear channel, set aside for aircraft in difficulty. It can and should be used any time a pilot encounters a situation of uncertainty or distress.

A major deterrent to requesting assistance is the pilot's ego. The perceived embarrassment and repercussions of a request have in many instances turned a bad situation into an impossible one. For example, a pilot attempting to locate an uncontrolled field in reduced visibility became critically low on fuel and landed in an open field. He never requested assistance during his hour and a half, futile search, for the airport. Several days later, under similar conditions, another pilot called the local FSS and advised them of his situation. Using VOR and DF the FSS brought the pilot and his family to another airport in the area, obtained a special VFR clearance for the pilot, and he landed safely. Both pilots were invited to have a little chat with the Flight Standards District Office about the circumstances. One pilot also talked to his insurance company.

FAR 91.3 specifies the responsibility and authority of the pilot in command. Under this rule, the pilot is responsible, and the final authority, for the operation of the aircraft. The pilot in an emergency might deviate from any rule to meet that emergency. The pilot might be required to send a written report of that deviation.

Pilots who request flight assistance usually don't deviate from FARs. However, their actions might be reviewed by the FAA. With few exceptions, this results in counseling from the Accident Prevention Specialist, unless there is evidence of excessive pilot deficiencies. Flight assistance service cannot be continually used by a few pilots who refuse to obtain or maintain basic proficiency.

When a student pilot requires assistance the FAA wants to talk to the flight instructor. I know, because I've been in that position. We ironed out the problems, I became a better instructor and, in my favor, my students knew whom to contact for assistance.

I provide and recommend that my students receive experience and training, respectively in the use of DF steers before they begin solo cross-country flights. The worst time to receive a first DF steer is during an actual flight assist. Facilities are usually quite willing to provide practice DF steers and approaches where commissioned.

Then there was the pilot who called and requested a practice DF steer. When told the facility was to busy, he said, "Well, how about the real thing."

As stated in the Airman's Information Manual, "When you are in doubt of your position, or feel apprehensive for your safety, do not hesitate to request assistance. The FAA's Air Traffic Service facilities are ready and willing to help."

15
IFR Flight Planning

A<small>N IFR FLIGHT PLAN ALLOWS AN APPROPRIATELY RATED AND CURRENT PILOT</small>
with a properly equipped aircraft to operate in weather conditions that are less than
VFR. The IFR flight plan also provides separation between known aircraft and alerts
search and rescue in case of an accident. When less than VFR conditions exist in controlled airspace, FARs require the pilot to file an IFR flight plan and obtain a clearance.
An IFR flight plan is also required in positive control airspace when congestion, or aircraft speed, or both, require positive, ground-controlled separation.

The proper filing of an IFR flight plan can make the difference between an on-time
departure or a lengthy delay. The more a pilot knows about the filing and processing of an
IFR flight plan, the better he or she will be able to make maximum use of DUAT, the
FAA's Air Traffic Control system, and their flying activity.

In the early days of aviation, locations were abbreviated by two letters (NK, Newark).
As the number of NAVAIDs and airports increased, three-letter identifiers came into use
(ATL, Atlanta); international identifiers use four letters (CYVR, Vancouver, British
Columbia, Canada). Some publishers have placed the four-letter, international identifiers
on domestic charts. On domestic flight plans, use only the three-letter identifiers.

Originally, airway intersections were given local names, for example Twin Lakes.
These were abbreviated with number-letter identifiers (4TW). NAVAIDs in the vicinity of
airports were often given the same name and identifier as the nearby airport. Computer-
ization has impacted LCIDs two ways. All intersections are now identified by five letters
(EUGEN). In our computerized ATC system, to ensure accurate flight data processing and

eliminate ambiguity, NAVAIDs that are not collocated with airports will have different LCIDs. Some still remain, but all will eventually be changed.

FLIGHT PLAN INFORMATION

With a few important differences, the IFR flight plan is completed in much the same way as the VFR flight plan in Chapter 14; type (IFR), full aircraft identification, aircraft type, and special equipment codes are similar. Aircraft identification must include the N (N1252Y). Approved lifeguard and air taxi operators should prefix the N with L or T, as appropriate (LN8148F or TN1115R).

Operators with approved three-letter call signs can be used (AMF123, Amflight one twenty-three). DUAT users must use appropriate aircraft type designators contained in Appendix A, Abbreviations.

The *Airman's Information Manual* (AIM) recommends pilots file the maximum transponder or navigation capability for their aircraft. This will provide ATC with the necessary information to utilize the system to its maximum. Refer to FIG. 14-3 for special equipment suffix codes.

Pilots should file /R (or other appropriate area navigation and transponder code) when the aircraft is equipped with any FAA approved and certified area navigation (RNAV) system. This includes VORTAC RNAV, inertial, omega, and loran.

True airspeed, point of departure, proposed time of departure, and initial cruising altitude are similar to the VFR flight plan. The departure point must be a fix (airport, NAVAID, radial-distance, or latitude-longitude). For IFR *in controlled airspace*, the pilot can file for any altitude. This might be advantageous because of aircraft ceiling limitations, icing, or passenger comfort. ATC will normally approve these altitudes based on traffic. On top (OTP) is also a perfectly good altitude, but, the pilot should specify the requested on top altitude (OTP/175, on top at 17,500 feet).

Information is computer processed, so route of flight on an IFR flight plan must be accurate, even the smallest route or fix error will result in a reject. For example, the IFR En Route Chart in FIG. 15-1 shows V485 almost directly over the San Jose (SJC) VOR. The airway, however, is actually made up of a radial from the Sausalito (SAU) VOR. Figure 15-2 is an example of a flight plan route filed SJC V485. . . . The computer-generated error message specifies that the FIX SJC is NOT ON ROUTE V485. Close does not count. The route is corrected by inserting the intersection LICKE (FIG. 15-1). The computer responds with an acknowledgment message (R, roger message number 001).

Although airway to airway routes can be filed (V28 V334), unless the computer can define the intersection, the flight plan will be rejected. It's always best to file the intersection (V28 ALTAM V334), which is required with DUAT. One purpose of filing airways is to allow the pilot to file a route and omit intermediate fixes. Unfortunately, a few pilots still file V25 SNS V25 PRB V25 RZS. The purpose of the airway is to allow the pilot to file V25 RZS.

Due to limitations of ATC computers, not all LCIDs can be stored. A pilot using DUAT can file ROM V485 HENER V186. . . . DUAT will respond ''Posting FIX

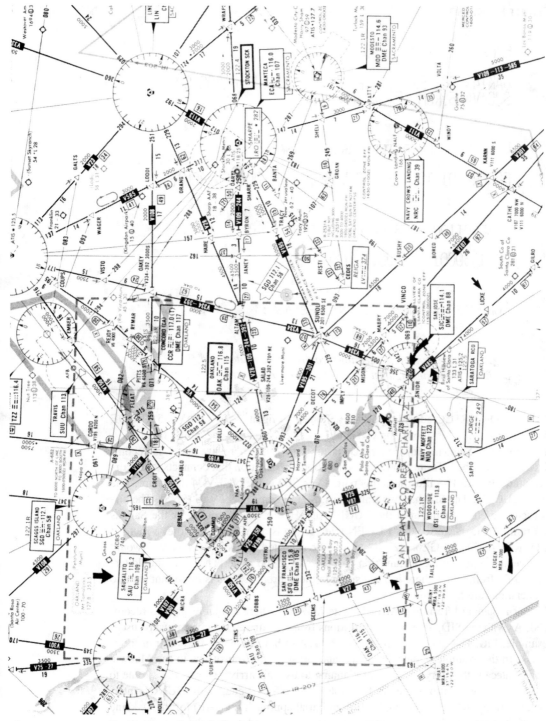

Fig. 15-1. *Pilots must be careful when specifying routes on IFR flight plans. Thorough review of the charts will prevent errors.*

275

Filed by pilot:

OAK1425001 FP N1115R C150/T 90 SJC P1800 90
SJC.V485.ROM..PRB/0100

Comupter generated error message:

ERROR 001 10 RTE SJC.V485. FIX NOT ON ROUTE

Correction message entered by FSS:

OAK1430001 CM SJC..LICKE.V485.

Computer acknowledgment message:

R001

Fig. 15-2. *Computer processing requires that routes and fixes connect. Even the slightest error will result in an error or reject message.*

REDDE for ZOA ARTCC adaption purposes. Route of Flight . . .? ROM V485 REDDE V485 HENER. . . ." This allows the Oakland Center computer to accept the flight.

The use of a Standard Instrument Departures (SID), where available, is recommended. However, the SID must have an intersection or transition that connects to the airway structure. Figure 15-3 illustrates this point. The SID is the NUEVO4 departure. The exit fix is EUGEN. The SID has two transitions, SHOEY and SALINAS (SNS). The airway structure filed must begin at the EUGEN or SHOEY intersections, or the Salinas VOR. From FIG. 15-1, we see that EUGEN intersection is on V-27. Therefore, a route of flight OAK NUEVO4 EUGEN V27 . . . would be accepted; OAK NUEVO4 V27 would not be accepted. The exit fix or transition must be part of the route. The route should terminate at a fix from which there is a transition to the approach. This is important if radio communciations are lost.

Use of a Standard Terminal Arrival Route (STAR), where available, is also recommended. As with the SID, appropriate transitions from the airway structure must be used. For example, FIG. 15-4 shows a typical STAR. STARs have an entry fix and transitions like SIDs. In the example, Coaldale, Mina, and Mustang are transitions to the Madwin arrival. Manteca is the entry fix. A pilot planning to use this arrival should file a route to one of the transition fixes or the entry fix. Note that the STAR ends at the SUNOL intersection and, from FIG. 15-5, that SUNOL is an initial approach fix (IAF) for the Oakland ILS RWY 29 approach. The STAR provides routes and altitudes from the en route structure to the airport.

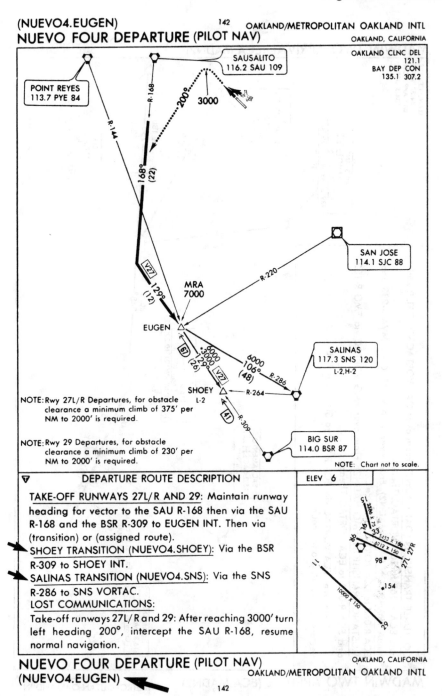

(NUEVO4.EUGEN)   142   OAKLAND/METROPOLITAN OAKLAND INTL
NUEVO FOUR DEPARTURE (PILOT NAV)   OAKLAND, CALIFORNIA

OAKLAND CLNC DEL
121.1
BAY DEP CON
135.1 307.2

SAUSALITO
116.2 SAU 109

POINT REYES
113.7 PYE 84

R-168

200°

3000

R-144

168°
(22)

V27 129°
(12)

MRA
7000

R-220

SAN JOSE
114.1 SJC 88

EUGEN

V27 (3000) (26)

3000

6000
106°
(48) R-286

SALINAS
117.3 SNS 120
L-2, H-2

SHOEY   L-2   R-264

(41) R-309

BIG SUR
114.0 BSR 87

NOTE: Rwy 27L/R Departures, for obstacle
clearance a minimum climb of 375' per
NM to 2000' is required.

NOTE: Rwy 29 Departures, for obstacle
clearance a minimum climb of 230' per
NM to 2000' is required.

NOTE: Chart not to scale.

▽   DEPARTURE ROUTE DESCRIPTION

TAKE-OFF RUNWAYS 27L/R AND 29: Maintain runway
heading for vector to the SAU R-168 then via the SAU
R-168 and the BSR R-309 to EUGEN INT. Then via
(transition) or (assigned route).
► SHOEY TRANSITION (NUEVO4.SHOEY): Via the BSR
R-309 to SHOEY INT.
► SALINAS TRANSITION (NUEVO4.SNS): Via the SNS
R-286 to SNS VORTAC.
LOST COMMUNICATIONS:
Take-off runways 27L/R and 29: After reaching 3000' turn
left heading 200°, intercept the SAU R-168, resume
normal navigation.

ELEV 6

98°

154

NUEVO FOUR DEPARTURE (PILOT NAV)   OAKLAND, CALIFORNIA
(NUEVO4.EUGEN) ◄   OAKLAND/METROPOLITAN OAKLAND INTL
                    142

Fig. 15-3. *Standard Instrument Departures (SID) should be filed, where available. Exit fixes and transitions must connect with the filed en route structure.*

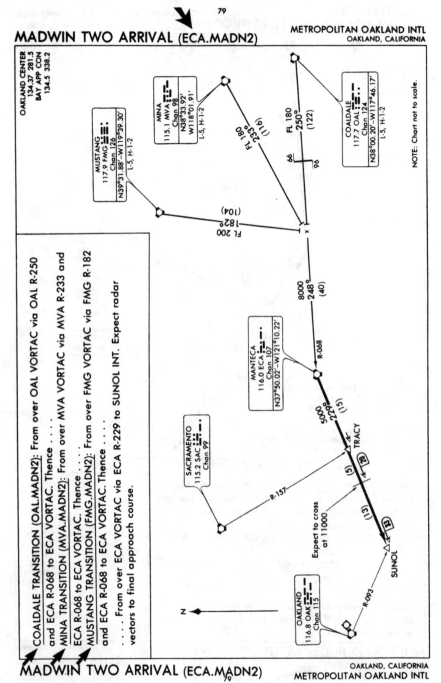

Fig. 15-4. *Standard Terminal Arrival Routes (STAR) are recommended. Pilots should file to the STAR transition or entry fix.*

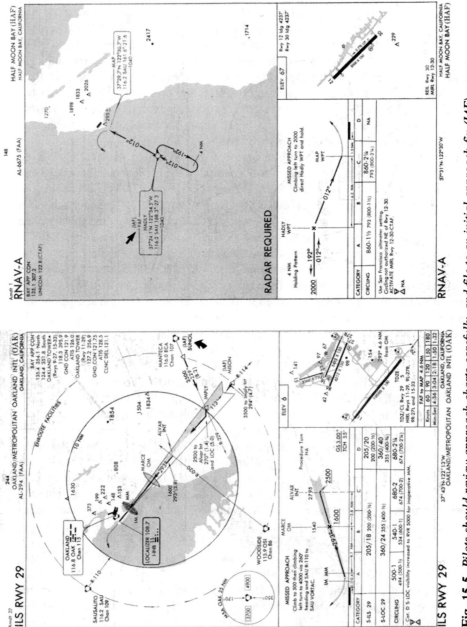

Fig. 15-5. *Pilots should review approach charts carefully, and file to an initial approach fix (IAF).*

Routes should be filed to an IAF. Figure 15-5 shows HADLY as an IAF for the Half Moon Bay RNAV-A approach. Referring to FIG. 15-1, HADLY is also an intersection on V27. Therefore, the route V27 HADLY HAF could be filed. Certain pilots think they must file to the final approach fix (FAF); the FAF for the Oakland ILS RWY 29 approach (FIG. 15-5) is the MARCE outer marker. It is not necessary to file, for example, SUNOL IMPLY MARCE OAK because this route segment is part of the published transition. In fact, because of computer storage capability, not all intermediate and final approach fixes can be stored. Pilots using DUAT might receive rejection messages indicating "fix not stored." Routes should be filed using preferred routes contained in the *Airport/Facility Directory*. Not all preferred routes appear in the Directory, so the local FSS can often help pilots with preferred SIDs and routes in their area.

Pilots flying aircraft equipped with an approved area navigation system might wish to file direct or point-to-point. The random route portion of the flight should begin and end over appropriate departure and arrival fixes. The use of SIDs and STARs is advisable. The route must be defined using radial-distance fixes from appropriate navigational aids. As a minimum, one way point must be filed for each ARTCC through which the flight will be conducted. These way points must be located within 200 nm of the preceding ARTCC's boundary. This requirement is, again, due to the storage capability of the computer.

If the computer does not recognize the fix, the flight plan will be rejected. For example, a pilot wished to file RNAV direct from Hollister, CA, to John Day, OR. When asked, he was unable to provide a way point. The specialist pulled out a chart and acceptable way points were determined. The flight plan, as filed by the pilot, would have been rejected.

Unfortunately, a few pilots engage in rather poor flight planning. They usually use the excuse, "They're going to send me the way they want anyway." DUAT does not discriminate against pilots filing at any altitude for any direct route. For example, DUAT will accept an IFR flight plan from Marin Ranch, CA (CA35), in the San Francisco Bay area direct to Rosmond, CA (L00), in the Mojave Desert. Because L00 is not stored in the ZOA computer, DUAT inserts the L00 lat-long 3452N/11813W for the destination.

Irate center supervisors have called demanding that the FSS include appropriate departure fixes. Well, that's not the FSS's job, it's the pilot's. Even when accepted by the computer, these flight plans don't work; someone, somewhere has to fix them, which results in delays for everyone. One pilot using this rationale filed from San Jose direct to Denver. I pulled out the SID book and he accepted an appropriate SID to an en route fix. Pilots with aircraft equipped with latitude/longitude coordinate navigation capability can file random RNAV routes at and above FL390, within the conterminous United States, using lat-long coordinates. Appropriate SIDs and STARs should be used.

After the departure fix, the pilot must include each turn point and the arrival fix for the destination. The arrival fix must be identified by both lat-long and fix identifier: OAK OAK3 OAK LIN 3910/10542 SHREW DEN. This route specifies the Oakland three departure to the Linden (LIN) VOR, direct to 3910/10542 which is the lat-long coordinate for the SHREW intersection. SHREW is the entry fix for the Denver (DEN) profile descent arrival.

The remarks section of the flight plan should contain information on the nonavailability of SIDs and STARs (SSNO), or oxygen. This section can be used to indicate a desire to climb VFR to cruising altitude. Pilots using authorized three-letter air taxi call signs should write out the radio telephony in remarks (Amflight). Enter only remarks pertinent to ATC or to clarify other flight plan information. Requests for specific approaches, multiple approaches, or altitude changes en route should be made directly with the controller.

When required, an alternate airport should be entered in block 13. Remember it is the pilot's responsibility to determine the requirement for an alternate. Pilots will, from time to time, ask the FSS specialist if an alternate is necessary. Although the specialist can often be helpful selecting an appropriate alternate, he or she is not responsible for this determination.

At an accident prevention meeting, an FAA FSDO representative insisted that pilots file separate flight plans from the destination to alternate in case of radio failure and a missed approach; do not do this. It serves no practical purpose and only congests computer systems that are already nearly saturated.

Fuel on board, pilot's name, etc., number aboard, and color are entered in the same manner as a VFR flight plan.

FLIGHT PLAN FILING AND PROCESSING

IFR flight plans are filed like a VFR flight plans. Basic filing procedures contained in Chapter 14 should be followed.

As stated in the *Airmen's Information Manual*, "Pilots should file IFR flight plans at least 30 minutes prior to estimated time of departure to preclude possible delay in receiving a departure clearance from ATC." DUAT flight plans must be filed at least one hour prior to departure. IFR flight plans can normally be accepted up to a maximum of 24 hours in advance. Pilots became accustomed to filing the day before during the General Aviation Reservation Program after the controller's strike of 1981. I do not recommend this procedure, however. Too many things change. From a technical and regulatory point of view it is not possible to determine time en route, alternates, or facility outages (NOTAMs). Additionally, all too often, pilots have to call the FSS with amendments. The following example illustrates a common occurrence. The Citation pilot called the evening before and filed four flight plans—Oakland to Mendicino, to Friday Harbour, to Denver, to Dallas. The following morning he calls back to change everything. The time required to make all the changes, which required coordination with three ARTCCs took twice as long as would have been necessary to simply code the flight plans. This procedure also encourages pilots to depart without a preflight briefing.

Upon receipt of an IFR flight plan, the FSS will usually transmit most of the information to the appropriate departure ARTCC no more than two hours prior to departure time. Normally, the information is transmitted via the FAA's Service B Telecommunications System to the center's computer. The computer checks the message for format and errors. Computer error and reject messages come from several sources. The largest percentage are incorrect routes.

Error messages can also be caused by typing errors, telecommunications trouble, or internal computer problems. When an error or reject is received, the FSS attempts to correct the problem. This can be time-consuming, especially during periods of heavy traffic.

When the flight plan is correct, the computer generates an acknowledgment message, as illustrated in FIG. 15-2.

Thirty minutes prior to departure time, the computer sends a departure strip, containing the flight plan information, to the center departure sector, and approach control or tower, as appropriate. The information will not be readily available before this time. Pilots should advise the controller of the filed departure time when calling for clearance more than 30 minutes before the filed P (proposed) time. This will allow the controller to request the flight plan. Pilots calling for clearance two hours before filed departure time, most often, will not receive a clearance.

It is not unheard of for a pilot to change aircraft at the last minute, just like VFR, and become very indignant when the controller cannot find the flight plan—filed under a different identification. Centers retain flight plans from one to three hours after proposed departure time. The exact time depends on individual centers and computer storage capacity. Because of these factors it's to the pilot's advantage to file within several hours of proposed departure time, and revise departure time when it differs by more than one hour.

Pilots filing with one FSS for a later departure from an airport served by another FSS have called to change information such as proposed departure time only to find there is no flight plan. Pilots cannot expect ATC to have their flight plan prior to two hours before P time. And, some pilots routinely call the FSS to see if the center has their flight plan. This is a redundant procedure. It's usually easiest for all concerned, including the pilot, to file as close to 30 minutes prior to departure time as possible. DUAT transmits the IFR proposal to the departure center one hour prior to P time. Flight plan amendments can only be made through a DUAT computer terminal prior to one hour, after that time any amendments will have to be made through an FSS.

To facilitate flight plan processing, pilots should file a separate IFR flight plan for each leg of a flight. Even if merely a low approach is intended, a separate flight plan to the next destination will result in faster, more efficient service. There is, in effect, no such thing as a round-robin IFR flight plan, or IFR with landings en route. This does not preclude the pilot, however, from filing from point of departure to an en route fix and back to the departure airport during instrument flight training.

This is often a valid procedure because it provides ATC with all essential flight plan information, upon which to issue a clearance. The computer has been programmed to reject a route, for example, HAF direct HAF; the error message will come back ZERO DISTANCE. Referring to FIG. 15-5, a pilot who wishes to depart Half Moon Bay, shoot the approach, and land, should file HAF HADLY HAF. This is a perfectly acceptable route.

Many metropolitan areas have established abbreviated flight plan procedures, through letters of agreement between ATC facilities, whereby controllers enter local flight plans. Pilots can request local, or Tower En Route Clearances, from ground or clearance delivery without filing an IFR flight plan. Pilots, however, should not expect this service in all areas. A check with local pilots or the FSS can determine if abbreviated procedures are available. Otherwise, the pilot must plan to file a complete flight plan.

In effect, ATC, acting for the Administrator, has authorized deviation from the FAR that requires the pilot file a flight plan. This procedure, however, does not relieve the pilot from complying with FARs as far as alternate airports and fuel requirements. How does a pilot comply with these regulations?

By filing an IFR flight plan, if the pilot wants to be on record. Most pilots are also aware they can obtain a clearance directly from the control facility in-flight. The controller, although not required to do so, has authorized the pilot to deviate from the FAR requirement to file a flight plan. When the controller gets busy, he or she might not have the time or inclination to accommodate pilots. The best procedure is to file a flight plan.

COMPOSITE FLIGHT PLANS

Composite flight plans (VFR-IFR or IFR-VFR) are accepted by the FSS as stated in the *Airmen's Information Manual*. However, the instructions in the AIM are oversimplified, incomplete, and do not reflect today's ATC system. From a practical point of view, and for DUAT users, composite flight plans are actually two separate flight plans.

A composite VFR-IFR flight plan is fairly simple. The pilot files and specifies a point to pick up IFR. However, don't be surprised if the FSS wants two flight plans because they are handled separately. The VFR portion is suspended and the IFR portion is transmitted to the appropriate center; it must be closed by the pilot, preferably prior to picking up IFR. The exact procedure should be agreed upon between the pilot and FSS specialist at the time of filing. After departure, the VFR portion is opened. This allows transmission of the VFR flight notification message to the appropriate FSS.

The pilot files a composite IFR-VFR flight plan in the usual manner and specifies the point where IFR is to be terminated. Again, don't be surprised if the FSS wants two flight plans. The FSS will transmit the IFR portion to the center and the VFR proposal to the FSS responsible for the location where VFR is to begin. The pilot will have to activate the VFR portion after canceling IFR. Here again, a procedure should be agreed upon with the FSS specialist at filing.

OBTAINING AND CANCELING IFR CLEARANCES

Clearances are normally obtained from the departure ground or clearance delivery controller. At uncontrolled airports, receiving a clearance can be as simple as a request through a remote frequency for center or FSS, or perhaps require a clearance void time over the phone. Because the controller must have the flight plan information, pilots must file prior to departure. Preflight and runup should be completed before requesting clearance. The pilot should provide the FSS or ATC specialist with aircraft ident, departure and destination, and how soon the pilot can depart after the clearance is received.

Clearance void times tie up airspace, so controllers are reluctant to issue times beyond 15 minutes. Pilots must be ready for an immediate departure. If the pilot decides not to go for any reason, he or she must advise the FSS or ATC. Otherwise, ATC must assume the pilot has departed and is experiencing radio trouble. The airspace must be sterilized—cleared of all known traffic—resulting in extensive delays.

IFR flight plans are automatically canceled by an operating tower upon arrival. However, the pilot must close an IFR flight plan upon arrival at other locations. The failure to close can needlessly tie up airspace and cause delays for hours. Often the control facility will specify how the pilot is to close. In any case, the flight plan can always be closed with an FSS. A pilot flying a twin Cessna arrived at Santa Rosa after the tower closed. The FSS, center, and sheriff's department spend a good part of the night searching for this aircraft, which was neatly tucked away in its hangar.

USING IFR FLIGHT PLAN SERVICE

A topical subject these days is whether a pilot should routinely file IFR, even when weather conditions are VFR. An IFR flight plan has the advantage that ATC helps the pilot precisely fly from A to B. It relieves the pilot of knowing what type of airspace he or she is traversing and who to contact (Airport Radar Service Areas, Terminal Control Areas, Airport Traffic Areas, etc.).

Finally, at the destination, ATC usually sequences the arrival with other IFR and VFR traffic. Certain aviators consider radar traffic advisories an additional safety factor. Departure and arrival delays, out-of-the-way routings and approaches, less than advantageous cruising altitudes, and increased pilot workload might be the price for an ATC clearance.

A pilot should also consider his or her experience, and aircraft capability. A newly rated instrument pilot without experience should carefully consider the advisability of filing IFR in congested airspace. Single-pilot operations in these areas, even when the weather is VFR, are extremely demanding. The pilot must control and navigate the aircraft, and communicate, often all at the same time. These individuals should seek training from a competent instructor before venturing single-pilot IFR in these areas.

A Cessna 150 or Tomahawk pilot who demands his or her right to the ILS at a major, congested airport makes friends of no one. Pilots should consider their obligations as well as their rights when filing IFR. There is little advantage with struggling to 11,000 or 12,000 feet in a Cessna 172 or Piper Cherokee just to go IFR.

If we decide to go IFR, the first task is to file the flight plan as outlined in previous sections of this chapter. I planned a proficiency training flight out of Livermore, CA. I had reserved an airplane and scheduled an instructor. My plan was to go to Stockton, then Sacramento, and return, and I filed three abbreviated flight plans with flight service; a letter of agreement exists within this area that authorizes this procedure. The weather was clear and alternate airports were not required. Flight plan from blocks one through 10 were provided for each leg. During each request for clearance, I advised ground control that we had prefiled. Each clearance was readily available, with no delay. Had this been a longer training flight, with delays in excess of one hour, I would have filed the successive leg at the departure airport, prior to departure.

On this occasion the L.A. Basin had a deeper than usual marine cloud layer. Tops were around 7,000 feet. Under such conditions pilots who prefer IFR-to-on-top might have to file because they will have to enter center airspace. (Abbreviated flight plans are normally restricted to approach control airspace.) I filed IFR to the Lake Hughes VOR. This procedure afforded me the IFR clearance through the Basin and out of the stratus condition. If I had wanted VFR flight plan protection beyond Lake Hughes, I would have filed a VFR flight plan from Lake Hughes to my destination. After canceling IFR, I would have activated the VFR portion with the Lancaster FSS. I determined Lancaster has flight plan responsibility for Lake Hughes from the *Airport/Facility Directory*. This is an example of an IFR-VFR flight plan combination.

As promised from Chapter 14, let's go back to my Lovelock, Van Nuys odyssey. California coastal sections are often covered with stratus. My route had few direct airways; those that were available had minimum altitudes far above a reasonable cruise altitude for the Cessna 150. In any case, there was no need for IFR because the desert weather was clear.

I filed my usual VFR flight plan, but changed the destination to the Palmdale VOR. In remarks I noted, "pickup IFR O/PMD-VNY." I filed a separate IFR flight plan from PMD to VNY. Over Palmdale I canceled VFR with Lancaster Radio, the tie-in for Palmdale, and contacted Los Angeles Center for my IFR clearance to Van Nuys. This is an example of a VFR-IFR flight plan combination.

IFR flight plans must be complete and accurate, especially for pilots using DUAT. Aircraft type must be the FAA-approved type identifier. Route of flight must also be complete and accurate for computer acceptance. The use of SIDs and STARs is recommended. Pilots filing RNAV routes must remember to include one way point in every center's airspace, not more than 200 miles from the preceding center's boundary. Routes should begin with a SID, follow the preferred routing, and end over a STAR transition or entry fix, or an initial approach fix.

IFR flight plans should be filed at least 30 minutes prior to departure. Fast-File and DUAT users must allow at least one hour. Flight plans are normally not transmitted to the departure center until two hours (one hour for DUAT) before the proposed time, and not to the sector or tower until 30 minutes before filed departure time. DUAT users will have to amend flight plans prior to one hour before departure, through a DUAT computer terminal, less than one hour prior to departure, through an FSS.

Clearances are normally obtained directly from ATC. In remote areas, a clearance might be relayed by phone from an FSS. The pilot must have filed a flight plan, and be ready for departure, before requesting clearance. The clearance will contain a void time. If the pilot is unable to make the void time, he or she must, as soon as possible, notify ATC. IFR flight plans are canceled by an operating tower; at airports without an operating tower, the pilot is responsible for providing ATC with a cancellation. Failure to notify ATC of an unused void time or cancellation creates delays.

Despite certain equipment restrictions, general aviation has complete access to the ATC system. There is no question that system complexity is growing. Only by knowing the system, and working within it, can a pilot realize its maximum benefit.

Appendix A
Abbreviations

MANY CONTRACTIONS ARE USED ON AVIATION WEATHER REPORTS AND forecasts to save space on telecommunication circuits, in computer equipment, and on charts. The contractions will normally be used for any derivative of the root word. If confusion would result, variations might be shown by adding the following letters to the contraction of the root word.

able	**BL**	ening	**NG**	ing	**G**
al	**L**	er,ier,or	**R**	ity	**TY**
ally,erly,ly	**LY**	ern	**RN**	ment	**MT**
ary,ery,ory	**RY**	ically	**CLY**	ous	**US**
ance,ence	**NC**	ive	**V**	s,es,ies	**S**
der	**DR**	iest,est	**ST**	tion,ation	**N**
ed,ied	**D**	iness,ness	**NS**	ward	**WD**

Continued.

The following contractions are normally used on aviation weather reports, PIREPs, forecasts, charts, and Notices to Airmen.

A

A	absolute (temperature)
A	Arctic air mass
A	hail
AC	altocumulus
ACCAS	altocumulus castellanus
ACSL	standing lenticular altocumulus
ACLTG	accelerating
ACYC	anticyclonic
ADRNDCK	Adirondack
ADV	advise
ADVCTN	advection
ADVY	advisory
A/FD	*Airport/Facility Directory*
AFDK	after dark
AIM	*Airman's Information Manual*
ALF	aloft
ALGHNY	Allegheny
ALNOT	alert notice
ALQDS	all quadrants
ALSEC	all sectors
ALTA	Alberta
ALUTN	Aleutian
ALWF	actual wind factor
AMPLTD	amplitude
AMS	air mass
ANLYS	analysis
APLCN	Appalachian
ARFF	airport rescue and fire fighting
AS	altostratus
ATLC	Atlantic
AURBO	Aurora Borealis
AWIPS	Advance Weather Interactive Processing System
AWW	alert weather watch

B

B	beginning of precipitation (time in minutes)
BC	British Columbia

BCH	beach
BCKG	backing
BD	blowing dust
BDA	Bermuda
BFDK	before dark
BINOVC	breaks in overcast
BKN	broken
BL	between layers
BLD	build
BLDUP	buildup
BLKHLS	Black Hills
BLKT	blanket
BLZD	blizzard
BN	blowing sand
BNDRY	boundary
BOVC	base of overcast
BRF	brief
BRK	break
BRKHIC	breaks in higher overcast
BRKSHR	Berkshire
BRM	barometer
BS	blowing snow
BTWN	between
BY	blowing spray
C	
C	continental air mass
CAN	Canada
CARIB	Caribbean
CASCDS	Cascades
CAVOK	cloud and visibility OK
CAVU	clear or scattered clouds and visibility greater than 10 miles
CBMAM	cumulonimbus mamma
CC	cirrocumulus
CCLKWS	counterclockwise
CCSL	standing lenticular cirrocumulus
CDFNT	cold front
CFP	cold front passage
CHC	change
CHSPK	Chesapeake
CI	cirrus

CIG	ceiling
CLD	cloud
CLR	clear
CLRS	clear and smooth
CNCL	cancel
CNDN	Canadian
CNVTV	convective
COND	condition
CONFDC	confidence
CONT	continuous
CONTDVD	Continental Divide
CONTRAILS	condensation trails
CS	cirrostratus
CST	coast
CTGY	category
CTSKLS	Catskills
CU	cumulus
CUFRA	cumulus fractus
CWA	center weather advisory
CYC	cyclonic
CYCLGN	cyclogenesis

D

D	dust
DABRK	daybreak
DF	direction finder
DFUS	diffuse
DH	decision height
DKTS	Dakotas
DLAD	delayed
DMSH	diminish
DNS	dense
DNSLP	downslope
DNSTRM	downstream
DP	deep
DPNG	deepening
DPTH	depth
DRFT	drift
DRZL	drizzle
DSIPT	dissipate
DTRT	deteriorate
DURGC	during climb
DURGD	during descent
DVV	downward vertical velocity

DWNDFTS	downdrafts
DWPNT	dew point

E

E	ending of precipitation (time in minutes)
E	equatorial air mass
E	estimated ceiling
ELNGT	elongate
EMBDD	embedded
ENERN	east-northeastern
ENEWD	east-northeastward
EOF	expected operations forecast
ESERN	east-southeastern
ESEWD	east-southeastward
EXTRAP	extrapolate
EXTRM	extreme

F

F	fog
FA	area forecast
FAF	final approach fix
FAH	Fahrenheit
FD	wind and temperature aloft forecast
FIBI	filed but impracticable to transmit
FILG	filling
FINO	weather report will not be filed for transmission
FL	flight level
FLG	falling
FLRY	flurry
FNT	front
FNTGNS	frontogenesis
FNTLYS	frontolysis
FORNN	forenoon
FRMG	forming
FROPA	frontal passage
FROSFC	frontal surface
FRST	frost
FRWF	forecast wind factor
FRZ	freeze
FRZN	frozen
FT	terminal forecast

G

G	gust reaching
GF	ground fog
GFDEP	ground fog estimated (feet) deep
GICG	glaze icing
GLFALSK	Gulf of Alaska
GLFCAL	Gulf of California
GLFMEX	Gulf of Mexico
GLFSTLAWR	Gulf of St. Lawrence
GNDFG	ground fog
GOES	Geostationary Operational Environmental Satellite
GOESNEXT	Next Generation GOES
GRAD	gradient
GRBNKS	Grand Banks
GRDL	gradual
GRTLKS	Great Lakes
GSTS	gusts
GSTY	gusty
GV	ground visibility

H

H	haze
HCVIS	high clouds visible
HDEP	haze layer estimated (feet) deep
HDFRZ	hard freeze
HDSVLY	Hudson Valley
HI	high
HIFOR	high level forecast
HLSTO	hailstones
HLTP	hilltop
HLYR	haze layer aloft
HURCN	hurricane
HUREP	hurricane report
HX	high index

I

IAF	initial approach fix
IC	ice crystals
ICAO	International Civil Aviation Organization
ICG	icing
ICGIC	icing in clouds

ICGICIP	icing in clouds and precipitation
ICGIP	icing in precipitation
IF	ice fog
IMDT	immediate
INLD	inland
INREQ	information request
INSTBY	instability
INTMT	intermittent
INTR	interior
INTRMTRGN	inter-mountain region
INTS	intense
INTSFY	intensify
INVRN	inversion
IOVC	in overcast
IP	ice pellets
IPV	improve
IR	ice on runway
ISA	International Standard Atmosphere
ISOLD	isolated
ITCZ	intertropical convergence zone
J	
JTSTR	jet stream
K	
K	cold air mass
K	smoke
KDEP	smoke layer estimated (feet) deep
KFRST	killing frost
KLYR	smoke layer aloft
KOCTY	smoke over city
L	
L	drizzle
LABRDR	Labrador
lat-long	latitude/longitude
LCL	lifted condensation level
LFC	level of free convection
LFT	lift
LGRNG	long range
LGT	light

LIFR	low IFR
LK	lake
LLWS	low level wind shear
LN	line
LSR	loose snow on runway
LTG	lightning
LTGCC	lightning cloud-to-cloud
LTGCCCG	lightning cloud-to-cloud, cloud-to-ground
LTGCG	lightning cloud-to-ground
LTGCW	lightning cloud-to-water
LTGIC	lightning in clouds
LTLCG	little change
LTNG	lightning
LVL	level
LWR	lower
LX	low index
LYR	layer or layered or layers

M

M	maritime air mass
M	measured ceiling
M	missing
MA	map analysis
MAN	Manitoba
MB	millibar
MDA	minimum descent altitude
MDT	moderate
MEA	minimum en route altitude
MEGG	merging
MEX	Mexico
MHKVLY	Mohawk Valley
MIDN	midnight
MIFG	patches of shallow fog no deeper than two meters
MIS	meteorological impact statement
MLTLVL	melting level
MNLD	mainland
MOA	military operations area
MOGR	moderate or greater
MONTR	monitor
MOV	move
MRGL	marginal

MRNG	morning
MRTM	maritime
MS	minus
MSTLY	mostly
MSTR	moisture
MTN	mountain
MTR	military training route
MULT	multiple
MVFR	marginal VFR
MXD	mixed

N

NAFAX	national facsimile circuit
NASA	National Aeronautics and Space Administration
NAS	National Airspace System
NAVAID	navigational aid
NB	New Brunswick
NCWX	no change in weather
NELY	northeasterly
NERN	northeastern
NEW ENG	New England
NFLD	Newfoundland
NGT	night
NL	no layers
NMBR	number
NMRS	numerous
NNERN	north-northeastern
NNEWD	north-northeastward
NNWRN	north-northwestern
NNWWD	north-westward
NOSPL	no specials
NPRS	nonpersistent
NRW	narrow
NS	nimbostratus
NS	Nova Scotia
NS	nonsignificant radar echoes
NVA	negative vorticity advection
NWLY	northwesterly
NWRN	northwestern

O

OAOI	on and off instruments
OAT	outside air temperature
OBS	observation

Abbreviations

OBSC	obscure
OCFNT	occluded front
OCLD	occlude
OCLN	occlusion
OCNL	occasional
OFP	occluded frontal passage
OFSHR	offshore
OMTNS	over mountains
ONSHR	on shore
ONT	Ontario
ORGPHC	orographic
OTAS	on top and smooth
OTLK	outlook
OTP	on top
OTRW	otherwise
OVC	overcast
OVHD	overhead
OVRNG	overrunning

P

P	polar air mass
P time	proposed departure time
PAC	Pacific
PBL	probable
PCPN	precipitation
PDMT	predominant
PDMT	predominate
PDW	priority delayed weather
PEN	peninsula
PGTSND	Puget Sound
PIBAL	pilot balloon observation
PLW	plow (snow)
PNHDL	panhandle
PPINA	radar weather report not available
PPINE	radar weather report not echoes observed
PPINO	radar weather report equipment inoperative
PPIOK	radar weather report equipment operation resumed
PPIOM	radar weather report equipment out for maintenance
PRBLTY	probability

PRES	pressure
PRESFR	pressure falling rapidly
PRESRR	pressure rising rapidly
PRJMP	pressure jump
PROG	prognostic
PRSNT	present
PS	plus
PSG	passage
PSG	passing
PSR	packed snow on runway
PTCHY	patchy
PTLY	partly
PTN	portion
PVA	positive vorticity advection

Q

Q	squall
QSTNRY	quasistationary
QUAD	quadrant
QUE	Quebec

R

R	rain
RABAL	radiosonde balloon wind data
RADAT	radiosonde observation data
RAFRZ	radiosonde observation freezing levels
RAICG	radiosonde observation icing at
RAOB	radiosonde observation
RAREP	radar weather report
RAWIN	upper winds observation
RCC	Rescue Coordination Center
RCD	radar cloud detection report
RCKY	Rockies (mountains)
RDG	ridge
RESTR	restrict
RGD	ragged
RH	relative humidity
RHINO	radar echo height information not available
RHINO	radar range height indicator not operating on scan
RIOGD	Rio Grande
RNFL	rainfall

ROBEPS	radar operating below prescribed standard
RPD	rapid
RS	record special observation
RSG	rising
RUF	rough
RVR	runway visual range
RVRM	runway visual range (midpoint)
RVRNO	RVR not available
RVRR	runway visual range (rollout)
RVRT	runway visual range (touchdown)
RVV	runway visibility value
RVVNO	RVV not available
RW	rain shower

S

S	snow
SA	surface aviation observation
SASK	Saskatchewan
SBSD	subside
SC	stratocumulus
SCSL	standing lenticular stratocumulus
SCT	scattered
SD	radar report (RAREP)
SELS	severe local storms
SELY	southeasterly
SERN	southeastern
SG	snow grains
SGD	Solar-Geophysical Data
SGFNT	significant
SHFT	shift
SHLW	shallow
SHRTLY	shortly
SHRTWV	shortwave
SHWR	shower
SIERNEV	Sierra Nevada
SIR	snow and ice on runway
SKC	sky clear
SLD	solid
SLGT	slight
SLR	slush on runway
SLT	sleet

SMK	smoke
SMTH	smooth
SNBNK	snowbank
SNFLK	snowflake
SNOINC	snow depth increase in past hour
SNRS	sunrise
SNST	sunset
SNW	snow
SNWFL	snowfall
SP	special observation
SP	snow pellets
SP	station pressure
SPKL	sprinkle
SPLNS	South Plains
SPRD	spread
SQAL	squall
SQLN	squall line
SR	sunrise
SS	sunset
SSERN	south-southeastern
SSEWD	south-southeastward
SSNO	no STARs, no SIDs
SSWRN	south-southwestern
SSWWD	south-southwestward
ST	stratus
STAGN	stagnation
STFR	stratus fractus
STFRM	stratiform
STG	strong
STM	storm
STNRY	stationary
SVR	severe
SVRL	several
SW	snow showers
SWLG	swelling
SWLY	southwesterly
SWRN	southwestern
SX	stability index
SXN	section
SYNOP	synoptic
SYNS	synopsis
SYS	system

T

T	thunderstorm
T	trace
T	tropical air mass
TCU	towering cumulus
TDWR	Terminal Doppler Weather Radar
TEMP	temperature
THD	thunderhead
THDR	thunder
THK	thick
THN	thin
TMPRY	temporary
TOP	cloud top
TOVC	top of overcast
TPG	topping
TRIB	tributary
TROF	trough
TROP	tropopause
TRPCD	tropical continental air mass
TRPCL	tropical
TRPLYR	trapping layer
TRRN	terrain
TSHWR	thundershower
TSQLS	thundersqualls
TSTM	thunderstorm
TURBC	turbulence
TURBT	turbulent
TWD	toward
TWRG	towering

U

U	intensity unknown
UA	pilot report
UDDF	up and downdrafts
UNOFFL	unofficial
UNSBL	unseasonable
UNSTBL	unstable
UNSTDY	unsteady
UNSTL	unsettle
UPDFTS	updrafts
UPR	upper
UPSLP	upslope

UPSTRM	upstream
USP	urgent special observation
UTC	Coordinated Universal Time
UUA	urgent pilot report
UVV	upward vertical velocity
UWNDS	upper winds
V	
V	variable
VCNTY	vicinity
VLCTY	velocity
VLNT	violent
VLY	valley
VR	veer
VRBL	variable
VRISL	Vancouver Island, BC
VRT MOTN	vertical motion
VSBY	visibility
VSBYDR	visibility decreasing rapidly
VSBYIR	visibility increasing rapidly
W	
W	indefinite ceiling
W	warm air mass
WA	AIRMET
WDLY	widely
WDSPRD	widespread
WEA	weather
WFP	warm front passage
WINT	winter
WK	weak
WMO	World Meteorological Organization
WND	wind
WNWRN	west-northwestern
WNWWD	west-northwestward
WPLTO	Western Plateau
WR	wet runway
WRM	warm
WRMFNT	warm front
WRNG	warning
WS	SIGMET
WSHFT	wind shift

WSR	wet snow on runway
WST	Convective SIGMET
WSTCH	Wasatch Range
WSWRN	west-southwestern
WSWWD	west-southwestward
WTR	water
WTSPT	waterspout
WV	wave
WW	Severe Weather Watch
WX	weather

X

X	sky obscured
−X	sky partially obscured
XCP	except
XPC	expect

Z

Z	Coordinated Universal Time (UTC)
ZL	freezing drizzle
ZR	freezing rain

IDENTIFIERS

This section contains major report (SA) and forecast (FT and FD) locations for the contiguous states, Alaska, and Hawaii. Many locations provide part-time or AWOS observations, therefore, observations and forecasts are not always available. Selected military locations are included; discrepancies will occur.

Depending on the retrieval system, some locations might not be available. Part-time and AWOS reporting locations might only be available locally. Reporting locations are continually being added and deleted.

Locations are identified by city and state (WESTFIELD MA). When more than one airport is listed under the same city, the airport name precedes the city name (Jeffco, DENVER CO). Military bases are identified by name, city, and state, except where the base name is the same as the associated city (New Orleans NAS, LA).

A

AAP	Andrau Airpark, HOUSTON, TX
ABE	ALLENTOWN, PA
ABI	ABILENE, TX
ABQ	ALBUQUERQUE, NM
ABR	ABERDEEN, SD
ABY	ALBANY, GA
ACK	NANTUCKET, MA
ACT	WACO, TX

ACV	ARCATA, CA
ACY	ATLANTIC CITY, NJ
ADK	ADAK ISLAND, AK
ADQ	KODIAK, AK
ADW	Andrews AFB, CAMP SPRINGS, MD
AEL	ALBERT LEA, MN
AEX	England AFB, ALEXANDRIA, LA
AGC	Allegheny Co., PITTSBURGH, PA
AGS	AUGUSTA, GA
AHN	ATHENS, GA
AIA	ALLIANCE, NE
AID	ANTIGO, WI
AIZ	KAISER/LAKE OZARK, MO
AKN	KING SALMON, AK
AKO	AKRNO, CO
ALB	ALBANY, NY
ALI	ALICE, TX
ALM	ALAMOGORDO, NM
ALN	St. Louis Regional, ALTON/ST. LOUIS, IL
ALO	WATERLOO, IA
ALS	ALAMOSA, CO
ALW	WALLA WALLA WA
AMA	AMARILLO, TX
AMG	ALMA, GA
ANB	ANNISTON, AL
ANC	ANCHORAGE, AK
AND	ANDERSON, SC
ANE	Janes Field, MINNEAPOLIS, MN
ANI	ANIAK, AK
ANN	ANNETTE, AK
ANW	AINSWORTH, NE
AOO	ALTOONA, PA
APA	Centennial, DENVER, CO
APC	NAPA, CA
APF	NAPLES, FL
APN	ALPENA, MI
AQQ	APALACHICOLA, FL
ARA	NEW IBERIA, LA
ARB	ANN ARBOR, MI
ARR	Aurora, CHICAGO, IL
ART	WATERTOWN, NY
ASE	ASPEN, CO
ASG	SPRINGDATE, AR

ASH	NASHUA, NH
AST	ASTORIA, OR
ATL	Hartsfield, ATLANTA, GA
ATW	APPLETON, WI
ATY	WATERTOWN, SD
AUG	AUGUSTA, ME
AUS	AUSTIN, TX
AUW	WAUSAU, WI
AVL	ASHEVILLE, NC
AVP	WILKES-BARRE/SCRANTON, PA
AVX	Catalina, AVALON, CA
AWY	ERIE, PA
AXN	ALEXANDRIA, MN
AXO	GRAND ISLE, LA
AYS	WAYCROSS, GA
AZO	KALAMAZOO, MI

B

BAB	Beal AFB, MARYSVILLE, CA
BAD	Barksdale AFB, BOSSIER CITY, LA
BAF	WESTFIELD, MA
BAM	BATTLE MOUNTAIN, NV
BBW	BROKEN BOW, NE
BCE	BRYCE CANYON, UT
BDL	Bradley, WINDSOR LOCKS, CT
BDR	BRIDGEPORT, CT
BED	BEDFORD, MA
BET	BETHEL, AK
BEH	BENTON HARBOR, MI
BFD	BRADFORD, PA
BFF	SCOTTSBLUFF, NE
BFI	Boeing Field, SEATTLE, WA
BFL	BAKERSFIELD, CA
BFM	Brookley, MOBILE, AL
BGM	BINGHAMTON, NY
BGR	BANGOR, ME
BHB	BAR HARBOR, ME
BHM	BIRMINGHAM, AL
BID	BLOCK ISLAND, RI
BIE	BEATRICE, NE
BIG	DELTA JUNCTION/FT. GREELY, AK
BIH	BISHOP, CA
BIL	BILLINGS, MT

BIS	BISMARCK, ND
BIX	Keesler AFB, BILOXI, MS
BJC	Jeffco, DENVER, CO
BJI	BEMIDJI, MN
BKE	BAKER, OR
BKH	KEKAHA, KAUAI, HI
BKL	Lakefront, CLEVELAND, OH
BKF	Buckley ANGB, AURORA, CO
BKW	Raleigh, BECKLEY, WV
BKX	BROOKINGS, SD
BLF	BLUEFIELD, WV
BLH	BLYTHE, CA
BLI	BELLINGHAM, WA
BLU	BLUE CANYON, CA
BLV	Scott AFB, BELLEVILLE, IL
BMG	BLOOMINGTON, IN
BMI	BLOOMINGTON/NORMAL, IL
BML	BERLIN, NH
BNA	NASHVILLE, TN
BNO	BURNS, OR
BNY	BURNEY, CA
BOI	BOISE, ID
BOS	BOSTON, MA
BOW	BARTOW, FL
BPI	BIG PINEY, WY
BPT	BEAUMONT/PORT ARTHUR, TX
BQK	BRUNSWICK, GA
BRD	BRAINERD, MN
BRL	BURLINGTON, IA
BRO	BROWNSVILLE, TX
BRW	BARROW, AK
BSM	Bergstrom AFB, AUSTIN, TX
BTI	BARTER ISLAND, AK
BTL	BATTLE CREEK, MI
BTM	BUTTE, MT
BTR	BATON ROUGE, LA
BTT	BETTLES, AK
BTV	BURLINGTON, VT
BUF	BUFFALO, NY
BUO	BEAUMONT, CA
BUR	BURBANK, CA
BVE	BOOTHSVILLE, LA
BVI	BEAVER FALLS, PA
BVO	BARTLESVILLE, OK

BVY	BEVERLY, MA
BWD	BROWNWOOD, TX
BWG	BOWLING GREEN, KY
BWI	BALTIMORE, MD
BYH	Eaker AFB, BLYTHEVILLE, AR
BYI	BURLELY, ID
BZN	BOZEMAN, MT

C

CAE	COLUMBIA, SC
CAG	CRAIG, CO
CAK	NORTH CANTON, OH
CAR	CARIBOU, ME
CBM	Columbus AFB, COLUMBUS, MS
CCR	CONCORD, CA
CCY	CHARLES CITY, IA
CDB	COLD BAY, AK
CDC	CEDAR CITY, UT
CDH	CAMDEN, AR
CDR	CHADRON, NE
CDS	CHILDRESS, TX
CDV	CORDOVA, AK
CDW	Essex, CALDWELL, NJ
CEC	CRESCENT CITY, CA
CEW	CRESTVIEW, FL
CEZ	CORTEZ, CO
CGF	Cuyahoga, CLEVELAND, OH
CGI	CAPE GIRARDEAU, MO
CGX	Meigs, CHICAGO, IL
CHA	CHATTANOOGA, TN
CHD	Williams AFB, CHANDLER, AZ
CHO	CHARLOTTESVILLE, VA
CHS	CHARLESTON, SC
CIC	CHICO, CA
CID	CEADAR RAPIDS, IA
CIU	Chippewa, SAULT STE MARIE, MI
CKB	CLARKSBURG, WV
CKL	CENTREVILLE, AL
CKV	CLARKSVILLE, TN
CLE	Hopkins, CLEVELAND, OH
CLL	COLLEGE STATION, TX
CLM	PORT ANGELES, WA
CLT	CHARLOTTE, NC
CMA	CAMARILLO, CA

CMH	COLUMBUS, OH
CMI	CHAMPAIGN/URBANA, IL
CMX	HANCOCK, MI
CNK	CONCORDIA, KS
CNM	CARLSBAD, NM
CNO	CHINO, CA
CNU	CHANUTE, KS
CNY	Canyonlands, MOAB, UT
COD	CODY WY
COE	COEUR D ALENE, ID
COF	Patrick AFB, COCOA BEACH, FL
CON	CONCORD, NH
COS	COLORADO SPRINGS, CO
COT	COTULLA, TX
COU	COLUMBIA, MO
CPR	CASPER, WY
CPS	CAHOKIA/ST LOUIS, IL
CRE	NORTH MYRTLE BEACH, SC
CRG	Craig, JACKSONVILLE, FL
CRP	CORPUS CHRISTI, TX
CRQ	Palomar, CARLSBAD, CA
CRW	CHARLESTON, WV
CSG	COLUMBUS, GA
CSM	CLINTON, OK
CSV	CROSSVILLE, TN
CTB	CUT BANK, MT
CVG	COVINGTON/CINCINNATI, OH
CVN	CLOVIS, NM
CVO	CORVALLIS, OR
CVS	Cannon AFB, CLOVIS, NM
CWA	MOSINEE, WI
CWF	LAKE CHARLES, LA
CWI	CLINTON, IA
CXY	Capital, HARRISBURG, PA
CYS	CHEYENNE, WY
CZD	COZAD, NE
CZK	CASCADE LOCKS, OR

D

DAB	DAYTONA BEACH, FL
DAG	DAGGETT, CA
DAL	Love Field, DALLAS, TX
DAN	DANVILLE, VA
DAY	DAYTON, OH

DBQ	DUBUQUE, IA
DCA	National, WASHINGTON, DC
DDC	DODGE CITY, KS
DEC	DECATUR, IL
DEN	Stapleton, DENVER, CO
DET	Detroit City, DETROIT, MI
DFW	DALLAS-FORT WORTH, TX
DHN	DOTHAN, AL
DHT	DALHART, TX
DLF	Laughlin AFB, DEL RIO, TX
DLG	DILLINGHAM, AK
DIK	DICKINSON, ND
DLH	DULUTH, MN
DLN	DILLON, MT
DLS	THE DALLES, OR
DMA	Davis-Monthan AFB, TUSCON, AZ
DMN	DEMING, NM
DNV	DANVILLE, IL
DOV	Dover AFB, DOVER, DE
DPA	Dupage, CHICAGO, IL
DRA	Desert Rock, MERCURY, NV
DRO	DURANGO, CO
DRT	DEL RIO, TX
DSM	DES MOINES, IA
DTL	DETROIT LAKES, MN
DTN	Downtown, SHREVEPORT, LA
DTW	Wayne, DETROIT, MI
DUG	DOUGLAS BISBEE, AZ
DUJ	DU BOIS, PA
DUT	UNALASKA, AK
DVL	DEVILS LAKE, ND
DVT	Deer Valley, PHOENIX, AZ
DWH	David Wayne Hooks, HOUSTON, TX
DYR	DYERBURG, TN
DYS	Dyess AFB, ABILENE, TX
DXR	DANBURY, CT

E

EAR	KEARNEY, NE
EAT	WENATCHEE, WA
EAU	EAU CLAIRE, WI
EBS	WEBSTER CITY, IA
ECG	ELIZABETH CITY, NC
EDW	Edwards AFB, EDWARDS, CA

EED	NEEDLES, CA
EEN	KEENE, NH
EFD	Ellington AFB, HUSTON, TX
EGE	EAGLE, CO
EKM	ELKHART, IN
EKN	ELKINS, WV
EKO	ELKO, NV
ELD	EL DORADO, AR
ELM	ELMIRA, NY
ELN	ELLENSBURG, WA
ELO	ELY, MN
ELP	EL PASO, TX
ELY	ELY, NV
EMP	EMPORIA, KS
EMT	EL MONTE, CA
ENA	KENAI, AK
END	Vance AFB, ENID, OK
ENM	EMMONAK, AK
ENN	NEHANA, AK
EPH	EPHRATA, WA
ERI	ERIE, PA
ERV	KERRVILLE, TX
ESC	ESCANABA, MI
ESF	ALEXANDRIA, LA
EST	ESTHERVILLE, IA
ETM	EAST SIMPSON, AK
EUG	EUGENE, OR
EVV	EVANSVILLE, IN
EVW	EVANSTON, WY
EWB	NEW BEDFORD, MA
EWN	NEW BERN, NC
EWR	NEWARK, NJ
EYW	KEY WEST, FL
F	
FAI	FAIRBANKS, AK
FAR	FARGO, ND
FAT	FRESNO, CA
FAY	FAYETTEVILLE, NC
FBG	Simmons AAF, FORT BRAGG, NC
FBL	FARIBAULT, MN
FCA	KALISPELL, MT
FCL	FORT COLLINS, CO
FCM	Flying Cloud, MINNEAPOLIS, MN

FDY	FINDLAY, OH
FFO	Wright-Patterson AFB, DAYTON, OH
FFM	FERGUS FALLS, MN
FFZ	Falcon Field, MESA, AZ
FHU	FT. HUACHUCA, AZ
FKL	FRANKLIN, PA
FLG	FLAGSTAFF, AZ
FLL	Hollywood, FORT LAUDERDALE, FL
FLO	FLORENCE, SC
FLV	FT. LEAVENWORTH, KS
FMN	FARMINGTON, NM
FMY	FORT MYERS, FL
FNB	FALLS CITY, NE
FNL	FORT COLLINS/LOVELAND, CO
FNR	FUNTER BAY, AK
FNT	FLINT, MI
FOD	FORT DODGE, IA
FOE	Forbes, TOPEKA, KS
FOK	Suffolk, WESTHAMPTON BEACH, NY
FRG	Republic, FARMINGDALE, NY
FRM	FAIRMONT, MN
FSD	SIOUX FALLS, SD
FSM	FORT SMITH, AR
FTK	FT. KNOX, KY
FTW	FORT WORTH, TX
FTY	Fulton Co, ATLANTA, GA
FUL	FULLERTON, CA
FVE	FRENCHVILLE, ME
FVM	FIVE MILE, AK
FWA	FORT WAYNE, IN
FWH	Carswell AFB, FORT WORTH, TX
FXE	Executive, FORT LAUDERDALE, FL
FYU	FORT YUKON, AK
FYV	FAYETTEVALE, AR

G

GAG	GAGE, OK
GAL	GALENA, AK
GAM	GAMBELL, AK
GBG	GALESBURG, IL
GBH	GALBRAITH LAKE, AK
GCC	GILLETTE, WY
GCK	GARDEN CITY, KS

GCN	GRAND CANYON, AZ
GDV	GLENDIVE, MT
GEG	International, SPOKANE, WA
GFA	Malmstrom AFB, GREAT FALLS, MT
GFK	GRAND FORKS, ND
GFL	GLENS FALLS, NY
GGG	LONGVIEW, TX
GGW	GLASGOW, MT
GJT	GRAND JUNCTION, CO
GKN	GULKANA, AK
GLD	GOODLAND, KS
GLH	GREENVILLE, MS
GLS	GALVESTON, TX
GMU	GREENVILLE, SC
GNT	GRANTS, NM
GNV	GAINSVILLE, FL
GON	GROTON/NEW LONDON, CT
GPT	Boloxi, GULFPORT, MS
GPZ	Itasca Co., GRAND RAPIDS, MN
GRB	GREEN BAY, WI
GRF	Gray AAF, TACOMA, WA
GRI	GRAND ISLAND, NE
GRR	Kent Co., GRAND RAPIDS, MI
GSB	Seymour Johnson AFB, GOLDSBORO, NC
GSO	GREENSBORO, NC
GSP	GREER, SC
GST	GUSTAVUS, AK
GTF	GREAT FALLS, MT
GTR	COLUMBUS/W POINT/STARKVILL, MS
GUC	GUNNISON, CO
GUP	GALLUP, NM
GUS	Grissom AFB, PERU, IN
GVT	GREENSVILLE, TX
GVW	Richards-Gebaur AFB, KANSAS CITY, MO
GWO	GREENWOOD, MS
GXY	GREELEY, CO
GYR	Goodyear, PHOENIX, AZ
GYY	GARY, IN

H

HAT	HATTERAS, NC
HBR	HOBART, OK

HDN	HAYDEN, CO
HDO	HONDO, TX
HEZ	NATCHEZ, MS
HFD	HARTFORD, CT
HGR	HAGERSTOWN, MD
HHF	CANADIAN, TX
HHR	HAWTHORNE, CA
HIB	HIBBING, MN
HIF	Hill AFB, OGDEN, UT
HIO	Hillsboro, PORTLAND, OR
HKY	HICKORY, NC
HLC	HILL CITY, KS
HLG	Ohio Co., WHEELING, WV
HLN	HELENA, MT
HMN	Halloman AFB, ALAMOGORDO, NM
HMS	HANFORD, WA
HNL	HONOLULU, HI
HNM	HANA, HI
HOB	HOBBS, NM
HOM	HOMER, AK
HON	HURON, SD
HOT	HOT SPRINGS, AR
HOU	Hobby, HOUSTON, TX
HPN	Weschester, WHITE PLAINS, NY
HQM	HOQUIAM, WA
HRL	HARLINGEN, TX
HRO	HARRISON, AR
HSI	HASTINGS, NE
HSP	HOT SPRINGS, VA
HSS	HOT SPRINGS, NC
HST	Homestead AFB, HOMESTEAD, FL
HSV	HUNTSVILLE, AL
HTH	HAWTHORNE, NV
HTL	HOUGHTON LAKE, MI
HTS	HUNTINGTON, WV
HUF	TERRE HAUTE, IN
HUL	HOULTON, ME
HUM	HOUMA, LA
HUT	HUTCHINSON, KS
HVN	Tweed, NEW HAVEN, CT
HVR	HAVRE, MT
HWD	HAYWARD, CA
HYA	HYANNIS, MA
HYS	HAYS, KS

I

IAB	McConnel AFB, WICHITA, KS
IAD	Dulles, WASHINGTON, DC
IAG	NIAGRA FALLS, NY
IAH	Intercontinental, HOUSTON, TX
ICT	WICHITA, KS
IDA	IDAHO FALLS, ID
IGM	KINGMAN, AZ
IKK	KANKAKEE, IL
ILE	KILLEEN, TX
ILG	WILMINGTON, DE
ILI	ILIAMNA, AK
ILM	WILMINGTON, NC
IML	IMPERIAL, NE
IMT	IRON MOUNTAIN/KINGSFORD, MI
IND	INDIANAPOLIS, IN
INK	WINK, TX
INL	INTERNATIONAL FALLS, MN
INT	WINSTON SALEM, NC
INW	WINSLOW, AZ
IPL	IMPERIAL, CA
IPT	WILLIAMSPORT, PA
IRK	KIRKSVILLE, MO
ISN	WILLISTON, ND
ISO	KINSTON, NC
ISP	MacArthur, ISLIP, NY
ISW	WISCONSIN RAPIDS, WI
ITH	ITHACA, NY
ITO	HILO, HI
IWD	IRONWOOD, MI
IWS	Lakeside, HOUSTON, TX
IYK	INYOKERN, CA
IXD	Johnson Co., OLATHE, KS

J

JAC	Jackson Hole, JACKSON, WY
JAN	JACKSON, MS
JAX	JACKSONVILLE, FL
JBR	JONESBORO, AR
JEF	JEFFERSON CITY, MO
JFK	JFK, NEW YORK, NY
JHM	LAHAINA, HI
JHW	JAMESTOWN, NY
JKL	JAKSON, KY

JLN	JOPLIN, MO
JMS	JAMESTOWN, ND
JNU	JUNEAU, AK
JST	JOHNSTOWN, PA
JVL	JANESVILLE, WI
JXN	JACKSON, MI

K

KLS	KELSO, WA
KOA	KAILUA/KONA, HI
KSM	ST MARY'S, AK
KTN	KETCHIKAN, AK

L

LAF	Purdue, LAFAYETTE, IN
LAL	LAKELAND, FL
LAM	LOS ALAMOS, NM
LAN	LANSING, MI
LAR	LARAMIE, WY
LAS	LAS VEGAS, NV
LAW	LAWTON, OK
LAX	International, LOS ANGELES, CA
LBB	LUBBOCK, TX
LBE	LATROBE, PA
LBF	NORTH PLATTE, NE
LBL	LIBERAL, KS
LBX	ANGLETON/LAKE JACKSON, TX
LCH	LAKE CHARLES, LA
LCI	LACONIA, NH
LEB	LEBANON, NH
LEX	LEXINGTON, KY
LFI	Langley AFB, HAMPTON, VA
LFK	LUFKIN, TX
LFT	LAFAYETTE, LA
LGA	La Guardia, NEW YORK, NY
LGB	LONG BEACH, CA
LGD	LA GRANDE, OR
LGU	LOGAN, UT
LHX	LA JUNTA, CO
LIC	LIMON, CO
LIH	LIHUE, HI
LIT	LITTLE ROCK, AR
LIZ	Loring AFB, LIMESTONR, ME
LMS	LOUISVILLE, MS
LMT	KLAMATH FALLS, OR

LND	LANDER, WY
LNK	LINCOLN, NE
LNN	WILLOUGHBY, OH
LNR	LONE ROCK, WI
LNS	LANCASTER, PA
LNY	LANAI CITY, HI
LOL	LOVELOCK, NV
LOU	Bowman Field, LOUISVILLE, KY
LOZ	LONDON, KY
LRD	LAREDO, TX
LRF	Little Rock AFB, JACKSONVILLE, AR
LRU	LAS CRUCES, NM
LSF	FORT BENNING, GA
LSE	LA CROSSE, WI
LSV	Nellis AFB, LAS VEGAS, NV
LUF	Luke AFB, GLENDALE, AZ
LUK	Lunken, CINCINNATI, OH
LVK	LIVERMORE, CA
LVM	LIVINGSTON, MT
LVS	LAS VEGAS, NV
LWB	LEWISBURG, WV
LWM	LAWRENCE, MA
LWS	LEWISTON, ID
LWT	LEWISTON, MT
LXV	LEADVILLE, CO
LYH	LYNCHBURG, VA

M

MAF	MIDLAND, TX
MAZ	MAYAGUEZ, PR
MBL	MANISTEE, MI
MBS	SAGINAW, MI
MCB	MC COMB, MS
MCE	MERCED, CA
MCC	McClellan AFB, SACRAMENTO, CA
MCF	MacDill AFB, TAMPA, FL
MCG	MC GRATH, AK
MCI	International, KANSAS CITY, MO
MCK	MC COOK, NE
MCN	MACON, GA
MCO	International, ORLANDO, FL
MCW	MASON CITY, IA
MDH	CARBONDALE/MURPHYSBORO, IL

MDO	MIDDLETON ISLAND, AK
MDT	Harrisburg, MIDDLETOWN, PA
MDW	Midway, CHICAGO, IL
MEI	MERIDIAN, MS
MEM	International, MEMPHIS, TN
MER	Castle AFB, MERCED, CA
MEV	MINDEN, NV
MFD	MANSFIELD, OH
MFE	MC ALLEN, TX
MFI	MARSHFIELD, WI
MFR	MEDFORD, OR
MGM	MONTGOMERY, AL
MGR	MOULTRIE, GA
MGW	MORGANTOWN, WV
MHE	MITCHELL, SD
MHK	MANHATTAN, KS
MHM	MINCHUMINA, AK
MHN	MULLEN, NE
MHR	Mather AFB, SACRAMENTO, CA
MHT	MANCHESTER, NH
MHV	MOJAVE, CA
MIA	International, MIAMI, FL
MIB	Minot AFB, MINOT, ND
MIC	Crystal, MINNEAPOLIS, MN
MIE	MUNCIE, IN
MIV	MILLVILLE, NJ
MKC	Downtown, KANSAS CITY, MO
MKE	Mitchell, MILWAUKEE, WI
MKG	MUSKEGON, MI
MKK	Molokai, KAUNAKAKAI, HI
MKL	JACKSON, TN
MKT	MANKATO, MN
MLB	MELBORNE, FL
MLC	MC ALESTER, OK
MLD	MALAD CITY, ID
MLF	MILFORD, UT
MLI	MOLINE, IL
MLS	MILES CITY, MT
MLT	MILLINOCKET, ME
MLU	MONROE, LA
MMH	MAMMOTH LAKES, CA
MML	MARSHALL, MN
MMO	MARSEILLES, IL
MMU	MORRISTOWN, NJ

MMV	MC MINNVILLE, OR
MNM	MENOMINEE, MI
MOB	MOBILE, AL
MOD	MODESTO, CA
MOT	MINOT, ND
MPV	BARRE/MONTPELIER, VT
MQI	MANTEO, NC
MQM	MONDIA, MT
MQT	MARQUETTE, MI
MRB	MARTINSBURG, WV
MRF	MARFA, TX
MRI	Merrill Field, ANCHORAGE, AK
MRY	MONTEREY, CA
MSL	MUSCLE SHOALS, AL
MSN	MADISON, WI
MSO	MISSOULA, MT
MSP	International, MINNEAPOLIS, MN
MSS	MASSENA, NY
MSY	Moisant, NEW ORLEANS, LA
MSV	MONTICELLO, NY
MTJ	MONTROSE, CO
MTN	Martin State, BALTIMORE, MD
MTW	MANITOWOC, WI
MUE	Waimeakohala, KAMUELA, HI
MVN	MOUNT VERNON, IL
MUO	Mountain Home AFB, ID
MUE	KAMUELA, HI
MVY	MARTHAS VINEYARD, MA
MWA	MARION, IL
MWC	Timmerman, MILWAUKEE, WI
MWH	MOSES LAKE, WA
MWL	MINERAL WELLS, TX
MWN	MOUNT WASHINGTON, NH
MWS	MOUNT WILSON, CA
MXF	Maxwell AFB, MONTGOMERY, AL
MYF	Montgomery, SAN DIEGO, CA
MYL	MC CALL, ID
MYR	Myrtle Beach AFB, SC
MYU	MEKORYUK, AK
MYV	MARYSVILLE, CA
MZZ	MARION, IN

N

NBC	Beaufort MCAS, SC

NBE	Hensley NAS, DALLAS, TX
NBG	New Orleans NAS, LA
NBU	Glenview NAS, IL
NCA	New River MCAS, JACKSONVILLE, NC
NEW	Lakefront, NEW ORLEANS, LA
NFL	Fallon NAS, NV
NGP	Corpus Christi NAS, TX
NGU	Norfolk NAS, VA
NGZ	Alameda NAS, CA
NHK	Patuxent River NAS, MD
NHZ	Brunswick NAS, ME
NID	China Lake NAS, CA
NIP	Jacksonville NAS, FL
NIR	Chase Field NAS, BEEVILLE, TX
NJK	El Centro NAS, CA
NKT	Cherry Point MCAS, NC
NKX	Miramar NAS, SAN DIEGO, CA
NLC	Lemoore NAS, CA
NPA	Pensacola NAS, FL
NQA	Memphis NAS, MILLINGTON, TX
NQI	Kingsville NAS, TX
NRB	Mayport NAS, FL
NSI	SAN NICOLAS ISLAND, CA
NTD	Point Nugu NAS, CA
NTU	Oceana NAS, VIRGINIA BEACH, VA
NUC	SAN CLEMENTE ISLAND, CA
NUQ	Moffett NAS, CA
NUW	Whidbey Is NAS, OAK HARBOR, WA
NXX	Willow Grove NAS, PA
NYG	Quantico MCAF, VA
NZC	Cecil NAS, FL
NZJ	El Toro MCAS, SANTA ANA, CA
NZW	South Weymouth NAS, MA
NZY	North Island NAS, SAN DIEGO, CA

O

OAJ	JACKSONVILLE, NC
OAK	OAKLAND, CA
OAR	Ft. Ord, MONTEREY, CA
OCF	OCALA, FL
OCV	BERING SEA, AK
ODX	ORD NE

OFF	Offutt AFB, OMAHA, NE
OFK	NORFOLD, NE
OGD	OGDEN, UT
OGG	KAHULUI, HI
OGS	OGDENSBURG, NY
OJC	OLATHE, KS
OKC	Will Rogers, OKLAHOMA CITY, OK
OLE	OLEAN, NY
OLF	WOLF POINT, MT
OLM	OLYMPIA, WA
OLU	COLUMBUS, NE
OMA	OMAHA, NE
OME	NOME, AK
ONL	O NEILL NE
ONM	SOCORRO, NM
ONO	ONTARIO, OR
ONP	NEWPORT, OR
ONT	ONTARIO, CA
OPF	Opa Locka, MIAMI, FL
OQU	NORTH KINGSTOWN, RI
ORD	O Hare, CHICAGO, IL
ORF	NORFOLK, VA
ORG	ORANGE, TX
ORH	WORCESTER, MA
ORL	Executive, ORLANDO, FL
ORT	NORTHWAY, AK
OSC	Wurtsmith AFB, OSCODA, MI
OSH	OSHKOSH, WI
OSU	Ohio State, COLUMBUS, OH
OTG	WORTHINGTON, MN
OTH	NORTH BEND, OR
OTM	OTTUMWA, IA
OTZ	KOTZEBUE, AK
OVN	WSO, OMAHA, NE
OWB	OWENSBORO, KY
OWD	NORWOOD, MA
OWY	OWYHEE, NV
OXR	OXNARD, CA
OZR	Cairns AAF, FT RUCKER, AL
P	
PAE	Paine Field, EVERETT, WA
PAH	PADUCAH, KY
PAO	PALO ALTO, CA

PAQ	PALMER, AK
PBF	PINE BLUFF, AR
PBG	Plattsburgh AFB, NY
PBI	WEST PALM BEACH, FL
PDK	Peachtree, ATLANTA, GA
PDT	PENDLETON, OR
PDX	PORTLAND, OR
PFN	PANAMA CITY, FL
PGA	PAGE, AZ
PHF	NEWPORT NEWS, VA
PHL	Int'l, PHILADELPHIA, PA
PHX	Sky Harbor, PHOENIX, AZ
PIA	PEORIA, IL
PIB	LAUREL/HATTIESBURG, MS
PIE	ST. PETERSBURG/CLEARWATER, FL
PIH	POCATELLO, ID
PIR	PIERRE, SD
PIT	International, PITTSBURGH, PA
PKB	PARKERSBURG, WV
PKG	PARKERSBURG, WV
PKD	PARK RAPIDS, MN
PLN	PELLSTON, MI
PNC	PONCA CITY, OK
PNE	Northeast, PHILADELPHIA, PA
PNM	PRINCETON, MN
PNS	PENSACOLA, FL
POB	Pope AFB, FAYETTEVILLE, NC
POC	Brackett, LA VERNE, CA
POE	Polk AAF, LA
POU	POUGHKEEPSIE, NY
PPC	PROSPECT CREEK, AK
PPF	PARSONS, KS
PQI	PRESQUE ISLE, ME
PRB	PASO ROBLES, CA
PRC	PRESCOTT, AZ
PSB	PHILIPSBURG, PA
PSC	PASCO, WA
PSF	PITTSFIELD, MA
PSG	PETERSBURG, AK
PSK	DUBLIN, VA
PSM	Pease AFB, PORTSMOUTH, NH
PSP	PALM SPRINGS, CA
PSX	PALACIOS, TX
PTH	PORT HEIDEN, AK

PUB	PUEBLO, CO
PUC	PRICE, UT
PUO	PRUDHOE BAY, AK
PUW	PULLMAN/MOSCOW, WA
PVC	PROVINCETOWN, MA
PVD	PROVIDENCE, RI
PVU	PROVO, UT
PVW	PLAINVIEW, TX
PWA	Wiley Post, OKLAHOMA CITY, OK
PWM	PORTLAND, ME
PWT	BREMERTON, WA
PYM	PLYMOUTH, MA

R

RAL	RIVERSIDE, CA
RAP	RAPID CITY, SD
RBD	Redbird, DALLAS, TX
RBG	ROSEBURG, OR
RBL	RED BLUFF, CA
RCA	Ellsworth AFB, RAPID CITY, SD
RDD	REDDING, CA
RDG	READING, PA
RDM	REDMOND, OR
RDR	Grand Forks AFB, ND
RDU	RALEIGH/DURHAM, NC
REE	Reese AFB, LUBBOCK, TX
RFD	ROCKFORD, IL
RHI	RHINELANDER, WI
RHV	Reid-Hillview, SAN JOSE, CA
RIC	RICHMOND, VA
RIE	RICE LAKE, WI
RIL	RIFLE, CO
RIW	RIVERTON, WY
RIV	March AFB, RIVERSIDE, CA
RKD	ROCKLAND, ME
RKP	ROCKPORT, TX
RKS	ROCK SPRINGS, WY
RME	Griffiss AFB, ROME, NY
RMG	ROME, GA
RND	Randolph AFB, UNIVERSAL CITY, TX
RNO	RENO, NV
RNT	RENTON, WA
ROA	ROANOKE, VA

ROC	ROCHESTER, NY
ROW	ROSWELL, NM
RPE	SABRINE PASS, TX
RSL	RUSSELL, KS
RST	ROCHESTER, MN
RSW	SW Regional, FORT MYERS, FL
RUI	RUIDOSO, NM
RUT	RUTLAND, VT
RWF	REDWOOD FALLS, MN
RWI	ROCKY MOUNT, NC
RWL	RAWLINS, WY

S

SAC	Executive, SACRAMENTO, CA
SAF	SANTA FE, NM
SAN	Lindbergh, SAN DIEGO, CA
SAT	SAN ANTONIA, TX
SAV	SAVANNAH, GA
SAW	K.I. Sawyer AFB, GWINN, MI
SBA	SANTA BARBARA, CA
SBD	Norton AFB, SAN BERNARDINO, CA
SBN	SOUTH BEND, IN
SBP	SAN LUIS OBISPO, CA
SBS	STEAMBOAT SPRINGS, CO
SBY	SALISBURY, MD
SCC	DEADHORSE, AK
SCH	SCHENECTADY, NY
SCK	STOCKTON, CA
SDF	Standiford, LOUISVILLE, KY
SDL	SCOTTSDALE, AZ
SDM	Brown Field, SAN DIEGO, CA
SDP	SAND POINT, AK
SDY	SIDNEY, MT
SEA	Seattle-Tacoma, SEATTLE, WA
SEE	Gillespie Field, SAN DIEGO, CA
SEP	STEPHENVILLE, TX
SFB	SANFORD, FL
SFF	Felts Field, SPOKANE, WA
SFO	SAN FRANCISCO, CA
SGF	SPRINGFIELD, MO
SGU	ST. GEORGE, UT
SGY	SKAGWAY, AK
SHD	STAUNTON/WAYNESBORO/ HARRISONBURG, VA

SHH	SHISHMAREF, AK
SHN	SHELTON, WA
SHR	SHERIDAN, WY
SHV	Regional, SHREVEPORT, LA
SIT	SITKA, AK
SIY	Siskiyou, MONTAGUE, CA
SJC	SAN JOSE, CA
SJT	SAN ANGELO, TX
SKA	Fairchild AFB, SPOKANE, WA
SKF	Kelly AFB, SAN ANTONIO, TX
SKW	SKWENTNA, AK
SLC	SALT LAKE CITY, UT
SLE	SALEM, OR
SLK	SARANAC LAKE, NY
SLN	SALINA, KS
SMF	Metropolitan, SACRAMENTO, CA
SMO	SANTA MONICA, CA
SMP	STAMPEADE PASS, WA
SMX	SANTA MARIA, CA
SNA	SANTA ANA, CA
SNP	ST. PAUL ISLAND, AK
SNS	SALINAS, CA
SNY	SIDNEY, NE
SOW	SHOW LOW, AZ
SPA	SPARTANBURG, SC
SPG	Whitted, ST. PETERSBURG, FL
SPI	SPRINGFIELD, IL
SPS	WICHITA FALLS, TX
SQL	SAN CARLOS, CA
SRQ	SARASOTA/BRADENTON, FL
SSI	BRUNSWICK, GA
SSU	WHITE SULPHUR SPRINGS, WV
STC	ST. CLOUD, MN
STJ	ST. JOSEPH, MO
STL	Lambert, ST. LOUIS, MO
STP	ST. PAUL, MN
STS	SANTA ROSA, CA
SUE	STURGEON BAY, WI
SUN	Sun Valley Friedman, HAILEY, ID
SUS	Spirit of St. Louis, ST. LOUIS, MO
SUU	Travis AFB, FAIRFIELD, CA
SUX	SIOUX CITY, IA

323

SVA	SAVOONGA, AK
SVC	SILVER CITY, NM
SVE	SUSANVILLE, CA
SWO	STILLWATER, OK
SWF	NEWBURGH, NY
SXA	SOLDOTNA, AK
SYR	SYRACUSE, NY
SZL	Whiteman AFB, KNOB NOSTER, MO
S06	MULLAN, ID

T

TAD	TRINIDAD, CO
TAL	TANANA, AK
TCC	TUCUMCARI, NM
TCL	TUSCALOOSA, AL
TCM	McChord AFB, TACOMA, WA
TCS	TRUTH OR CONSEQUENCES, NM
TDO	TOLEDO, WA
TEB	TETERBORO, NJ
TEX	TELLURIDE, CO
TIK	Tinker AFB, OKLAHOMA CITY, OK
TIW	Tacoma Narrows, TACOMA, WA
TIX	TITUSVILLE, FL
TKA	TALKEETNA, AK
TLH	TALLAHASSEE, FL
TMB	Tamiami, MIAMI, FL
TOA	TORRANCE, CA
TOL	TOLEDO, OH
TOP	TOPEKA, KS
TPA	TAMPA, FL
TPH	TONOPAH, NV
TPL	TEMPLE, TX
TRI	BRISTOL/JOHNSON/KINGSPORT, TN
TRK	TRUCKEE, CA
TRM	THERMAL, CA
TSP	TEHACHAPI, CA
TTD	Troutdale, PORTLAND, OR
TTN	TRENTON, NJ
TUL	TULSA, OK
TUP	TUPELO, MS
TUS	TUCSON, AZ
TVC	TRAVERSE CITY, MI
TVF	THIEF RIVER FALLS, MN
TVL	SOUTH LAKE TAHOE, CA

TWF	TWIN FALLS, ID
TXK	TEXARKANA, AR
TYR	TYLER, TX
TYS	KNOXVILLE, TN

U

UCA	UTICA, NY
UIL	QUILLAYETE, WA
UIN	QUINCY, IL
UKI	UKIAH, CA
UMT	UMIAT, AK
UNK	UNALAKLEET, AK
UNV	STATE COLLEGE, PA
UOX	OXFORD, MS

V

VAD	Moody AFB, VALDOSTA, GA
VBG	Vandenberg AFB, LOMPOC, CA
VCT	VICTORIA, TX
VCV	George AFB, VICTORVILLE, CA
VDZ	VALDEX, AK
VEL	VERNAL, UT
VIH	ROLLA/VICHY, MO
VLD	VALDOSTA, GA
VNY	VAN NUYS, CA
VPS	Eglin AFB, VALPARAISO, FL
VRB	VERO BEACH, FL
VRX	GULF OF MEXICO, LA
VSF	SPRINGFIELD, VT
VTN	VALENTINE, NE
VUW	EUGENE ISLE, LA
VWS	WSO, VALDEZ, AK

W

WAL	WALLOPS ISLAND, VA
WCR	CHANDALAR LAKE, AK
WDG	ENID, OK
WJF	LANCASTER, CA
WMC	WINNEMUCCA, NV
WRB	Robins AFB, WARNER ROBINS, GA
WRG	WRANGELL, AK
WRI	McGuire AFB, WRIGHTSTOWN, NJ
WRL	WORLAND, WY
WYS	WEST YELLOWSTONE, MT

Y

YAK	YAKUTAT, AK
YIP	Willow Run, DETROIT, MI
YKM	YAKIMA, WA
YKN	YANKTON, SD
YNG	YOUNGSTOWN, OH
YUM	YUMA, AZ

Z

ZZV	ZANESVILLE, OH

AIRCRAFT DESIGNATORS

This listing contains FAA civil, general aviation, aircraft type designators. Type designators consist of two to four character alphanumeric groups, required for proper flight plan processing. Listings are alphabetical by aircraft manufacturer. Because some models have been built by more than one company, types are cross-referenced when necessary.

Most types are simple and self-explanatory. A Cessna 150's type designator is C150. Others might not be as obvious. Certain manufacturers produce a basic aircraft with several different engine options. A Piper Cherokee or Warrior might be equipped with one of several different engines. The manufacturer might designate the aircraft as PA-28-151 and PA-28-181. The FAA designator, however, for both Cherokee and Warrior, with either engine, is PA28. A similar situation exists for the Mooney Mark 20 series. Mooney Mark 20 201, 231, and 252 airplanes are designated M020.

Manufacturer's designators often contain references to turbocharging, retractable landing gear, and T-tails; FAA designators most often do not contain these references. A Piper Cherokee Six, Lance, and Saratoga, regardless of landing gear, turbocharging, or T-tail configuration would be designated PA32. Likewise, Beech might designate the airplane as a Bonanza V35 or Bonanza A36TC; FAA designators are BE35 and BE36 respectively.

FAA aircraft type designators are continuously revised. FAA Handbook 7340.1 *Contractions* contains the latest information.

Consult a Flight Service Station for aircraft type designators not contained within this listing, or to resolve questions about correct codes.

	Aero Commander, *see* **Rockwell**
	Aeronca
AR58	Aeronca Champion
AR11	Chief/Super Chief
AR15	Sedan
	Aerospatiale
HR30	Alouette II
HR60	Alouette III
HR36	Dauphin

HR35	Ecureuil/Astar
HR34	Gazelle
S880	Rallye
S892	Rallye Commodore
S894	Rallye Minerva
TB10	Tabago
TB9	Tampico
TB20	Trinidad
TB21	Trinidad TC
HR55	Twin Star
	Alon
F02	Aircoupe
	Aircoupe, *see* **Alon**
	Beech
BE99	Airliner
BE55	Baron 55
BE58	Baron 58
BE02	Beech 1900
BE40	Beech 400
BE9F	Beech F90
BE35	Bonanza 35 (V-Tail)
BE36	Bonanza 36
BE33	Debonair/Bonanza 33
BE76	Duchess 76
BE60	Duke 60
BE10	King Air 100
BE90	King Air 90
BE45	Mentor (T34)
BE65	Queen Air 65/70
BE80	Queen Air 80
BE88	Queen Air 88
BE24	Sierra 24
BE77	Skipper 77
BE19	Sport/Musketeer 19
BE17	Staggerwing 17
BE23	Sundowner/Musketeer 23
BE8S	Super 18
BE20	Super King Air 200
BE30	Super King Air 300
BE3L	Super King Air 300LW
BE95	Travelair 95
BE18	Twin Beech 18
BE50	Twin Bonanza

Bell

BH14	Biglifter
BH04	Iroquois 204
BH05	Iroquois 205
BH12	Iroquois/Twin
BH22	Model 222
BH06	Jet/Long/Sea Ranger
BH47	Sioux/Trooper 47
BHST	Super Transport 214ST

Bellanca

CH8	Challenger
CH5	Champion
CH10	Citabria
CH9	Citabria 7ECA
BL14	Cruisemaster
BL30	Decathlon
CH40	Lancer 402
BL28	Scout
CH7	Traveler 7EC
BL31	Turbo-Viking
BL26	Viking

Boeing

B75	Stearman
B105	Model 105
HV07	Seaknight

Brantly

HB43	Model 305
HB42	Model B-2A/B-2B

Britten-Norman

BN2	Islander
BN3	Trislander

Canadair

CL60	Challenger (AV)
CL61	Challenger (GE)

Cessna

C188	Agwagon 188
C305	Bird Dog
C208	Caravan I
C177	Cardinal
C120	Cessna 120
C140	Cessna 140
C150	Cessna 150
C152	Cessna 152
C170	Cessna 170

C172	Cessna 172/Skyhawk/Cutlass
C175	Cessna 175/Skylark
C180	Cessna 180/Skywagon
C182	Cessan 182/Skylane
C185	Cessna 185/Skywagon
C190	Cessna 190
C195	Cessna 195
C205	Cessna 205
C206	Cessna 206/Super Skywagon
C207	Cessna 207/Stationair
C210	Cessna 210/Centurion
C303	Cessna 303/Crusader
C310	Cessna 310
C320	Cessna 320/Skynight
C335	Cessna 335
C336	Cessna 336/Skymaster
C337	Cessna 337/Super Skymaster
C340	Cessna 340
C401	Cessna 401
C402	Cessna 402
C404	Cessan 404/Titan
C411	Cessna 411
C414	Cessna 414/Chancellor
C421	Cessna 421/Golden Eagle
C425	Cessna 425/Conquest
C441	Cessna 441/Conquest
C500	Cessna 500/Citation I
C501	Cessna 501/Citation I/SP
C550	Cessna 550/Citation II/ S/2
C551	Cessna 551/Citation II/SP
C560	Cessna 560/Citation V
C650	Cessna 650/Citation III
CT50	Crane/Bobcat
	Champion, *see* **Aeronca/Bellanca**
	Commander, *see* **Rockwell**
	Dessault
DA50	Falcon
DA10	Falcon 10
FFJ	Falcon 20/Fan Jet
	DeHavilland
DH91	Albatross
DH2	Beaver
DH5	Buffalo
DH4	Caribou

DH1	Chipmunk
DH7	DASH 7
DH8	DASH 8
DH10	Dove
SH11	Heron
DH3	Otter
DH2T	Turbo Beaver
DH6	Twin Otter
	Learjet
LR23	Learjet 23
LR24	Learjet 24
LR25	Learjet 25
LR28	Learjet 28
LR29	Learjet 29
LR35	Learjet 35
LR36	Learjet 36
LR54	Learjet 54
LR55	Learjet 55
	Grumman American
G164	Ag-Cat
G28	Cheetah
GA7	Cougar AA7
AA5	Traveler
AA1	Yankee/Trainer
	Gulfstream Aerospace
GA84	Commander 840/900/980/1000
G159	Gulfstream I
G2	Gulfstream II
G3	Gulfstream III
G4	Gulfstream IV
	Handley Page
HP13	Jetstream
	Hawker-Siddeley
HS25	Model HS/DH/BH125
	Heilo
HE1	Courier
HE4	Model 500
HE5	Stallion
HE3	Super Courier
	Hughes
HU30	Model 269/300
HU50	Pawnee 369/500
	Israel Aircraft
WW25	Astra 1125

WW23	Westwind 1123
WW24	Westwind 1124
	Lake
LA4	Skimmer/Buccaneer
	Lear Jet, *see* **Learjet**
	Lockheed
L329	Jetstar
L18	Lodestar
	Luscombe, *see* **Silvaire**
	Martin
M202	Model 202
M404	Model 404
	Maule
ML4	Rocket
	McDonnell-Douglas
DC3	Skytrain
	Mitsubishi
MU3	Diamond
MU2	Marquise/Solitaire
	Mooney
MO10	Cadet
MO20	Mark 20
MO21	Mark 21
MO22	Mark 22
	Navion
NA1	Rangemaster
NA16	Twin Navion
	(*see also* Rockwell International; Navion)
	Piaggio
P136	Royal Gull
P166	Super Gull
P808	Vespa Jet
	Piper
PA60	Aerostar
PA23	Apache
PA29	Archer
PAZT	Aztec
PA28	Cherokee
PARO	Cherokee Arrow
PA32	Cherokee Six/Lance/Saratoga
PA41	Cheyenne 400
PAYE	Cheyenne I/II
PA42	Cheyenne III/IV

PA16	Clipper
PA24	Comanche
PA5	Cruiser
PA11	Cub Special
PA2	Cub Trainer
PA14	Family Cruiser
PA46	Malibu
PA31	Navajo
PA20	Pacer
PA44	Seminole
PASE	Seneca
PA12	Super Cruiser
PA18	Super Cub
PA38	Tomahawk
PA22	Tri-Pacer/Colt
PA30	Twin Comanche
PA15	Vagabond Trainer
PA17	Vagabond
PA28	Warrior
	Riley
RY65	Rocket/Model 65
RY21	Eagle 21
RY40	Turbo-Executive
	Robinson
RH22	Robinson R22
	Rockwell International
AC85	Aero Commander
AC72	Air Cruiser
AC12	Commander 112
AC2A	Commander 112A
AC2T	Commander 112TC
AC14	Commander 114
AC20	Commander 200
AC50	Commander 500
AC52	Commander 520
AC56	Commander 560
AC10	Darter 100/150
AC60	Grand Commander 680
AC21	Jet Commander
AC69	Jet Prop
LARK	Lark
N145	Navion
N265	Subreliner
AC68	Super Commander

AC6T	Turbo Commander
Short	
SHD6	Model 360
SHD3	Short
SH7	Skyvan
Sikorsky	
SK51	Model S51
SK52	Model S52
SK59	Model S59
SK62	Model S62
SK76	Model S76
SK64	Skycrane
Silvaire	
SL8	Observer/Luscombe
Stearman, *see* **Boeing**	
Stinson	
ST77	Reliant
ST75	Voyager
Swearingen	
SW2	Merlin IIA/B
SW3	Merlin IIIA/B/C
SW4	Merlin IV/Metro III
Swift, *see* **Vought**	
Taylorcraft	
TC19	Sportsman
TC20	Topper
TC15	Tourist
Ted Smith	
TS60	Aerostar
Varga	
VG21	Kachina 2150A
Vertol, *see* **Boeing**	
Vought	
GC1	Swift
Westwind, *see* **Israel Aircraft**	

Appendix B
Forecast and Report
Locations

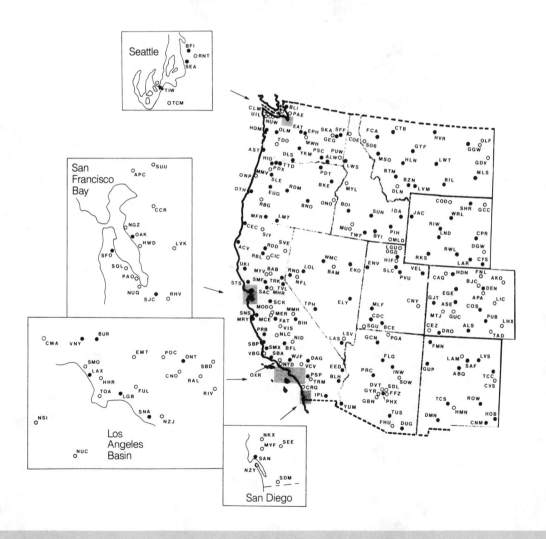

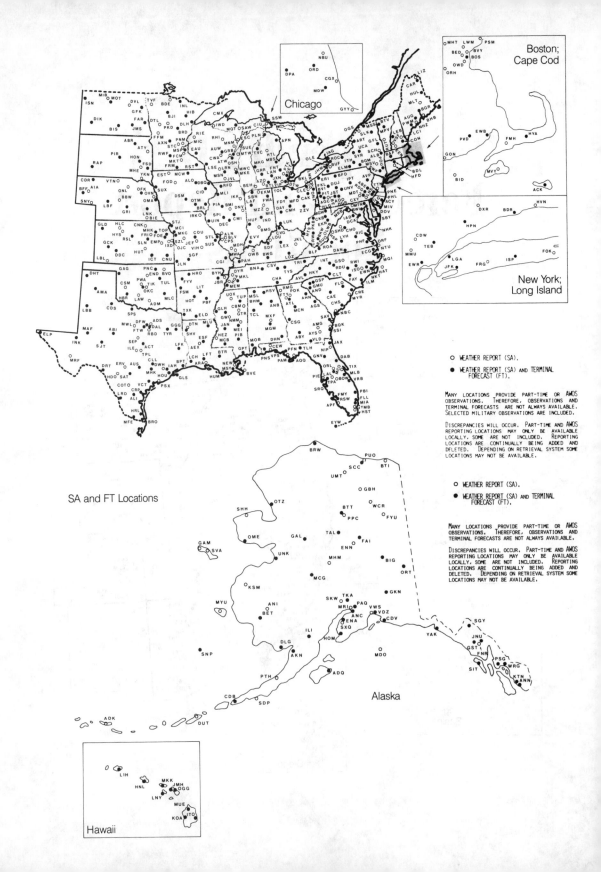

SA and FT Locations

Chicago

Boston; Cape Cod

New York; Long Island

○ WEATHER REPORT (SA).

● WEATHER REPORT (SA) AND TERMINAL
FORECAST (FT).

MANY LOCATIONS PROVIDE PART-TIME OR AWOS
OBSERVATIONS. THEREFORE, OBSERVATIONS AND
TERMINAL FORECASTS ARE NOT ALWAYS AVAILABLE.
SELECTED MILITARY OBSERVATIONS ARE INCLUDED.

DISCREPANCIES WILL OCCUR. PART-TIME AND AWOS
REPORTING LOCATIONS MAY ONLY BE AVAILABLE
LOCALLY. SOME ARE NOT INCLUDED. REPORTING
LOCATIONS ARE CONTINUALLY BEING ADDED AND
DELETED. DEPENDING ON RETRIEVAL SYSTEM SOME
LOCATIONS MAY NOT BE AVAILABLE.

○ WEATHER REPORT (SA).

● WEATHER REPORT (SA) AND TERMINAL
FORECAST (FT).

MANY LOCATIONS PROVIDE PART-TIME OR AWOS
OBSERVATIONS. THEREFORE, OBSERVATIONS AND
TERMINAL FORECASTS ARE NOT ALWAYS AVAILABLE.

DISCREPANCIES WILL OCCUR. PART-TIME AND AWOS
REPORTING LOCATIONS MAY ONLY BE AVAILABLE
LOCALLY. SOME ARE NOT INCLUDED. REPORTING
LOCATIONS ARE CONTINUALLY BEING ADDED AND
DELETED. DEPENDING ON RETRIEVAL SYSTEM SOME
LOCATIONS MAY NOT BE AVAILABLE.

Alaska

Hawaii

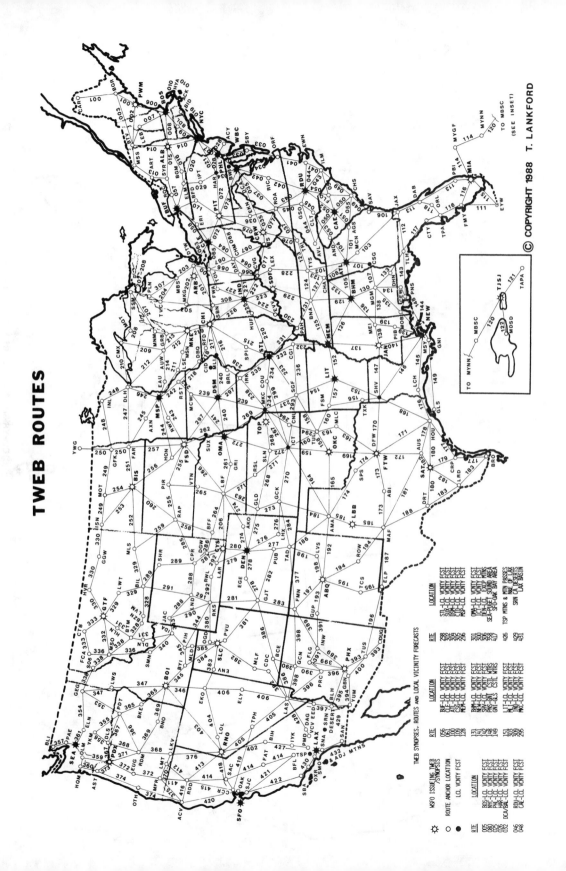

TWEB ROUTES

© COPYRIGHT 1988 T. LANKFORD

FD LOCATIONS

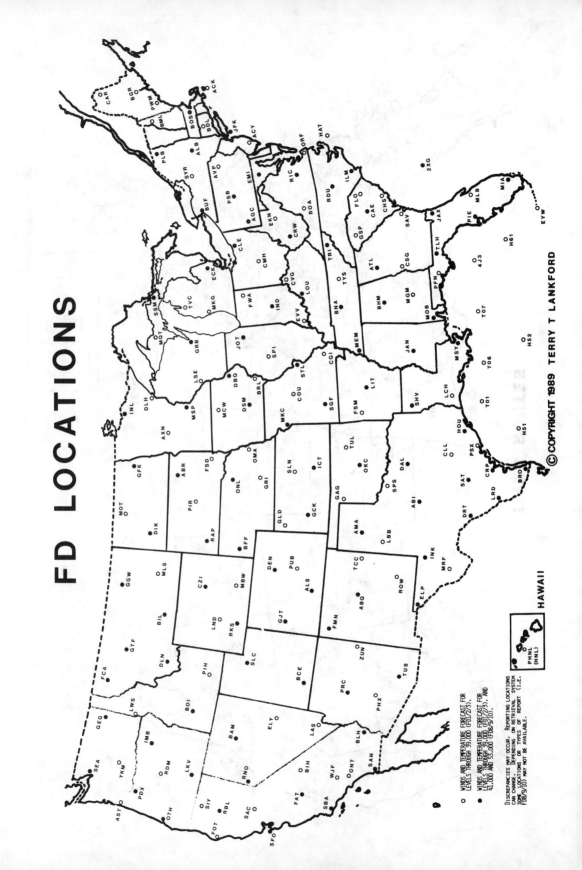

○ WINDS AND TEMPERATURE FORECAST FOR
  LEVELS THROUGH 39,000 (FDU/2/3).

● WINDS AND TEMPERATURE FORECAST FOR
  LEVELS THROUGH 39,000 (FDU/2/3), AND
  41,000 AND 53,000 (FB9/9/10).

DISCREPANCIES MAY OCCUR. REPORTING LOCATIONS
CAN CHANGE, DEPENDING ON RETRIEVAL SYSTEM
OR LOCATIONS OR TYPES OF REPORT (I.E.
FB6/9/10) MAY NOT BE AVAILABLE.

HAWAII

PHNL
(HNL)

© COPYRIGHT 1989 TERRY T LANKFORD

FD LOCATIONS

ALASKA

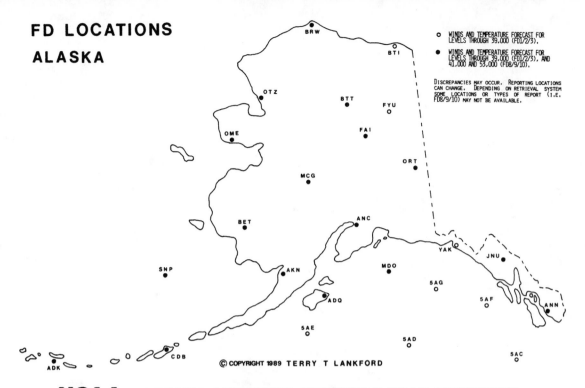

WINDS AND TEMPERATURE FORECAST FOR
LEVELS THROUGH 39,000 (FD1/2/3).

WINDS AND TEMPERATURE FORECAST FOR
LEVELS THROUGH 39,000 (FD1/2/3), AND
41,000 AND 53,000 (FD8/9/10).

DISCREPANCIES MAY OCCUR. REPORTING LOCATIONS
CAN CHANGE. DEPENDING ON RETRIEVAL SYSTEM
SOME LOCATIONS OR TYPES OF REPORT (I.E.
FD8/9/10) MAY NOT BE AVAILABLE.

© COPYRIGHT 1989 TERRY T LANKFORD

NOAA NATIONAL WEATHER SERVICE RADAR NETWORK

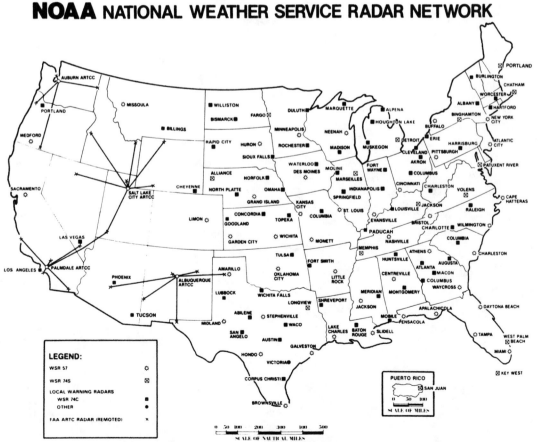

Appendix C
Plotting Identifiers

The following location identifiers appear on the In-flight Advisory Plotting Chart.

A

ABI	ABILENE, TX
ABQ	ALBUQUERQUE, NM
ABR	ABERDEEN, SD
ABY	ALBANY, GA
ACK	NANTUCKET, MA
ACT	WACO, TX
ACY	ATLANTIC CITY, NJ
ADM	ARDMORE, OK
AEX	ALEXANDRIA, LA
AGS	AUGUSTA, GA
AHN	ATHENS, GA
AKO	AKRON,CO
ALB	ALBANY, NY
ALS	ALAMOSA, CO
AMA	AMARILLO, TX
AMG	ALMA, GA
AND	ANDERSON, SC
APN	ALPENA, MI
ARG	WALNUT RIDGE, AR
ATL	ATLANTA, GA
AUS	AUSTIN, TX

AVP	SCRANTON, PA
AXN	ALEXANDRIA, MN

B

BCE	BRYCE CANYON, UT
BDF	BRADFORD, IL
BDR	BRIDGEPORT, CT
BFF	SCOTTSBLUFF, NE
BFL	BAKERSFIELD, CA
BGR	BINGHAMTON, NY
BGR	BANGOR, ME
BHM	BIRMINGHAM, AL
BIL	BILLINGS, MT
BIS	BISMARCK, ND
BJI	BEMIDJI, MN
BKW	BECKLEY, WV
BLI	BELLINGHAM, WA
BML	BERLIN, NH
BNA	NASHVILLE, TN
BNO	BURNS, OR
BOI	BOSE, ID
BRL	BURLINGTON, IA
BRO	BROWNSVILLE, TX
BTR	BATON ROUGE, LA
BTY	BEATTY, NV
BUF	BUFFALO, NY
BUM	BUTLER, MO
BVL	BONNEVILLE, UT
BWG	BOWLING GREEN, KY
BWI	BALTIMORE, MD
BZN	BOZEMAN, MT

C

CAR	CARIBOU, ME
CDS	CHILDRESS, TX
CEW	CRESTVIEW, FL
CHA	CHATTANOOGA, TN
CHE	HAYDEN, CO
CHO	CHARLOTTESVILLE, VA
CHS	CHARLESTON, SC
CID	CEDAR RAPIDS, IA
CLE	CLEVELAND, OH
CLT	CHARLOTTE, NC
CMH	COLUMBUS, OH
COD	CODY, WY

CON	CONCORD, NH
COU	COLUMBIA, MO
CPR	CASPER, WY
CRP	CORPUS CHRISTI, TX
CTY	CROSS CITY, FL
CUU	CHIHAUHAU, MEX
CVG	COVINGTON, KY

D

DAG	DAGGETT, CA
DBQ	DUBUQUE, IA
DEC	DECATUR, IL
DEN	DENVER, CO
DFW	FORT WORTH, TX
DHT	DALHART, TX
DIK	DICKINSON, ND
DLH	DULUTH, MN
DMN	DEMING, NM
DPR	DUPREE, SD
DRT	DEL RIO, TX
DSM	DES MOINES, IA
DTA	DELTA, UT
DTW	DETROIT, MI
DVC	DOVE CREEK, CO
DYR	DYERSBURG, TN

E

EAT	WENATCHEE, VA
EAU	EAU CLAIRE, WI
EED	NEEDLES, CA
EEY	WINCHESTER, VA
EKN	ELKINS, WV
EKO	ELKO, NV
ELD	EL DORADO, AR
ELP	EL PASO, TX
ELY	ELY, NV
ERI	ERIE, PA
EUG	EUGENE, OR
EVV	EVANSVILLE, IN
EWR	NEWARK, NJ
EYW	KEY WEST, FL

F

FAM	FARMINGTON, MO
FAR	FARGO, ND

FAT	FRESNO, CA
FCA	KALISPELL, MT
FDY	FINDLAY, OH
FLO	FLORENCE, SC
FMN	FARMINGTON, NM
FMY	FORT MYERS, FL
FOT	FORTUNA, CA

G

GCC	GILLETTE, WY
GCK	GARDEN CITY, KS
GEG	SPOKANE, WA
GFK	GRAND FORKS, ND
GGG	LONGVIEW, TX
GGW	GLASGOW, MT
GJT	GRAND JUNCTION, CO
GLD	GOODLAND, KS
GRB	GREEN BAY, WI
GRI	GRAND ISLAND, NE
GRW	GREENWOOD, MS
GSO	GREENSBORO, NC
GTF	GREAT FALLS, MT
GUC	GUNNISON, CO
GUP	GALLUP, NM

H

HAR	HARRISBURG, PA
HAT	HATTERAS, NC
HNN	HENDERSON, WV
HQM	HOQUIAM, WA
HRO	HARRISON, AR
HVE	HANKSVILLE, UT
HVR	HAVRE, MT
HYS	HAYS, KS

I

IAH	HOUSTON, TX
ICT	WICHITA, KS
IGB	COLUMBUS, MS
ILC	WILSON CREEK, NV
ILM	WILINGTON, NC
IND	INDIANOPOLIS, IN
INL	INTERNATIONAL FALLS, MN
INW	WINSLOW, AZ
IRK	KIRKSVILLE, MO

ISN	WILLISTON, ND
IWD	IRONWOOD, MI

J

JAC	JACKSON, WY
JAN	JACKSON, MS
JAX	JACKSONVILLE, FL
JCT	JUNCTION, TX
JST	JOHNSTOWN, PA

L

LAA	LARMAR, CO
LAF	LAFAYETTE, IN
LAR	LARAMIE, WY
LAS	LAS VEGAS, NV
LAX	LOS ANGELES, CA
LBB	LUBBOCK, TX
LBF	NORTH PLATTE, NE
LBL	LIBERAL, KS
LCH	LAKE CHARLES, LA
LFK	LUFKIN, TX
LIT	LITTLE ROCK, AR
LKT	SALMON, ID
LKV	LAKEVIEW, OR
LOU	LOUISVILLE, KY
LOZ	LONDON, KY
LSE	LA CROSSE, WI
LVS	LAS VEGAS, NM
LWS	LEWISTON, ID
LWT	LEWISTOWN, MT
LYH	LYNCHBURG, VA

M

MAF	MIDLAND, TX
MBS	SAGINAW, MI
MCB	MCCOMB, MS
MCN	MACON, GA
MCW	MASON CITY, IA
MEI	MERIDIAN, MS
MEM	MEMPHIS, IN
MFR	MEDFORD, OR
MGM	MONTGOMERY, AL
MIA	MIAMI, FL
MKC	KANSAS CITY, MO
MKE	MILWAUKEE, WI

MKG	MUSKEGON, MI
MLC	MC ALESTER, OK
MLP	MULLAN PASS, ID
MLS	MILES CITY, MT
MLT	MILLINOCKET, ME
MLU	MONROE, LA
MOB	MOBILE, AL
MOD	MODESTO, CA
MOT	MINOT, IN
MOV	MONCLOVA, MEX
MPV	MONTPELIER, VT
MQT	MARQUETTE, MI
MRF	MARFA, TX
MSL	MUSCLE SHOALS, AL
MSN	MADISON, WI
MSO	MISSOULA, MT
MSP	MINNEAPOLIS, MN
MSY	NEW ORLEANS, LA
MTU	MYTON, UT
MYL	MC CALL, ID

O

OKC	OKLAHOMA CITY, OK
OMA	OMAHA, NE
ONL	O NEILL, NE
ONP	NEWPORT, OR
ORD	CHICAGO, IL
ORF	NORFOLK, VA
ORL	ORLANDO, FL
OSW	OSWEGO, KS

P

PBI	WEST PALM BEACH, FL
PDT	PENDLETON, OR
PDX	PORTLAND, OR
PEQ	PECOS CITY, TX
PGS	PEACH SPRINGS, AZ
PHX	PHOENIX, AZ
PIT	ST. PETERSBURG, FL
PIH	POCATELLO, ID
PIR	PIERRE, SD
PIT	PITTSBURGH, PA
PKB	PARKERSBURG, WV
PPE	PUNTA PENASCO, MEX
PSP	PALM SPRINGS, CA

PSX	PALACIOS, TX
PUB	PUEBLO,CO
PVD	PROVIDENCE, RI
PWE	PAWNEE CITY, NE
PWM	PORTLAND, ME

R

RAP	RAPID CITY, SD
RBL	RED BLUFF, CA
RDM	REDMOND, OR
REO	ROME, OR
RHI	RHINELANDER, WI
RIC	RICHMOND, VA
RIW	RIVERTON, WY
RKS	ROCK SPRINGS, WY
RNO	RENO, NV
ROW	ROSWELL, NM
RWF	REDWOOD FALLS, MN
RWI	ROCKY MOUNT, NC

S

SAC	SACRAMENTO, CA
SAN	SAN DIEGO, CA
SAT	SAN ANTONIO, TX
SAV	SAVANNAH, GA
SBA	SANTA BARBARA, CA
SBN	SOUTH BEND, IN
SBY	SALISBURY, MD
SEA	SEATTLE, WA
SFO	SAN FRANCISCO, CA
SGF	SPRINGFIELD, MO
SHR	SHERIDAN, WY
SJN	ST. JOHNS, AZ
SJT	SAN ANGELO, TX
SLC	SALT LAKE CITY, UT
SLK	SARANAC LAKE, NY
SLN	SALINA, KS
SLT	SLATE RUN, PA
SNS	SALINAS, CA
SPS	WICHITA FALLS, TX
SSM	SAULT STE MARIE, MI
SSO	SAN SIMON, AZ
STL	ST. LOUIS, MO
SUX	SIOUX CITY, IA
SYR	SYRACUSE, NY

T

TBC	TUBA CITY, AZ
TBE	TOBE, CO
TCC	TUCUMCARI, NM
TCS	TRUTH OR CONSEQUENCES, NM
TLH	TALLAHASSEE, FL
TOU	TATOOSH, WA
TPH	TONOPAH, NV
TRI	BRISTOL, TN
TUL	TULSA, OK
TUS	TUCSON, AZ
TVC	TRAVERSE CITY, MI
TWF	TWIN FALLS, ID
TXK	TEXARKANA, AR
TYS	KNOXVILLE, TN

U

UKI	UKIAH, CA

V

VBI	SIOUX NARROWS, ONT
VIH	ROLLA/VICHY, MO
VRB	VERO BEACH, FL
VTN	VALENTINE, NE

W

WMC	WINNEMUCCA, NV

Y

YDC	PRINCETON, BC
YDR	BROADVIEW, SASK
YKM	YAKIMA, WA
YOW	OTTAWA, ONT
YQB	QUEBEC, QUE
YQL	LETHBRIDGE, ALTA
YQT	THUNDER BAY, ONT
YSC	SHERBROOKE, QUE
YSJ	ST. JOHN, NB
YUM	YUMA, AZ
YVV	WIARTON, ONT
YWG	WINNIPEG, MAN
YXH	MENDICINE HAT, ALTA
YYN	SWIFT CURRENT, SASK
YYZ	TORONTO, ONT

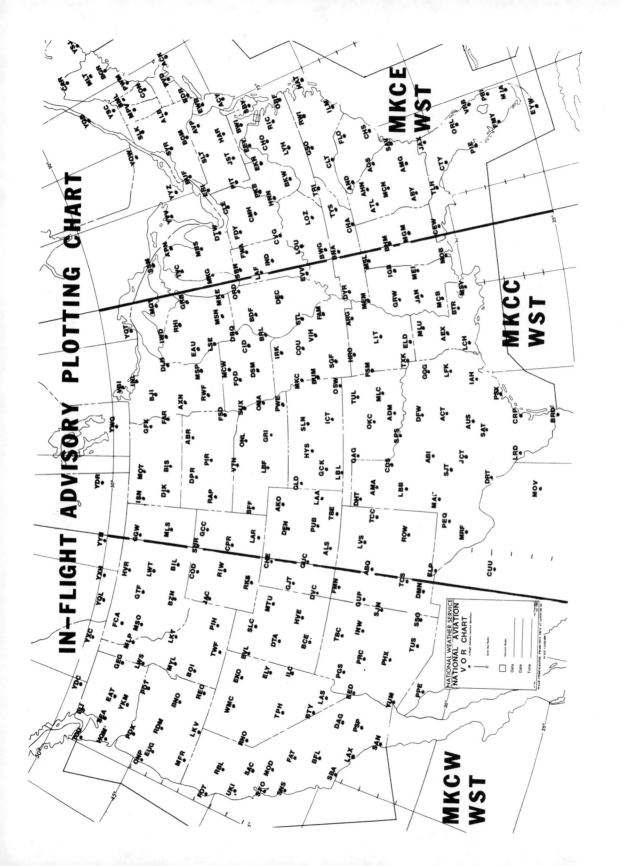

IN-FLIGHT ADVISORY PLOTTING CHART

MKCE WST

MKCC WST

MKCW WST

NATIONAL WEATHER SERVICE
NATIONAL AVIATION
V O R CHART
In-Flight Advisory Plotting Chart

Data
Date
Time

Appendix D
Area Designators

FA Designators

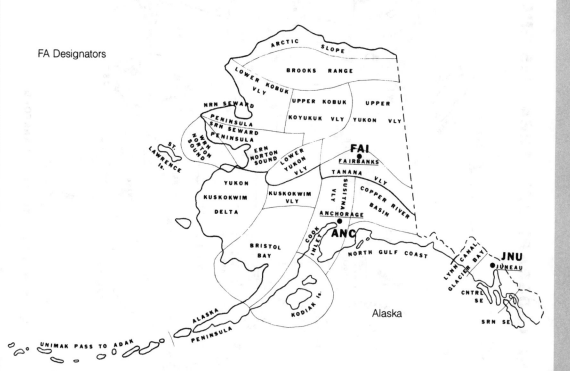

Alaska

Hawaii

© COPYRIGHT 1988 TERRY T LANKFORD

COMMON GEOGRAPHICAL AREA DESIGNATORS

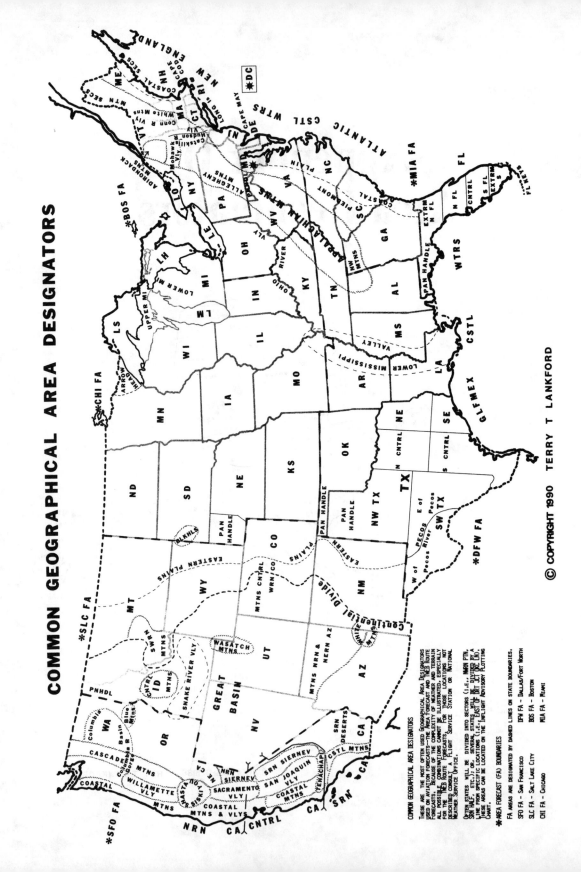

COMMON GEOGRAPHICAL AREA DESIGNATORS

THESE ARE THE MOST OFTEN USED GEOGRAPHICAL AREA DESIGNATORS USED ON AVIATION FORECASTS—THE AREA FORECAST AND THEIR ROUTE FORECASTS. BECAUSE OF THE COMPLEXITY OF WEATHER AND TERRAIN ALL POSSIBLE ROUTE FORECASTS CANNOT BE ILLUSTRATED. ESPECIALLY FOR THE DESCRIBED CONSULT THE NEAREST FLIGHT SERVICE STATION OR NATIONAL WEATHER SERVICE OFFICE.

OFTEN STATES WILL BE DIVIDED INTO SECTORS (i.e., MARN FTN, SRN VLY, ETC.). OR SEVERAL STATES COMBINED. STATES DIVIDED BY A LINE FROM SPECIFIC LOCATIONS (i.e., EAST OF DEF. CITY, ETC.). THESE AREAS CAN BE LOCATED ON THE INFLIGHT ADVISORY PLOTTING CHART.

*AREA FORECAST (FA) BOUNDARIES

FA AREAS ARE DESIGNATED BY DASHED LINES ON STATE BOUNDARIES.

SFO FA – SAN FRANCISCO   DFW FA – DALLAS/FORT WORTH
SLC FA – SALT LAKE CITY   BOS FA – BOSTON
CHI FA – CHICAGO   MIA FA – MIAMI

© COPYRIGHT 1990   TERRY T LANKFORD

Appendix E
Weather Products

SURFACE OBSERVATIONS (SA)

ACY SA 2050 250 −SCT 5H 108/87/75/2009/985/ 722 1001
JFK SA 2050 −X 5H 102/78/73/1918/983/H4/ 730
LGA SA 2250 40 SCT E70 BKN 130 OVC 4TRW+ 119/78/70/2720G23/988/
    WSHFT 27 TB13 W MOVG SE FQT LTGICCCCG W−NW PRESRR RB30
ABE SA 2253 E45 BKN 120 BKN 6F 112/75/73/E1705/987

NWS observers, like the military, have a talent for seeing a multitude of cloud layers.
This SFO report contains five.

SFO RS 1854 11 SCT 23 SCT M30 BKN 85 BKN 100 OVC 8
    122/46/44/1310/989/RE43 WSHFT 30

LAWRS Observations

MDT SA 2145 E50 OVC 3H 82/76/2405/986/PRESRR
RDG SA 2245 8 SCT E25 OVC 7 76/73/1610/988/TE05
STS SA 2048 CLR 30 110/54/1405/990
COE SA 2350 12 SCT E30 OVC 20 38/35/1412/994
APF SA 2345 20 SCT E20 BKN 7 76/M/0000/010
VIS SA 1645 W1 X 1/4F 39/0000/004
APC SA 0045 CLR 10 3605/998

AWOS/AMOS Observations

This AWOS observation from Sanford, ME (SFM), reports clear above 12,000. Obstructions to visibility are not available with this AWOS unit. The remarks indicate that precipitation has occurred.

```
FOD SA 2349 AWOS M12 OVC 10 24/19/0604/009
SFM SA 0013 AWOS 120 CLR 5 27/24/0607/006/ P001
```

This AWOS observation from Bremerton, WA, indicates that the wind direction is mission (M), speed seven knots.

```
PWT SA 2349 AWOS M6 OVC 10 44/42/M07/998
```

At Block Island, RI, the peak wind reported is 18 knots, and the pressure tendency and change during the past three hours is 020.

```
BID SP 0029 AMOS 39/ – 27/0513/998 PK WIND 18 020
```

WEATHER ADVISORIES

SIGMETs

This is an example of a Fairbanks, AK, SIGMET for volcanic ash released by Mt. Redoubt in December 1989.

```
FAIA UWS 151625
PAZA SIGMET ALPHA 1 VALID 151630/152030 PAFA –
VOLCANIC ASH BLO FL350 FCST TO MOV INTO AREA BOUNDED BY 160 SW
FAI TO TAL TO 80 N EAA TO 200 S EAA TO 40 S BIG TO 90 S FAI TO
160SW FIA.
```

Convective SIGMETs

```
MKCC WST 022155
CONVECTIVE SIGMET 46C
VALID UNTIL 2355Z
AR MS LA AL
FROM 40 S MEM – 30ESE IGB – MOB – 50ME MUL – 40S MEM
AREA TSTSM MOVG FROM 2410. TOPS ABV 450.

CONVECTIVE SIGMET 47C
VALID UNTIL 2355Z
KS OK TX
FROM 30NNW OSW – 30SSW SPS – 60WNW LBB
DVLPG LINE SVR TSTMS 40 MI WIDE MOVG FROM 2620. TOPS ABV 450.
HAIL TO 3 IN . . . WIND GUSTS TO 65 KT PSBL.

CONVECTIVE SIGMET 49C
```

VALID UNTIL 2355Z
NM
30NNW ROW
DVLPG ISOLD SVR TSTM D25 MOVG FROM 2720. TOPS ABV 450
TORNADOES . . . HAIL T0 3 IN . . . WIND GUSTS TO 70KT PSBL.
OUTLOOK VALID UNTIL 0355Z
FROM MCW – COU – FSM – DFW – SJT – LVS – VTN – MCW
REF WW 374. REF WW 375. VERY UNSTBL AMS HAS MOVED NWD INTO
CNTRL PLAINS AREA. SFC LI IN – 10 RANGE IN SOME AREAS. MSTR
CONVG ANAL SHOWS SEVERAL AREAS OF CONCERN . . . FIRST IN CDFNT MOVG
INTO NRN NE WHERE MDT – HIGH VALUES OBSVD ALSO INTO NRN IA. MDT
MSTR CONVG XTNDS SWD INTO WRN KS. OTHR AREAS OF MDT MSTR CONVG
OVER ERN OK AND W CRNTRL TX WHERE TSTMS ARE ALSO VERY STG ATTM.
TSTMS OVER LA/MS ARE XPCD TO DMSH NEXT 1 – 2 HOURS AS OUTFLOWS HAVE
STBLIZED MUCH OF THE AMS THERE.

Alert Weather Watch

MKC AWW 021930
WW 374 SVERE TSTM OK KS 022000Z – 030200Z
AXIS . . 70 STATUTE MILES EAST AND WEST OF LINE . .
20 SW ADM/ARDMORE OK/ – 30W CNU/CHANUTE KS/
HAIL SURFACE AND ALOFT . . 3 INCHES. WIND GUSTS . . 65 KNOTS.
MAX TOPS TO 550. MEAN WIND VECTOR 230/25.

MKC AWW 022003
WW 375 TORNADO TX NM 022020Z – 030300Z
AXIS . . 80 STATUTE MILES NORTH AND SOUTH OF LINE . .
20WSW ROW/ROSWELL NM/ – 60SSE CDS/CHILDRESSS TX/
HAIL SURFACE AND ALOFT . . 3 INCHES. WIND GUST . . 70 KNOTS.
TAX TOPS TO 550. MEAN WIND VECTOR 230/30.

Severe Weather Watch Bulletin

MKC WW 021935
BULLETIN – IMMEDIATE BROADCAST REQUESTED
SEVERE THUNDERSTORM WATCH NUMBER 374
NATIONAL WEATHER SERVICE KANSAS CITY MO
235 PM CDT FRI JUN 02 1989
A . . . THE NATIONAL SEVERE STORMS FORECAST CENTER HAS ISSUED A
    SEVERE THUNDERSTORM WATCH FOR
    MUCH OF CENTRAL AND EASTERN OKLAHOMA
    PARTS OF SOUTH – CENTRAL AND SOUTHEAST KANSAS

FROM 300 PM CDT UNTIL 900 PM CDT THIS FRIDAY AFTERNOON AND
EVENING

LARGE HAIL . . . DANGEROUS LIGHTNING AND DAMAGING THUNDERSTORM
WINDS
ARE POSSIBLE IN THESE AREAS.

THE SEVERE THUNDERSTORM WATCH AREA IS ALONG 70 STATUE MILES
EAST AND WEST OF A LINE FROM 20 MILES SOUTHWEST OF ARDMORE
OKLAHOMA TO 30 MILES WEST OF CHANUTE KANSAS.

REMEMBER . . . A SEVERE THUNDERSTORM WATCH MEANS CONDITIONS ARE
FAVORABLE FOR SEVERE THUNDERSTORMS IN AND CLOSE TO THE WATCH
AREA.
PERSONS IN THESE AREAS SHOULD BE ON THE LOOKOUT FOR THREATENING
WEATHER CONDITIONS AND LISTEN FOR LATER STATEMENTS AND POSSIBLE
WARNINGS.

C . . . A FEW SVR TSTMS WITH HAIL SFC AND ALOFT TO 3 IN. EXTRM TURBC
AND SFC WND GUST TO 65 KN. A FEW CBS WITH MAX TOPS TO 550. MEAN
WIND VECTOR 230/25.

D . . . TSTMS CONG TO DVLP OVR N CNTRL OK AND EXTRM S CNTRL KS IN VERY
MOIST AND UNSTABL AMS. SFC BASED LIFTED INDEX IS MINUS 10 OR
LESS. TCU/SML CBS ALSO BEGINNING TO DVLP OVR S CNTRL OK. TSTMS
EXPCD TO INTSFY FURTHER DURG AFTN HEATING PD WITH STGR CELLS LIKELY
REACHING SVR LVLS INTO EVE HRS.

E . . . OTR TSTMS . . . CONT VALID PTN OF WW 737.

. . . WEISS

Hurricane Bulletin

WINT32 KMIA 131842
BULLETIN
HURRICANE GILBERT INTERMEDIATE ADVISORY
NATIONAL WEATHER SERVICE MIAMI FL
3 PM EDT TUE SEP 13 1988

. . . GILBERT NOW PACKING 160 MPH WINDS . . .
HURRICANE WARNINGS ARE IN EFFECT FOR THE CAYMAN
ISLANDS . . . NORTHEASTERN YUCATAN FROM FELIPE CARILLO PUERTO TO
PROGRESO INCLUDING COZUMEL AND CANCUN . . . THE ISLE OF YOUTH AND
WESTERN CUBA WEST OF THE CITY OF PINAR DEL RIO.

AT 3 PM EDT . . . 1900Z . . . THE CENTER OF HURRICANE GILBERT WAS LOCATED
NEAR LATITUDE 19.3 NORTH . . . LONGITUDE 82.3 WEST . . . OR ABOUT 280
MILES . . . 450 KM . . . EAST SOUTHEAST OF THE ISLAND OF COZUMEL MEXICO.
GILBERT IS MOVING TOWARD THE WEST NORTHWEST NEAR 15 MPH . . . 24

KM/HR. THIS MOTION IS EXPECTED TO CONTINUE THIS AFTERNOON AND TONIGHT

NOAA RECONNASSANCE NOW REPORTS WINDS IN GILBERT HAVE REACHED 160 MPH WITH A CENTRAL PRESSURE OF 903 MILLIBARS . . . 26.66 INCHES. GILBERT MAY STILL INCREASE A LITTLE MORE IN STRENGTH.
TROPICAL STORM FORCE WINDS EXTEND OUTWARD UP TO 250 MILES . . . 400 KM . . . TO THE NORTH AND 200 MILES . . . 320 KM . . . TO THE SOUTH OF THE CENTER.

PEOPLE IN THE WARNED AREAS OF CUBA AND MEXICO SHOULD HAVE NEARLY COMPLETED PREPARATIONS FOR THIS SEVERE HURRICANE.

TIDES OF UP TO 8 TO 12 FEET AND HIGH WAVES ARE LIKELY NEAR AND TO THE RIGHT OF WHERE THE CENTER CROSSES THE COAST. LESSER VALUES WILL OCCUR ELSEWHERE IN THE WARNED AREAS. THESE CONDITIONS COULD UNDERMINE BUILDINGS ALONG THE BEACH.

SQUALLS ARE CURRENTLY PASSING THROUGH THE FLORIDA KEYS. SMALL CRAFT SHOULD REMAIN IN PORT FROM KEY LARGO TO DRY TOTUGAS. TIDES OF 1 TO 2 FEET ABOVE NORMAL WILL CONTINUE OVER THE FLORIDA KEYS.

RAINFALL TOTALS OF 5 TO 10 INCHES ACCOMPANY THE HURRICANE.

AREA FORECASTS

Alaska

ANCH FA 301440
HAZARDS VALID UNTIL 010300

AK SRN HLF EXCP SE AK . . .

FLT PRCTNS . . . IFR . . . ALUTNS . . KODIAK IS
                 ICG . . . ALUTNS
                 TURBC . . . ALUTNS

TSTMS IMPLY PSBL SVR OR GTR TURBC SVR ICG LLWS
NON MSL HGTS NOTED BY AGL OR CIG
THE FA ISSUANCE INCORPORATES THE FOLLOWING AIRMETS STILL IN EFFECT . . . NONE.

ANCS FA 301440
SYNOPSIS VALID UNTIL 010900
1033 MB LOW N MCG QSTNRY. 1031 MB LOW 120 S CYT DRFTG NW TO CDV. 983 MB LOW 550 SW PASY MOVG 320 SW PASY. OCFNT SEWD FM PT JUST SW PASY TO EXTD SE ACRS ADK 09Z.

ACNI FA 301440

ICING AND FRZLVL VALID UNTIL 010300
OCNL MDT RIME ICIC FRZLVL – 120 ALUTNS NR AKD SPRDG E TO Z11 03Z

FRZLVL . . .
050 – 075 NGLF CST . . COPPER RIVER BASIN . . KOKIAK IS . . COOK INLET . .
SUSITNA VLY . . SLPG TO 035 – 055 ELSW EXP 025 AK PEN.

ANCT FA 301440
TURBC VALID UNTILL 010300
OCNL MDT BLO 060 ALUTNS.

ANCC FA 301440
SGFNT CLD AND WX VALID UNTIL 010300 . . . OTLK VALID 010300 – 010900

. . . COOK INLET AND SUSITNA VLY . . .
NO SGFNT CLDS OR WX. OTLK . . . VFR.

. . . PASSES . . .
LK CLARK . . MERRILL . . RAINY . . WINDY . . CHICKALOON . . PORTAGE OPEN.

. . . COOPER RIVER BASIN . . .
70 SCT – BKN 80. OTLK . . . VFR.

. . . AK PEN PORT HEIDEN TO UNIMAK PASS . . .
PAC SIDE . . 25 BKN – OVC LYRS 130. FEW AREAS 15 OVC. MSTLY 25 SCT –
BKN BY 21Z. OTLK . . . MVFR CIG.
. . . UNIMAK PASS TO ADAK . . .
10 SCT – BKN 20 OVC LYRS 200. R – INVOF ADK SPRDG E TO Z11 END PD.
OTLK . . . MVFR CIG R.

. . . KOKIDA IS . . .
15 OVC OCNLY VRBL TO CIGS BLO 10 WDLY SCT VSBYS BLO 3F SE
EXPOSURES. BY 21Z MSTLY 20 SCT – BKN. TOPS 80. OTLK . . . MVFR CIG.

. . . N GLF CST . . .
MSTLY CLR. WDLY SCT CIGS BLO 10 VSBYS BLO 3F. LWR CONDS GEN
DISPTG BY 20Z ONSHR AND LFTG TO 15 OVC OVR WTR. TOPS 25.
OTLK . . . VFR.

. . . KUSKOKWIM VLY . . .
FEW PTCHS 80 BKN 100. OTRW CLR. OTLK . . . VFR

. . . YKN – KUSKOWIM DELTA . . .
50 SCT – BKN 80 BKN LYRS 200. ALG IMDT CST FEW PTCHS 15 OVC 25.
OTLK . . . VFR.

. . . BRISTOL BAY . . .

50 SCT – BKN 80 SCT – BKN LYRS 200. ALG IMDT CST FEW PTCHS 15 OVC
25. OTLK . . . VFR.

Hawaii

HNLH FA 301540
HAZARDS VALID UNTIL 010400
HAWAIIAN ISLANDS AND CSTL WTRS
FLT PRCTN . . . NONE XPCD.

TSTMS IMPLY PSBL SVR OR GTR TURBC SVR ICING AND LLWS.
NON MSL HGTS NOTED BY AGL OR CIG.

THIS FA ISSUANCE INCORPORATES THE FOLLOWING AIRMETS STILL IN
EFFECT . . . NONE.

HNLS FA 301540
SYNOPSIS VALID UNTIL 011000
STNRY SFC HI FAR NW OF HNL.

HNLI FA 301540
ICING AND FRZLVL VALID UNTIL 010400
NO SGFNT ICING XPCD. FRZLVL 150 LIH TO 130 ITO

HNLT FA 301540
TURBC VALID UNTIL 010400
NO SGFNT TURBC XPCD.

HNLC FA 301540
SGFNT CLOUDS AND WX VALID UNTIL 010400 . . . OTLK 010400Z TO 011000Z

OVR AND VCNTY BIG ISLAND.
20 BKN 40 BKN 80 BRF 15 OVC 3RW + . OTLK . . . VFR.

WNDWD/MTN SXNS AND WNDWD CSTL WTRS OF OTR ISLANDS.
25 SCT 40 BKN 80 BRF 20 BKN 5RW. OTLK . . . VFR.

ELSW.
25 SCT 45 SCT BRF 40 BKN 60 RW. OTLK . . . VFR.

Glossary

advection—The process of moving an atmospheric property from one location to another. Advection usually refers to the horizontal movement of properties (temperature, moisture, vorticity, etc.).

air mass—A large body of air, with homogeneous horizontal temperature and moisture characteristics.

anticyclonic—Having a clockwise rotation in the northern hemisphere, associated with the circulation around an anticyclone (high pressure area).

arc cloud—An arc-shaped line of convective clouds often observed in satellite imagery moving away from a dissipating thunderstorm area.

atmospheric phenomena—As reported on SAs, atmospheric phenomena is weather occurring at the station and any obstructions to vision. Obstructions to vision are only reported when the prevailing visibility is less than seven miles.

Automated Weather Observing System—AWOS is a computerized system that measures sky condition, visibility, precipitation, temperature, dew point, wind, and altimeter setting. It has a voice synthesizer to report minute by minute observations over radio frequencies, telephone lines, or local displays.

baroclinic—A state of the atmosphere where isotherms—lines of equal temperature—cross contours, temperature and pressure gradients are steep, and temperature advection takes place. A baroclinic atmosphere enhances the formation and strengthens the intensity of storms. It is characterized by an upper level wave one-quarter wave length behind the surface front.

barotropic—Barotropic is an absence of, or the opposite of baroclinic. Theoretically, an entirely barotropic atmosphere would yield constant pressure charts with no height or temperature gradients or vertical motion.

boundaries—Zones in the lower atmosphere characterized by sharp gradients or discontinuities of temperature, pressure, or moisture and often accompanied by convergence in the wind field. Examples include surface fronts, dry lines, and outflow boundaries. In the latter case, the boundary is produced by a surge of rain-cooled air flowing outward near the surface from the originating area of convection. In an unstable air mass, thunderstorms tend to develop along these zones and especially at intersections of two or more boundaries.

BWER/WER/LEWP—Bounded Weak Echo Region/Weak Echo Region/Line Echo Wave Pattern. All of these weather radar terms are indicators of strong thunderstorms and the development of severe weather.

chop—Reported with turbulence, chop refers to a slight, rapid, and somewhat rhythmic bumpiness without appreciable changes in altitude or attitude.

clear air turbulence (CAT)—Nonconvective, wind shear, turbulence occurring at or above 15,000 feet, although it usually refers to turbulence above 25,000 feet.

closed cell stratocumulus—Common over water, this term is used to describe satellite viewed oceanic stratocumulus associated with an inversion. They are associated with high pressure.

cloud band—A nearly continuous cloud formation with a distinct long axis, a length-to-width ratio of at least four to one, and a width greater than one degree of latitude (60 nm).

cloud element—The smallest cloud form that can be resolved on satellite imagery from a given satellite system.

cloud line—A narrow cloud band in which individual elements are connected and the line is less than one degree of latitude in width. Indicates strong winds, often 30 knots or greater over water.

cloud shield—A broad cloud formation that is not more than four times as long as it is wide. Often it is formed by cirrus clouds associated with a ridge or the jet stream.

cloud streets—A series of aligned cloud elements that are not connected. Several cloud streets usually line up parallel to each other and each street is not more than 10 miles wide.

cold-core low—A low pressure area that intensifies aloft. When this type of low contains closed contours at the 200 mb level, its movements tend to be slow and erratic.

cold pool—Generally refers to an area at 500 mbs in which the air temperature is colder than adjacent areas. Other atmospheric conditions being equal, thermodynamic instability is greater beneath cold pools, thus making thunderstorm development more likely.

comma cloud system—A cloud system that resembles the comma punctuation mark. The shape results from differential rotation of the cloud border and upward and downward moving air.

comma head—The rounded portion of the comma cloud system. This region often produces most of the steady precipitation.

comma tail—The portion of the comma cloud that lies to the right of, and often nearly parallel to, the axis of maximum winds.

confluence—A region where streamlines converge. The speed of the horizontal flow will often increase where there is confluence. It is the upper level equivalent of surface convergence.

Coordinated Universal Time—Formerly Greenwich Mean Time, also known as Z or ZULU time, Coordinated Universal Time (UTC) is the international time standard. UTC is used in all aviation time references, except control zone active times, which are expressed in local time.

convergence—Air flowing together near the surface is forced upward due to convergence. It is a vertical motion producer that tends to destabilize the atmosphere near the surface.

cyclonic—Having a counterclockwise rotation in the northern hemisphere, associated with the circulation around a cyclone or low pressure area.

deformation zone—An area within the atmospheric circulation where air parcels contract in one direction and elongate in the perpendicular direction. The narrow zone along the axis of elongation is called the deformation zone. Deformation is a primary factor in frontogenesis and frontolysis.

dew point front—*See* dry line.

difulence—The spreading apart of adjacent streamlines. The speed of horizontal flow often decreases with a diffluent zone. It is the upper air equivalent of surface divergence and activates or perpetuates thunderstorm development.

Direct User Access Terminal—A computer terminal where pilots can directly access meteorological and aeronautical information, plus file a flight plan without the assistance of an FSS.

divergence—Subsiding air diverges, or spreads, at the surface. Divergence is a downward motion producer that tends to stabilize the atmosphere near the surface.

dry line—An area within an air mass that has little temperature gradient, but significant differences in moisture. The boundary between the dry and moist air produces a lifting mechanism. Although not a true front, it has the potential to produce hazardous weather. It is also known as a dew point front.

dry slot—A satellite meteorology term used to describe a cloud feature associated with an upper level short wave trough. Generally speaking, the cloud system is shaped like a large comma. As the system develops, sinking air beneath the jet stream causes an intrusion of dry, relatively cloud-free air on the upwind side of the comma cloud. The air of the intrusion is the dry slot. It is commonly the location where lines of thunderstorms subsequently develop.

embedded thunderstorm—A thunderstorm that occurs within nonconvective precipitation. A thunderstorm that is hidden in stratiform clouds.

Enhanced Infrared (IR) Imagery—A process by which infrared imagery is enhanced to provide increased contrast between features to simplify interpretation. This is done by assigning specific shades of gray to specific temperature ranges.

enhanced V—A cloud top signature sometimes seen in enhanced infrared imagery in which the coldest cloud top temperatures form a V shape. Storms that show this cloud top feature are often associated with severe weather.

fine line/thin line—At times weather radar picks up dust or debris that appear as a fine or thin line caused by a dry front or gust front. It indicates the presence of low-level wind shear.

GOES—Geostationary Operational Environmental Satellites, normally located about 22,000 nm above the equator at 75° W and 135° W. The satellites provide half-hourly visible and infrared imagery.

gust front—A low-level windshift line created by the downdrafts associated with thunderstorms and other convective clouds. Acting like a front, these features might produce strong gustiness, pressure rises, and low-level wind shear.

Hadley Cell—A circulation theory describing how low pressure at the equator rises, moves toward the pole, and sinks in high pressure at the pole, then moves toward the equator.

hail shaft—A shaft of hail detected on weather radar.

hook echo—A bona fide hook echo indicates the existence of a mesolow associated with a large thunderstorm cell. Such mesolows are often associated with severe thunderstorms and tornadoes. Hook echoes are not seen on ATC radars.

impulse—A weak, mid to upper level and fast moving shortwave feature, that can kick off thunderstorms.

International Standard Atmosphere (ISA)—A hypothetical vertical distribution of atmospheric properties (temperature, pressure, and density). At the surface, the ISA has a temperature of 15° C (59° F), pressure of 1013.2 mb (29.92 in.), and a lapse rate of approximately 2° C in the troposphere.

intertropical convergence zone (ITCZ)—The dividing line between the southeast trade winds and the northeast trade winds of the southern and northern hemispheres respectively.

level of free convection (LFC)—The level at which a parcel of air lifted adiabatically until saturation would become warmer than its surrounding air, and become unstable.

LEWP—*See* BWER/WER/LEWP

lifted index—A measure of atmospheric instability that is computed on a thermodynamic chart by lifting a parcel of air near the surface to the 500 mb level and subtracting the temperature of the parcel from the temperature of the environment. A negative index means the lifted parcel is buoyant at 500 mb and will continue to rise, which is an unstable condition.

lifted condensation level (LCL)—The level at which a parcel of air lifted adiabatically would cool and become saturated. The level at which clouds would form.

location identifier—Consisting of three to five alphanumeric characters location identifiers are contractions used to identify geographical locations, navigational aids, and intersections.

long wave—*See* Rossby wave.

low-level wind shear—*See* wind shear.

mesolow—Also known as mesocyclone, a mesolow is a small area of low pressure within a severe thunderstorm. Tornadoes can develop within the vortex.

mesoscale—Small-scale meteorological phenomena that can range in size from that of a single thunderstorm to an area the size of the state of Oklahoma.

mesoscale convective complex (MCC)—A large homogeneous convective weather system on the order of 100,000 square miles. They tend to form during the morning hours.

microburst—A small-scale, severe, storm downburst less than two-and-half miles across. Reaching the ground, the burst continues as an expanding outflow producing severe wind shear.

moisture convergence—An objective analysis field combining wind flow convergence and moisture advection. Under certain circumstances, this field is useful for forecasting areas of thunderstorm development.

negative tilt—Refers to troughs with an axis in the horizontal plane tilting from northwest to southeast. These systems tend to cause more weather in California because they bring in warm, moist air.

overrunning—A condition in which air flow from one air mass is moving over another air mass of greater density. The term usually applies to warmer air flowing over cooler air as in a warm frontal situation. It implies a lifting mechanism that can trigger convection in unstable air.

positive tilt—Refers to troughs with an axis in the horizontal plane tilting from northeast to southwest.

positive vorticity advection (PVA)—Positive vorticity advection, usually applies to the 500 mb level and refers to areas where the wind flow implies advection from higher values of absolute vorticity to lower ones. These areas are presumed to mark zones where upward vertical motion will be supported or enhanced. A vertical motion producer.

Rossby waves—Also known as major waves, planetary waves, or long waves, they are characterized by their large length and significant amplitude. They tend to be slow moving.

severe thunderstorm—A thunderstorm that produces winds of 50 knots or more, or hail 3/4 in. in diameter or greater.

severe wind shear—*See* wind shear.

shear axis—An axis indicating maximum lateral change in wind direction, as in an elongated circulation. This lateral change or shear might be either cyclonic or anticyclonic.

short wave—With wave lengths shorter than long waves, they tend to move rapidly through the long wave circulation. They can intensify or dampen weather systems.

Standard Atmosphere—*See* International Standard Atmosphere.

stratosphere—The atmospheric layer above the tropopause. It is characterized by a slight increase in temperature with height and the near absence of water vapor. Occasionally severe thunderstorms will break through the tropopause into the stratosphere.

streamlines—A line that represents the wind flow pattern, and is parallel to the instantaneous velocity. Streamlines indicate the trajectory of the flow.

sublimation—The process by which ice changes directly to water vapor, or water vapor directly to ice. The sublimation of ice to vapor is a cooling process, and water vapor to ice is a warming process.

synoptic scale—Large-scale weather patterns the size of the migratory high and low pressure systems of the lower troposphere with wave lengths on the order of 1,000 miles.

thermal high—An area of high atmospheric pressure caused by the cooling of air by a cold surface. They remain relatively stationary over the cold ground.

thermal low—An area of low atmospheric pressure caused by intense surface heating. They are common to the continental subtropics in summer, remain stationary, and cyclonic circulation is generally weak and diffuse.

thin line—*See* fine line/thin line.

transverse cirrus banding—Irregularly spaced bandlike cirrus clouds that form nearly perpendicular to a jet stream axis. They indicate turbulence associated with the jet.

tropopause—The boundary between the troposphere and the stratosphere is called the tropopause. It consists of several discrete overlapping leaves, rather than a single continuous surface, and acts as a lid trapping almost all water vapor in the troposphere. It is marked by a decrease in wind speed, and constant temperature with an increase in height.

troposphere—The lower layer of the atmosphere, extending from the surface to an average of seven miles. Temperature normally decreases with height, and winds increase with height. It is the layer of the atmosphere where almost all weather occurs.

vort lobe—A contraction for vorticity lobe. It usually applies to the 500 mb level and identifies an area of relatively higher values of vorticity. It is synonymous with short wave trough or upper level impulse. Generally speaking, there is rising air ahead of the vort lobe and sinking air behind.

vort max—A contraction for vorticity maximum. It usually applies to the 500 mb level and refers to a point along a vorticity lobe where the absolute vorticity reaches a maximum value.

vortex—In the most general use, any flow possessing vorticity. More often the term refers to a flow with closed streamlines.

vorticity—Indicates a circulation or rotation within the atmosphere.

warm air advection—A condition in the atmosphere characterized by air flowing from a relatively warmer area to a cooler area. It is often accompanied by upward vertical motion that in the presence of sufficient instability leads to thunderstorm development.

warm core low—An area of low pressure that is warmer at its center than at its periphery. Thermal lows and tropical cyclones are examples.

wave—A pattern of ridges and troughs in the horizontal flow as depicted on upper level charts. At the surface, a wave is characterized by a break along a frontal boundary. A center of low pressure is frequently located at the apex of the wave.

WER—*See* BWER/WER/LEWP

wind field—Winds plotted at a specified level in the atmosphere are referred to as a wind field (surface, 5,000 feet, 300 mb, etc.). Wind fields show areas of convergence, divergence, and advection, which provide meteorologists with a valuable forecast tool.

wind shear—Any rapid change in wind direction or velocity. Low-level wind shear (LLWS) is generally shear that occurs within about 2,000 feet of the surface. LLWS is classified severe when a rapid change in wind direction or velocity causes an airspeed change greater than 15 knots or vertical speed change greater than 500 feet per minute.

zonal flow—A wind flow that is generally in a west to east direction.

Index

/FL altitude/flight level, PIREPs, 41, 42
/IC icing, PIREPs, 41, 43
/OV location, PIREPs, 40, 41, 42
/RM remarks, PIREPs, 41, 42, 43
/SK sky cover, PIREPs, 41, 42
/TA air temperature, PIREPs, 41, 43
/TB turbulence, PIREPs, 41, 43
/TM time, PIREPs, 41, 42
/TP type aircraft, PIREPs, 41, 42
/WX weather, PIREPs, 41, 42

300 mb and 200 mb constant pressure charts, 199-201
500 mb constant pressure chart, 195-199
850 mb and 700 mb constant pressure charts, 193-195

A

abbreviated briefings, 214, 221-223
  request for specific information, 223
  update requests, 223
abbreviations, 287-333
absolute vorticity, 205
accidents, weather-related, x, xii
adiabatic lapse rate, 6

advanced weather interactive processing system (AWIPS), 58
advection, 54, 195, 198, 205, 361
  negative vorticity (NVA), 205
  positive vorticity (PVA), 74, 205, 364
  warm air, 366
advection fog, 17, 187
adverse conditions, standard briefings, 219
advisories, xiii, 59-70, 354
  AIRMETs, 59-63
  alert weather watches (AWW), 60, 65-67
  area forecasts and, 59
  center weather advisories (CWA), 60, 67-68
  continuous AIRMETs and, 59
  convective SIGMETs, 59, 60, 64-66
  coverage of, charts and maps, 61, 62
  dissemination of, 69-70
  flash, 59
  hazards or flight precautions, 59
  meterological impact statements (MIS), 68
  "occasional" used in, 61
  PIREPs (UUA), 60
  public forecasts, 60
  severe local storms (SELs), 60
  severe weather watch bulletin (WW), 60, 66

advisories (*cont.*)
 SIGMETs, 59-63
AGL (ground level), 4, 74
Ahrens, C. Donald, 55
air analysis charts, 177-211
air density, 141
air mass (*see also* frontal systems), 361
air route traffic control centers (ARTCC),
 55, 60, 69, 216, 244
 flight watch and, 243
 IFR flight planning, 281
Air Traffic Bulletin, 73, 87-89
air traffic control, ix, xiii, 40, 54, 230, 241,
 273
 circular polarization radar, 146
 moving target indicator radar, 146
 radar for, 146
 sensitivity time control radar, 146
Air Traffic Control Handbook, 113
airborne radar, 145, 146, 149, 151, 245
aircraft performance standards, 140-141
aircraft type designators, 326-333
airline transport pilots, xi-xii
Airline Weather Services, 145
airmail, 213
Airman's Information Manual, x, 44, 274,
 281, 283
AIRMETs, 39, 59-63, 67, 73, 76, 77, 87,
 88, 230, 232
airport advisory service (AAS), 238
airport radar service areas (ARSA), 284
airport traffic areas (ATA), 284
Airport/Facility Directory, 2, 31, 36, 69, 99,
 133, 153, 172, 232, 238, 245, 247, 248,
 252, 257, 262, 264, 280
airspeed
 dramatic changes in (*see* wind shear), 173
 true vs. calibrated or equivalent, 141
airway communications stations, 213
airway intersections, 273, 274
airway radio stations, 213
alert weather watches (AWW), 60, 65-67,
 232, 355
altimeter settings, 24-25, 33, 36, 74, 113
altitudes, 140
altocumulus, 180, 181
 Castellanus, 26, 27, 36
 standing lenticular, 26, 28, 36
altostratus, 180, 181
amplitude modulation scope, radar, 148

anamometers, 24
anchors, TWEB forecasts, 100
anomalous propagation, radar, 148
anticyclones, 185, 203, 205, 361
 haze and, 18, 19
AOPA Pilot, 230
apparent visibility, 11
approach lighting systems (ALS), ceilings
 and, 7
Approach magazine, 26
arc cloud, 361
area forecasts (FA), 56, 59, 63, 71-97, 178,
 188, 208, 220, 236, 357-359
 adverse conditions, 90
 amendment criteria, 87
 ceilings, 94
 clouds and weather, 93
 coastal waters, 73
 conditional terms, 76-77
 convective SIGMETs, 94
 coverage area, 92
 dissemination of, 72
 freezing levels, 77-79, 92
 frequency of issuance, 72, 97
 geographical area designators, 93
 hazards or flight precautions, 59, 73-74,
 92
 high altitude significant weather prog,
 94-97, 94
 icing, 76-77, 92
 in-flight advisory plotting chart, 93
 limitations to, 97
 low-level wind shear, 80-82, 92
 obscuration, 93
 "occasional," 77
 outlook, 86-87
 sections of, 72
 significant clouds and weather section,
 82-86
 synopsis section, 74-76, 90
 thunderstorms, 92
 translation and use of, 89-94
 turbulence, 76-77, 80-82, 92
 TWEB forecasts and, 109
 valid time of, 92, 97
 visibility, 93, 94
Argo, Dominique, 97
ASOS Progress Report, 34
atmospheric data, 21-23
 altimeter settings, 24-25

clouds, 26-29
density altitude, 21, 22
dew point, 21
freezing levels, 31, 32
remarks on, 25-26
sea level pressure, 21
temperature, 21, 22
thermal turbulence, 22, 23
winds, 23-24
atmospheric phenomena, 12-21, 361
advection fog, 17
dust, 13, 14, 19
evaporation fog, 18
fog, 13-18
freezing rain/drizzle, 13, 14
frontal fog, 18
FSS observations of, 13
ground fog, 16
hail, 13, 14
haze, 13, 14, 18
ice crystals, 13, 14
ice fog, 13, 14, 16
ice pellets, 13, 14
icing conditions, 14, 15, 18
inversion layers, 18
inversion-induced wind shear turbulence,
    18, 19
low-level wind shear (LLWS), 12
microbursts, 12
obstructions to vision, 16-21
precipitation levels, 13, 14
radiation fog, 16
rain-induced fog, 18
rain/drizzle, 13, 14
sand, 13, 14, 19, 20
smoke, 13, 14, 18, 20
snow, 13, 14
snow, blowing, 13, 14, 21
steam fog, 18
stratus clouds, 17
thunderstorms, 12, 13
tornadoes, waterspouts, funnel clouds, 12,
    13
upslope fog, 18
weather phenomena, 12
wind gusts, 13
zero-zero conditions, 16
atmospheric pressure (see also frontal
    systems; high-pressure systems;
    low-pressure

systems), 3, 25, 100, 182-188, 354
constant pressure charts, 192-199
hurricanes, 211
international standard atmosphere (ISA),
    140
rapid changes, 29, 38
sea level, 21
automated flight service stations (AFSS), 2,
    99, 135, 215, 216, 241
automated weather observation systems
    (AWOS), x, xiii, 2, 33-38, 58, 121, 180,
    188, 354, 361, 367
location identifiers, abbreviations, 302-322
terminal forecasts (FT) based on, 118
automatic meteorological observing station
    (AMOS), 33, 354
automatic observing station (AUTOB), 33,
    118
automatic terminal information service
    (ATIS), 68, 69
aviation safety reporting service (ASRS), 229
Aviation Weather, xi, 58, 74
Aviation Weather Services, xi, 44, 161, 170

B

back scatter, radar, 146
balloons
ceilings measurement with, 6
winds and temperatures aloft from,
    133-134
baroclinic, 361
barotropic, 361
beam resolution, radar, 146
BINOVC (breaks in overcast), 29
Bjerknes, Vilhelm and Jakob, 186
BKN (broken sky cover), 3, 4
blowing sand (see sand), 20
boundaries (see frontal systems), 362
bounded weak echo region (BWEAR), 362
briefings, x-xii, 69, 96, 213-236
abbreviated, 214, 221-223
commercial weather briefing services,
    233-236
DUAT, 233-236
FAA pilot weather briefing service,
    228-233
in-flight, 214, 228
Model 1 system, 215-217
outlook, 214, 223-228
protocol for, 231-233

briefings (*cont.*)
  requirements for, 214
  standard, 214, 218-221
  teletype for, 214-215, 214
Buell, C.E., 145

C

calibrated airspeed, 141
call signs, IFR flight planning, 274
carburetor icing, 48, 49
Castellanus, altocumulus clouds, 26, 27, 36
cathode ray tubes (CRT), radar, 149
ceiling light, ceilings height measurement, 6
ceilings (*see also* clouds; sky cover;
    visibility), xiii, 3, 4-10, 17, 25, 34,
    36-38, 56, 63, 73, 74, 83, 84, 86, 94,
    105, 106, 108, 114, 116, 119, 123, 129,
    130, 132, 188, 244
  balloons to measure, 6
  ceiling light for, 6
  clinometer for, 6
  convective cloud height estimate, 6
  decision height (DH), 7
  estimated, 5
  indefinite, 5, 7
  landing requirements, FARs, 8
  lifted condensation level (LCL) and, 6
  measured, 5, 6, 7
  minimum descent altitudes (MDAs) and,
    10
  obscuration, 8
  obscuring phenomena, 7
  PIREPs to report, 6
  rotating beam ceilometer (RBC) for, 6, 7
  slant range distance/visibility, 8
  summation principle, 8, 9
  variable, 4
ceilometer (*see also* rotating beam
    ceilometer)
  laser, 33, 34
cells, 70, 151
center weather advisories (CWA), 39, 60.
    67-68, 87
Center Weather Service Units (CWSU), 55,
    60, 88, 152, 244
charts, xii-xiii, 61
  abbreviations used on, 288-302
  air analysis, 177-211
  composite moisture stability, 168-170
  constant pressure, 177, 192-199
  radar summary, 177
  sectional, 42
  severe weather outlook, 166-168, 170
  significant weather prognosis, 223-228
  surface analysis, 177-188, 206, 210
  upper air analysis, 192-202
  weather depiction, 177, 188-191, 206, 224
  winds and temperatures aloft, 137-138
  world aeronautical (WAX), 42
check rides, xi
Chinook winds, 187
chop, 43, 362
circular polarization (CP), radar, 146
cirrocumulus, 180, 181
  standing lenticular, 26
cirroform clouds, 103
cirrostratus, 180, 181
cirrus, 26, 86, 180, 181, 236
  transverse banding, 365
Civil Aeronautics Authority (CAA), 213
Civil Aeronautics Board (CAB), 145
Class II NOTAMs, 254
clear air turbulence (CAT), 43, 45, 63, 80,
    94, 245, 362
clear ice, 47, 77
clearances, IFR, 283-284
clinometer, ceilings height measurement, 6
closed cell stratocumulus, 362
cloud band, 362
Cloud Chart The, xiv
cloud elements, 34, 362
cloud line, 362
cloud shield, 362
cloud streets, 362
clouds (*see also* ceilings; sky cover;
    visibility), xii, xiv 25-29, 34, 36-39, 42,
    43, 47, 48, 63, 74, 78, 101, 103, 106,
    108, 111, 114, 118, 119, 124, 126, 129,
    146, 155, 157, 170, 171, 172, 179-182,
    187, 188, 193, 195, 206, 210, 224, 226,
    228, 234, 236, 353
  altocumulus, 180, 181
  altocumulus Castellanus, 26, 27, 36
  altostratus, 180, 181
  arc, 361
  area forecasts (FA) report, 82-86, 93
  base of, 6
  cirrocumulus, 180, 181

cirroform, 103
cirrostratus, 180, 181
cirrus, 26, 86, 180, 181, 236
climbs and descents through (FARs), 5
closed cell stratocumulus, 362
cloud band, 362
cloud element, 34, 362
cloud line, 362
cloud shield, 362
cloud streets, 362
comma systems, 362
convective, height of, 6
cumuliform, 23, 45, 47
cumulonimbus, 12, 14, 32, 36, 94, 96,
   180, 181
cumulonimbus Mamma, 29, 31
cumulus, 14, 25, 29, 70, 180, 181
   fair weather cumulus, 23
fractocumulus, 29
fractostratus, 180, 181, 182
funnel (see funnel clouds; tornadoes;
   waterspouts)
height of, 101, 102
nimbostratus, 181
roll clouds, 29
rotor, 36, 44
shelf clouds, 29
standing lenticular altocumulus, 26, 28, 36
standing lenticular cirrocumulus, 26
standing lenticular stratocumulus, 26
stratocumulus, 23, 180, 181
stratus, 11, 17, 26, 46, 75, 170, 180, 181,
   190
transverse cirrus banding, 365
TWEB forecasts report, 101
wall clouds, 29
CLR (clear sky cover), 3, 4
coastal marine layers, 75
coastal waters, 73
coke bottle (see clinometer)
cold fronts, 37, 75, 80, 187, 206, 208, 226
   cold low aloft, 198
cold pool, 362
cold-core low, 362
Collins, Richard, 230
comma cloud systems, 362
comma head, 362
comma tail, 362
commercial pilots, xi-xii

commercial weather briefing services, x,
   233-236
composite flight plans, IFR flight planning,
   283
composite moisture stability chart, 168-170
computers, 53, 57, 58, 89, 143
conditional terms, area forecasts (FA), 76-77
confluence, 362
constant pressure charts, 177, 192-199
   300 mb and 200 mb, 199-201
   500 mb, 195-199
   850-700 mb, 193-195
continuous AIRMETs, 59
contours, 192
contractions, 287-333
control towers (see also air traffic control),
   2, 40
controlled airspace, IFR flight planning, 274
convection/convective activity (see also
   thunderstorms), 12, 23, 43, 74, 94, 187
   level of free (LFC), 23, 364
   radar and, 145-175
convective outlook (AC), 164-166, 203
convective SIGMETs, 59, 60, 64-66, 94,
   166, 203, 232, 354
convergence, 185, 186, 193, 205, 362, 364
Coordinated Universal Time (UTC), 3, 41,
   42, 362
Coriolis force, 192, 203
crepuscular rays, 25
crosswind component, 24, 38
cumulonimbus, 12, 14, 32, 36, 83, 94, 96,
   180, 181
cumulonimbus Mamma, 29, 31
cumulus, 14, 23, 25, 29, 45, 47, 83, 124,
   180, 181
current conditions, standard briefings, 220
cyclones, 96, 203, 205, 362

D

de-icers, 22, 47
decision height (DH), 7
   visibility and, 12
Definitions and Abbreviations, 78
deformation zone, 363
density altitude, xiii, 21-23, 33, 141, 142,
   186
Department of Defense (DOD), 33, 149
depression, temperature/dewpoint, 192

destination forecast, standard briefings, 221
development, 54
dew point, 21, 33, 38, 66, 113, 172, 173, 179, 182, 187, 192, 193, 198, 363
   convective cloud height estimate using, 6
difluence, 206, 363
Direct User Access Terminal (DUAT), x, xiv, 1, 25, 42, 69, 85, 90, 97, 101, 111, 134, 179, 203, 233-236, 247, 257, 262, 264, 273, 280, 281
direction finders, 270
discrete frequency, FSS, 238
divergence, 185, 186, 193, 205, 206, 363
doppler radar (*see also* NEXRAD), 58, 149, 150, 172
downbursts, 171
downdrafts, 26, 29, 31, 61, 109, 142, 153, 171
downslope winds, 187, 205
drizzle (*see* rain/drizzle)
dry line, 66, 363
dry slot, 363
duplex communications, 238
dust, xiii, 11, 13, 14, 19, 43, 63, 96, 171, 172, 173, 180
dust devils, 25

E

echoes, radar, 155
Ely Low, 209
embedded microbursts, 172
embedded thunderstorms, 63, 64, 109, 363
emergencies, 270-272
en route flight advisory service (EFAS) (*see also* Flight Watch), 40, 55
en route forecast, standard briefings, 228
Enhanced Infrared (IR) imagery, 363
enhanced V, 363
equipment, 2
equivalent airspeed, 141
estimated ceilings, 5
evaporation fog, 18
evaporative cooling turbulence, 26, 82, 172
experience, xii, 2, 37, 43, 51, 75

F

FAA Aviation News, 151
fair weather cumulus, 23
fall streaks, 26
Fast-File service, VFR flight planning, 264

FD locations, 337
FDC NOTAM, 248, 253-254
Federal Aviation Administration (FAA), ix-xii, 2, 33, 36, 54, 56, 60, 145, 214, 215, 216, 221, 228, 229, 247
Federal Aviation Regulations (FAR), xi-xiv
   adverse weather forecasts, 73
   cloud distances, climbs and descents, 5
   fuel requirements, 139, 140
   landing requirements, ceilings, 8
fine line, 363
flash advisories, 59
flight advisory weather service offices, 59
flight assistance service, 270-272
flight planning, xiii-xiv, 66, 229
   composite, 283
   IFR, 273-285
   preflight planner, 261
   standard briefings and, 218-221
   VFR, 259-272
   winds and temperatures aloft used for, 143
flight precautions, area forecasts (FA), 59, 73-74
Flight Service, 43
Flight Service Station (FSS), ix-x, xiv, 5, 6, 11, 13, 25, 33, 40, 68, 69, 90, 96, 97, 101, 103, 111, 134, 152, 163, 179, 181, 199, 213, 214, 215, 228, 230, 231, 233, 236-241, 257, 259, 326
   AFSS procedures, 241
   aircraft identification for, 240
   airport advisory frequency, 238
   common frequency, 238
   discrete frequency, 238
   duplex communications, 238
   frequencies available for, 237
   identifying communication frequency for, 240
   limited remote communications/Navaid, 238
   monitoring frequency of, 240
   protocol for using, 240-241
   services available through, 237
   weather observation by, 2
Flight Services Handbook, xiv, 110, 220, 223, 367
flight standards district office (FSDO), 111, 233
flight testing, xi

Flight Watch, 40, 55, 99, 143, 152, 163, 179, 181, 221 241-246
  availability of, 242
  contacting, 244
  frequencies for, 246-246
  procedures for, 243-246
  stations for, 242
foehn winds, 19, 82
fog, xiii, 7, 11, 13-18, 25, 34, 38, 54, 56, 75, 83, 84, 86, 94, 108, 118, 120, 121, 170, 180, 182, 185, 187, 188, 189, 190, 226
forecasts and forecasting, xii-xiv, 39, 53-58, 241
  abbreviations used in, 287-333
  accuracy of, 54-56
  area (see area forecasts)
  composite moisture stability chart, 168-170
  convective outlook (AC), 164-166
  expectations of, 57-58
  interpolation of data from, 136
  limitations on, 56-58
  location identifiers, 302-326
  outlook, 57
  severe weather outlook chart, 166-168, 179
  specificity of, 56-57
  terminal, 56, 71, 83, 84
  TWEB route, 56
fractocumulus, 29
fractostratus, 180, 181, 182
freezing levels, 31, 32, 168, 170, 224, 226
  area forecasts (FA) report, 77-79, 92
  winds and temperatures aloft for, 143
freezing rain/drizzle, 13, 14, 22, 34, 47, 56
frictional effect, 136, 143, 192, 193
frontal fog, 18
frontal passage (FROPA), 29, 116, 117
frontal systems, 29, 37, 54, 56, 60, 66, 68, 74-76, 80, 82, 100, 101, 177, 178, 182-188, 206, 224
  boundaries, 96, 182, 185, 202
  cold, 187, 206, 208, 226
  dissipation (frontolysis), 182
  formation (frontogenesis), 182
  frontal or rain-induced fog, 18
  global waves, long-waves, 198
  hurricanes and, 211
  intensity and speed, 185
  jet stream and, 202
  movement of, 210

  occluded, 187
  polar, 186
  slope of, 187
  stationary, 187
  warm, 187
frontal turbulence, 82
frontogenesis, 182
frontolysis, 182
frost, 22
FT locations, 336
fuel requirements, 139, 140
funnel clouds (see also tornadoes; waterspouts), 12, 13, 25, 180

G

General Operating and Flight Rules, xiv, 367
geographical area designators, 61, 62, 68, 79, 84, 85, 93, 96, 102, 351-352
Geostationary Operational Environmental Satellites (GEOS), 363
global waves, 198
Glossary of Meteorology, 25
go/no-go decisions, xi-xiii, 5, 230
GOESNEXT satellites, 58
Greenwich Mean Time (see Coordinated Universal Time)
ground clutter, radar, 148
ground fog, 16
ground level (AGL), 4
gust front, 363
gusts (see also turbulence; winds), 29, 37, 38, 68, 71, 74, 83, 119, 153, 155, 171, 236
  load factors, 45

H

Hadley Cell, 363
hail, 12, 13, 14, 40, 47, 63, 64, 74, 94, 146, 148, 149, 155, 160
hail shaft, 363
halos, sun or moon, 181
hazardous in-flight weather advisory service (HIWAS), 69
hazards, area forecasts (FA), 59, 73-74, 92
haze, xiii, 9, 11, 13, 14, 18, 19, 25, 34, 86, 119, 126, 180
  top layer measurement, 19
high altitude flight watch, 55
high altitude significant weather prog, 94-97
high-level flight, xiii

high-level turbulence, 80
high-pressure systems, 74, 75, 100, 101,
   182-190, 226
   haze and, 18, 19
   thermal, 365
hook echo, 363
humidity, 18, 31, 32, 76, 170, 187, 195
hurricanes, 111, 131, 211
   bulletin for, 356-357

I

ice crystals, 13, 14
ice fog, 13, 14, 16
ice pellets, 13, 14, 47
ice protection equipment, 47
icing, xii-xiii, 14, 15, 18, 22, 26, 39, 40,
   43, 45-49, 51, 56, 63, 66, 68, 73, 74, 94,
   109, 131, 149, 170, 193, 195, 198, 220,
   224, 226, 231, 235, 244, 245
   area forecasts (FA) report, 76-79, 92
   carburetor, 48, 49
   clear, 47
   induction systems, 48
   layers of, 77
   mixed rime and clear, 47
   rime, 46, 63
   runway, 247
   sloping or lowering layers of, 77
   types of, 45-49
IFR/IFR flight planning, xiii-xiv, 7, 8, 11,
   15, 16, 36, 37, 38, 45, 56, 68, 70, 73,
   75, 86, 87, 93, 94, 117, 188, 189, 190,
   206, 209, 219, 224, 229, 273-285
   accuracy of, 274, 276
   air traffic control and, 273
   aircraft type identification, 274
   airspeed, departure, cruising altitude, 274
   airway intersections, 273, 274
   airway to airway routes, 274
   ARTCC and, 281
   call signs, 274
   clearances, obtaining and cancelling,
    283-284
   composite flight plans, 283
   computer processing of, 274, 276, 281-283
   controlled airspace, 274
   DUAT, 273, 280
   error messages, 281
   FAR requirements, 273
   filing requirements, 273, 281-283
   flight plan service, 284-285
   information required by, 274-281
   initial approach fix (IAF), 279, 280
   location identifiers, 273, 274
   minimums, 2, 9, 10
   navigation or transponder code, 274
   remarks, 281
   RNAV, 280
   standard instrument departures (SID), 276,
    277, 280
   standard terminal arrival route (STAR),
    276, 278, 280
   terminal forecasts (FT) and, 122, 130
   transponder or navigation capability, 274
impulse, 364
in-flight advisory plotting chart, 61, 62, 64,
   68, 76, 93, 96, 106
   location identifiers, 341-349
in-flight briefings, 214, 228
in-flight weather advisory program, 59
indefinite ceilings, 5, 7
induction system icing, 48
inertial navigation, 143
initial approach fix (IAF), IFR flight
   planning, 279, 280
instrument landing approach (ILS), 7, 170
Interim Voice Response System (IVRS), 2,
   99, 134, 221, 231, 233, 257
International Civil Aviation Organization
   (ICAO), 124
international standard atmosphere (ISA), 140,
   364
   temperature vs., 142
interpolation, 136
intersections, airway, 273, 274
intertropical convergence zone (ITCZ), 364
inversion layers, 18, 19, 82
inversion turbulence, 82
inversion-induced wind shear turbulence, 18, 19
isobars, 178, 182, 186, 192
isohumes, 170
isopleths, 168, 170
isotherms, 195

J

Jeppesen, 69
jet streams, 82, 96, 181, 199, 202, 206

K

Kraght, Peter E., 145

L

laser ceilometer, 33, 34
leased A and B systems (LABS), 215, 216
Leased Service A (LSAS), 2
lee side effect, 82
Letters to Airmen, 233
level of free convection (LFC), 23, 364
lifted condensation level (LCL), 6, 23, 364
lifted index, 168, 170, 364
lighting, runway, 247
lightning, 12, 13, 32, 37, 38, 50, 64, 74, 153, 173
limited aviation weather reporting station (LAWRS), 21, 353
limited fine mesh (LFM) model, winds and temperatures aloft, 133, 226
limited remote communications, 238
line echo wave pattern (LEWP), 362
local vicinity forecasts, 103-105
local warning radars, 155
location identifiers (LCID), 2, 42, 61, 158, 165, 235, 262, 273, 274, 335-337, 364
    abbreviations used, 302-326
    in-flight advisory plotting chart, 341-349
Location Identifiers handbook, 2, 165
long-wave ridges/troughs, 198, 364
LORAN, 143, 221
low instrument flight rules (LIFR), 119
low-level flight, xiii
low-level wind shear alert system (LLWAS), 36, 172, 173
low-level wind shear, 12, 24, 37, 38, 40, 43, 50, 56, 61, 66, 74, 101, 105, 109, 111, 115, 116, 131, 170-175, 226, 364
    area forecasts (FA) report, 80-82, 92
low-pressure systems, 74, 75, 100, 182-188, 206, 208, 209
    cold core, 362
    cold low aloft, 198
    Ely Low, 209
    hurricanes, 211
    mesolows, 155
    thermal, 365
    warm core, 366

M

mammatus (see cumulonimbus Mamma)
Manual of Meteorology, 53
maneuvering speed, turbulence vs., 45

mares' tails, 181
mean sea level (MSL), 5, 74
measured ceilings, 5, 6, 7
mechanical turbulence, 24, 68, 80, 82, 182, 195
melting level, radar and, 148
mesolows, 155, 364
mesoscale convective complex (MCC), 364
mesoscale weather systems, 55, 56, 364
meteorological impact statements (MIS), 68
Meteorology Today, 55
microbursts (see also low-level wind shear; wind shear), xiii, 27, 37, 38, 170-175, 364
    embedded, 172
    intensity of, 173
    recognition of, 171-174
Microbursts: A Handbook for Visual Identification, 171
Mike Monroney Aeronautical Center, 36
military operation areas (MOA), 221
military training routes, 221
military weather observation, 2, 25
minimum descent altitude (MDA), 31
    ceilings and, 10
    visibility and, 12
minimum en route altitudes (MEA), icing conditions and, 47
minimums
    IFR, 2, 9, 10
    VFR, 5
mixed ice, 47, 77, 79
Mode S transponders, 149
Model 1 system, 215, 216, 217
moisture convergence, 364
mountain obscurement (see obscuration)
mountain waves, 29, 30, 37, 44, 45, 68, 82, 109, 195, 245
mountainous terrain (see terrain)
moving target indicator, radar, 146
MSL (mean sea level), 5

N

NASA, 57, 153
National Aviation Weather Advisory Unit (NAWAU), 54, 59, 64, 67, 72, 73, 87-89
National Aviation Weather System, 53-54
National Meteorological Center (NMC), 54, 94

National Severe Storms Forecast Center
   (NSSFC), 54, 164-166
National Transportation Safety Board
   (NTSB), 70, 149, 214
National Weather Association, xiv
National Weather Service (NWS), x, 2, 11,
   25, 33, 34, 36, 39, 54, 55, 56, 58, 73,
   103, 120, 124, 145, 146, 153, 163, 178,
   179, 192, 228, 229, 233, 244, 245
NAVAID, 41, 69, 219, 238, 248, 270, 273,
   274
navigation, xiv
negative tilt, 364
negative vorticity advection (NVA), 205
nested grid model (NGM), winds and
   temperatures aloft   and, 133
NEXRAD, 58, 145, 146, 149, 150, 153, 172
night flight, visibility, 10
nimbostratus, 181
non-convective turbulence, 63
nonstandard refraction, radar, 148
NOTAMs, xiv, 36, 133, 213, 215, 219, 220,
   232, 233, 235, 236, 241, 247-257, 281
   abbreviations used in, 288-302
   Class II, 254
   FDC NOTAM, 248, 253-254
   issuance of, 247
   NOTAM (D), 248-252
   NOTAM (L), 248, 252-253
   standard briefings and, 221
   terminology of, 248
Notices to Airmen, 221, 247, 253, 254, 257

O
obscuration, 3, 8, 9, 25, 34, 63, 69, 83, 84,
   93, 101, 105, 124, 126, 219, 235
obscuring phenomena, 3, 7
observed winds aloft chart, 202-204
obstructions to vision, 16-21, 34, 83, 111,
   113, 118, 130, 132, 354
occasional, area forecasts (FA) usage, 77
occluded fronts, 187
offshore winds, 187, 226
onshore winds, 187
Operations Manual, 113
orographic lift, 205
outlook briefings, 214, 223-228
   significant weather prog chart, 223-228
outlook forecasts, 57, 66
   terminal forecasts (FT), 118-119

outlook, area forecasts (FA), 86-88
OVC (overcast sky cover), 3, 4
   breaks in (BINOVC), 29
overrunning, 364

P
Pacific Flyer, 71
Pilot Bulletins, 233
pilot reports (see PIREPs)
Pilot Windshear Guide, 171
Pilot's Guide to IVRS, A, 2, 233
Pilot/Controller Glossary, 78
pilots automatic telephone weather answering
   service (PATWAS), 99, 134, 221,
   231-233, 257
PIREPs, x, xii-xiii, 4, 38-53, 77, 80, 87-89,
   114, 115, 143, 173, 215, 220, 236, 241,
   244, 245
   abbreviations used in, 288-302
   air temperature: /TA, 41, 43
   altitude/flight level: /FL, 41, 42
   ceilings, 6
   en route flight advisory service (EFAS) for,
      40
   evaluation of, 51-52
   filing of, 40
   format for, 40-43
   haze layer tops, 19
   icing, types and degrees of, 45-49
   icing: /IC, 41, 43
   location identifiers, 42
   location: /OV, 40, 41, 42
   remarks: /RM, 41, 42, 43, 50-52
   routine (UA), 40
   sky cover: /SK, 41, 42
   time: /TM, 41, 42
   turbulence, degrees of, 44-45
   turbulence:/TB, 41, 43
   type aircraft: /TP, 41, 42
   urgent (UUA), 40, 60, 69
   weather: /WX, 41, 42
plan position indicator (PPI), radar, 146
polar fronts, 186
positive control area (PCA), 43
positive tilt, 364
positive vorticity advection (PVA), 66, 74,
   205, 364
precipitation (see also hail; rain; snow), xiii,
   13-15, 33, 83, 153, 171, 173, 178, 181,
   182, 193, 195, 198, 208, 224

attenuation of radar by, 149, 151
composite moisture stability chart, 168-170
intensity, intensity trend, 156
melting level, 148
radar and, 146
video integrator and processor (VIP), 156
preflight planner, 261
pressure (*see* atmospheric pressure)
pressure altitude, 140
pressure gradients, 192
prevailing visibility, 10, 11
Private Pilot, 33
private pilots, xi-xii
public forecasts, 60

R

Radar, 145, 153
radar, 39, 53, 58, 64, 89, 146-153, 270
   airborne (*see also* Radar), 145, 146, 149,
    151, 245
   amplitude modulation scope, 148
   ATC En Route, 146
   beam resolution, 146
   cathode ray tube (CRT) for, 149
   circular polarization, 146
   data acquisition units for, 149
   display units for, 149
   doppler (*see also* NEXRAD), 149, 150,
    172
   ground clutter (anomalous propagation),
    148
   local warning, 155
   melting level and, 148
   moving target indicator, 146
   next generation (NEXRAD), 145, 146,
    149, 150
   nonstandard refraction, 148
   NWS, 146
   plan position indicator (PPI), 146
   precipitation attenuation, 146, 149, 151
   product generation units for, 149
   Radar, 153
   radar facsimile circuit (RAFAX), 153, 163
   radar remote weather display system
    (RRWDS), 152-153
   radar summary chart, 161-163
   radar weather reports (RAREPs), 145,
    153-161, 163, 220, 236
   range attuation, 146
   range height indicator (RHI), 146, 148

reflected energy or back scatter for, 146
sensitivity time control, 146
Stormscope, 153, 245
Terminal Doppler Weather Radar (TDWR),
  172
thunderstorm predictions with, 145-175
translation and use of reports from,
  161-164
video integrator and processor (VIP), 156
radar facsimile circuit (RAFAX), 153, 163
radar precipitation intensity VIP levels, 64
radar remote weather display system
  (RRWDS), 152-153, 163, 245
radar summary chart, 161, 162, 163, 177
  plotted data, 157, 159
radar weather reports (RAREPs), 145,
  153-161, 163, 220, 236
  echo configuration and coverage, 155
  echo height, 157
  echo location and movement, 156-157
  information contained in, 155
  local warning radars and, 155
  location identifiers in, 158
  precipitation type, intensity, intensity trend,
   156
  radar summary chart vs., 157, 159, 161
  remarks section, 157-161
  storm detection (SD) report, 155
  translation and use of, 161-164
RADAT messages, 32, 170
radiation fog, 16, 54, 84, 189, 190, 226
radio beacons, 99
radio navigation aids (*see* NAVAID)
rain/drizzle, 7, 11, 13, 14, 22, 34, 37, 38,
  69, 71, 83, 94, 101, 102, 105, 108, 116,
  129, 146, 148, 149, 156, 161, 171, 172,
  173, 180, 181, 182, 226
rain-induced fog, 18
range attuation, radar, 146
range height indicator (RHI), radar, 146, 148
record weather reports, 2
recreational pilots, xi-xii
relative humidity, 18, 31, 32, 168, 170, 172
relative vorticity, 205
remarks, weather reports, 25-26, 36, 37,
  50-52
restricted visibility, 16
ridges, 184, 185, 195, 198, 205, 206, 210
rime ice, 46, 63, 77, 79
RNAV, IFR flight planning, 280

roll clouds, 29
Rossby wave, 364, 365
rotating beam ceilometer (RBC), 6, 7, 34
rotor clouds, 36, 44
routine PIREPs (UA), 40
RS weather reports, 2, 3
runway visibility (RVV), 12
runway visual range (RVR), 12, 36, 38

S

sand, 13, 14, 19, 20, 43, 63, 96
Santa Ana winds, 51, 82, 187
satellites, 39, 53, 54, 58, 64, 73, 89, 181,
   190, 211, 244, 363
saturation, 6, 23
Schuyler, Norman, 33
SCT (scattered sky cover), 3, 4
scud, 182
sea breezes, 82
sea level pressure, 21
search and rescue, 266
sectional charts, 42
sensitivity time control, radar, 146
service ceilings, 48
severe local storms (SELs), 60
severe shear, 171
severe thunderstorms, 13, 16, 37, 44, 64, 66,
   94, 145, 187, 365
severe weather, 2
severe weather forecast alerts, 232
severe weather outlook chart, 166-168, 170
severe weather watch bulletin (WW), 60, 66,
   168, 355, 356
Shaw, William N. (Sir), 53
shear (see wind shear)
shear axis, 365
shelf clouds, 29
short wave, 365
showers (see precipitation; rain; snow)
SIGMETs, 39, 44, 59-63, 67, 69, 73, 76,
   80, 87, 88, 92, 230, 231, 232, 354
   convective, 59, 60, 64-66, 94, 166, 203,
   232, 354
significant weather prognosis chart, 223-228
sky cover (see also ceilings; clouds;
   visibility) 3-5, 25, 26, 33, 34, 37, 42, 83,
   84, 101, 105, 113, 114, 117, 118, 120,
   124, 126, 130, 132, 179, 180, 182, 188,
   220, 226, 236
   breaks in overcast (BINOVC), 29

broken (BKN), 3, 4
   ceilings and, 3, 4
   clear (CLR), 3, 4
   climbs and descents through (FARs), 5
   height from ground level (AGL), 4
   obscuration (X), 3, 4
   obscuring phenomena, 3
   overcast (OVC), 3, 4
   partially obscured (-X), 8, 9
   PIREPs reporting, 4
   scattered (SCT), 3, 4
   summation principles for, 3, 4
   variable, 4
slant range visibility, 8
sleet (see ice pellets)
slope, frontal system, 187
Smith, Paul, 87-89
smoke, xiii, 7, 9, 11, 13, 14, 18, 20, 43, 86,
   119, 180
snow, 7, 11, 13, 14, 22, 26, 34, 47, 119,
   146, 148, 181, 182, 209, 226
   blowing, 13, 14, 21
   runway, 247
special VFR, 268-270
special weather reports (SP), 2, 3, 215
squalls, 24, 29, 31, 96, 153, 164, 184
Stalker, Lance, 71
standard atmosphere, 140
standard briefings, 214, 218-221
   adverse conditions, 219
   current conditions, 220
   destination forecast, 221
   en route forecast, 220
   NOTAMs and, 221
   synopsis of, 220
   VFR flight not recommended (VNR), 220
   winds aloft forecasts, 221
standard instrument departures (SID), IFR
   flight planning, 276, 277, 280
standard terminal arrival route (STAR), IFR
   flight planning, 276, 278, 280
standing lenticular altocumulus, 26, 28, 36
standing lenticular cirrocumulus, 26
standing lenticular stratocumulus, 26
station model
   weather depiction charts, 188
   surface analysis chart, 179-182
stationary fronts, 101, 187
steam fog, 18
storm detection (SD) report, 155

Stormscope, 145, 153, 245
stratocumulus, 23, 180, 181
  standing lenticular, 26
stratosphere, 96, 192, 199, 365
stratus clouds, 11, 17, 26, 46, 75, 170, 180, 181, 190
streamlines, 365
student pilots, xi-xii
sublimation, 26, 47, 365
summation principle, 3, 4, 8, 9, 42
surface analysis chart, 177-188, 206, 210
  frontal systems, 178
  isobars on, 178
  moisture patterns, 178
  sources for, 179
  station model and symbols for, 179-182
  symbols for, 96
  temperature, 178
  transmission times, 179
  winds, 178
surface heating, 143
surface observations (SA), xiii, 1-38, 353
surface visibility, 11
SW weather reports, 3
symbols, xii, 179-182
synoptic scale, 365
synoptic weather systems, 55, 56

T

tabulated winds and temperatures aloft, 134-137
telephone information briefing service (TIBS), 99, 134, 231, 232, 233, 257
temperature, 21, 22, 25, 33, 34, 38, 39, 43, 66, 76, 113, 133-144, 172, 173, 178, 179, 182, 185-187, 192, 193, 195, 198, 199, 210, 244
  convective cloud height estimate using, 6
  freezing levels and, 32
  international standard atmosphere (ISA) vs., 142
  interpolation of data on, 136
terminal aerodrome forecasts (TAF), 124-126
  optional codes, 126, 128, 126
  weather codes, 127
terminal control areas (TCA), 284
Terminal Doppler Weather Radar (TDWR), 172
terminal forecasts (FT), 56, 71, 83, 84, 111-132, 233, 236

accuracy of, 118, 130-131
altimeter settings, 113
amendment criteria, 120-124
AWOS observation-based, 118
ceiling, 114, 116, 119, 123, 129-132
clouds, 111, 114, 116, 118, 119, 129
conditional terms, 114-115
coverage, 113
dew point, 113
frontal passage, 116, 117
hurricanes, 111
icing and turbulence, 131
IFR flight planning and, 130
issuance times/validity, 113-114
limitations of, 130-131
low-level wind shear, 111, 115, 116
obstructions to visibility, 111, 113, 118, 130, 132
outlook, 118-119
sky cover, 113, 114, 117, 118, 120, 130, 132
synoptic situation and updates, 117
temperature, 113
terminal aerodrome forecasts (TAF), 124-126
thunderstorms, 119, 129
time references (UTC), 113
translation and use of, 126-132
visibility, 111, 113-123, 129, 130, 132
weather service forecast office preparation of, 111, 112
winds, 111, 113, 115, 116, 119, 120, 122, 129, 130, 132
terrain, xii, 26, 37, 70, 74, 80, 82, 83, 93, 142, 143, 187, 188
  mountain wave turbulence, 29, 30
  precipitation vs. visibility of, 15
  turbulence and, 24
testing and exams, xii
thermal high, 365
thermal low, 365
thermal turbulence, 22, 23, 54, 82
thin line, 363, 365
thunderstorms, xiii, 12, 13, 25, 26, 29, 31, 34, 37, 38, 54, 56, 63, 64, 66, 68, 70, 71, 73, 74, 75, 83, 92, 94, 96, 101, 105, 108, 109, 116, 119, 129, 131, 181, 182, 187, 195, 198, 206, 209, 210, 220, 226, 244, 245
  cells of, 151

thunderstorms (*cont.*)
composite moisture stability chart, 168-170
convective outlook (AC), 164-166
embedded, 63, 64, 109, 363
radar for, 145-175
severe, 13, 16, 37, 44, 64, 66, 94, 145, 187, 365
severe weather outlook chart, 166-168, 170
squall lines, 24, 164
wind shear and microbursts, 170-175
tilt, negative/positive, 364
tornadoes (*see also* funnel clouds; waterspouts), 2, 12, 13, 25, 40, 56, 63, 64, 66, 153, 155, 172, 173, 180
tower visibility, 11, 12
trace ice, 46
training, xii, 2, 32, 37, 43, 51, 75
transcribed information broadcast system, 221
transcribed weather broadcasts (TWEB), 69, 71, 83, 84, 87, 89, 99-109, 134, 178, 220, 221, 231, 232, 233, 257
accuracy and specificity of, 109
amendment criteria for, 105-106
anchors for, 100
area forecast and, 109
ceiling, 106, 108
clouds, 108
conditional terms, 102
coverage of, 106
fog, 108
frequencies for, 99
geographical area designators, 102
icing, 109
issuance of, 99, 100, 106
local vicinity forecasts, 103-105
low-level wind shear, 105, 109
mountain waves, 109
rain, 108
revisions, 100
route forecasts, 56
route numbers, 100
significant clouds and weather, 101-103
synopsis section of, 100-101
thunderstorms, 105, 108
translating and using, 106-109
turbulence, 109
up- and downdrafts, 109
valid time of, 99, 100, 106
VFR vs. IFR decision, 109

visibility, 106
transmissometer, 34
visibility measurement, 12
transponder codes, 274
Mode S, 149
transverse cirrus banding, 365
tropical storms, 75, 96
tropopause, 96, 192, 202, 365
winds and temperatures aloft for, 143
troposphere, 96, 192, 195, 199, 205, 365
troughs, 184-186, 195, 198, 199, 205, 206, 208, 236
true airspeed (TAS), 141
turbulence (*see also* gusts, wind shear; winds) xiii, 16, 24, 26, 27, 39, 40, 43-45, 47, 50, 51, 56, 60, 61, 63, 66, 68, 69, 70, 73, 74, 82, 94, 96, 97, 109, 131, 142, 153, 160, 170, 173, 174, 181, 185, 195, 198, 199, 202, 219, 220, 224, 226, 231, 235, 236, 244, 245
area forecasts (FA) report, 76-77, 80-82, 92
chop, 43
clear air (*see* clear air turbulence)
degrees of, 44-45
evaporative cooling, 172
inversion-induced, 18, 19
low-level, steam fog, 18
maneuvering speed vs., 45
mechanical, 24, 182, 195
mountain wave (*see* mountain waves)
non-convective, 63
squalls, 24
thermal, 22, 23, 54

U
Unisys Corporation, NEXRAD, 149
United States NOTAM system (USNS), 221
unrestricted visibility, 16
updrafts, 29, 31, 61, 109, 153
upper air analysis chart, 192-202
upper level weather systems, xiii, 205-211
upslope fog, 18, 54, 75, 190
upslope winds, 187, 205
urgent PIREPs (UUA), 40
USP weather reports, 2, 3

V
valley effect, 82
variable ceilings, 4

variable sky cover, 4
variable visibility, 10, 11
venturi effect, 140
VFR Pilot Exam-O-Gram, 36
VFR/VFR flight planning, xiii, xiv, 2, 8, 9,
    11, 15, 16, 36, 37, 38, 45, 57, 69, 75,
    86, 87, 94, 109, 117, 188, 206, 224,
    228, 259-272
  aircraft identification and type, 262, 263
  airspeed, departure time, 262
  alternate airports, 263
  estimated time en route, 263
  FAR requirements, 259, 263, 265
  Fast-File service, 264
  filing requirements, 259, 264
  flight assistance service, emergencies,
    270-272
  forms for, 260
  FSS procedures, 265-266
  fuel on board, 263
  information required on, 260-263
  minimums, 5
  not recommended (VNR), 220
  pilot, crew, passengers, 263
  preflight planner for, 261
  remarks, 263
  route and destination, 262
  search and rescue procedures, 266
  special equipment codes, 262
  special VFR, 268-270
  terminal forecasts (FT) amendment criteria
    and, 122
  VFR flight plan service for, 266-268
video integrator and processor (VIP), 156
virga, 26, 27, 171, 172, 173
visibility (*see also* ceilings; clouds; sky
    cover), xi, 10-12, 33, 34, 36, 37, 38, 42,
    43, 63, 83, 84, 86, 101, 102, 105, 106,
    111, 113-116, 118, 119, 121, 123, 124,
    126, 129, 130, 132, 182, 185, 188, 220,
    226, 228, 236, 244, 354
  aloft, 11
  apparent, 11
  area forecasts (FA), 93, 94
  blowing sand, 20
  blowing snow, 21
  day vs. night, 10
  decision height, 12
  downward and sideward, 15
  fog, 11

  forward, 15
  haze, 18
  inversion layers, 18
  minimum descent altitude (MDA), 12
  observations of, NWS and FSS, 11, 12
  precipitation vs., 15
  prevailing, 10, 11
  remarks, variable visibility, 11, 12
  restricted, 16
  runway (RVV), 12
  runway visual range (RVR), 12
  sectors of, prevailing, 10, 11
  slant range, 8
  smoke, 18
  statute mile measure of, 10
  stratus clouds, 11
  surface, 11
  tower, 11, 12
  transmissometer for, 12
  unrestricted, 16
  variable, 10, 11
  VFR vs. IFR, 11
  zero-zero conditions, 86
volcanic ash, 63, 354
VOR, 61, 69, 76, 99, 270
VORT MAX/VORT LOBE, 205, 365
vortex, 366
vorticity, xiii, 66, 74, 203, 205, 206, 366
  negative advection (NVA), 205
  positive advection (PVA), 205, 364
Voyager, 51

W

wall clouds, 29
warm air advection, 366
warm core low, 366
warm fronts, 187
waterspouts (*see also* funnel clouds;
    tornadoes), 12, 13, 180
waves, global or long-wave, 198, 366
weak echo region (WER), 362
weather avoidance system (*see* Radar)
Weather Bureau, 213, 214
Weather Decision, The, 58
weather depiction chart, 177, 188-191, 206,
    224
  analysis of, 188
  satellite imagery vs., 190
  station model and symbols for, 188
Weather for Aircrews, 14

weather log, 222, 233
weather observers, 2
weather products, 353-359
weather reports, xii-xiv, 1-2, 241
  abbreviations used on, 287-333
  altimeter settings, 24-25
  atmospheric data, 21-32
  atmospheric phenomena, 12-21
  ceilings, 5-10
  clouds, 26-29
  coding used in, 1
  Coordinated Universal Time (UTC) used
    in, 3
  density altitude, 21, 22
  dew point, 21
  freezing levels, 31, 32
  location identifier (LCID), 2, 302-326
  record, 2
  remarks on, 25-26
  RS (hourly special), 2, 3
  SA (hourly), 2, 3
  sea level pressure, 21
  sky cover, 3-5, 3
  SP (special), 2, 3
  SW (supplemental), 3
  temperature, 21, 22
  thermal turbulence, 22, 23
  USP (urgent special), 2, 3
  visibility, 10-12
  winds, 23-24
Weather Service Forecast Offices (WSFO),
  54, 63, 111
weather systems
  mesoscale, 55, 56
  synoptic, 55, 56
weather-related accidents, x, xii
Will Rogers World Airport, 36
Williams, Dick, 73, 97
wind fields, 366
wind profiler, 58, 143
wind shear (see also microbursts; turbulence;
  winds), xiii, 26, 36, 37, 38, 40, 43, 50,
  56, 61, 66, 74, 80-82, 92, 96, 101, 105,
  109, 111, 115, 116, 131, 153, 170-175,
  198, 226, 244, 245, 366
  intensity of, 173
  inversion-induced, 18, 19
  low-level (see low-level wind shear)
  probability of, 173
  recognition of, 171-174

  recovery from, 174-175
  severe, 365
  takeoff, approach, landing precautions, 174
wind vanes, 24
winds (see also gusts; turbulence; wind
  shear) xiii, 13, 18, 22-24, 33, 36, 37, 38,
  39, 44, 50, 51, 63, 64, 68, 71, 80, 86,
  101, 102, 111, 113, 115, 116, 119, 120,
  122, 124, 126, 129, 130-144, 173, 178,
  185, 186, 190, 192, 195, 199, 202, 220,
  226, 236, 244, 245, 354
  Chinook, 187
  convergence of fronts, 185
  Coriolis force, 192
  direction of, 23, 43, 80, 83, 102, 136,
    139, 179, 182, 192, 199
  divergence of fronts, 185
  foehn, 19, 82
  frictional effect, 136, 143, 192, 193
  gusting (see gusts)
  inertial navigation for, 143
  interpolation of data on, 136
  jet stream (see jet streams)
  LORAN for, 143
  measurement device: wind
    vane/anamometer, 24
  observed winds aloft chart, 202-204
  on- and offshore, 187
  peak, 24
  PIREPs and, 143
  pressure gradient, 192
  Santa Ana, 51, 82, 187
  shift, 24, 29, 38
  speed of, 23, 43, 80, 83, 102, 136, 139,
    179, 182, 192, 199
  speed of, dramatic changes in (see wind
    shear)
  squalls, 24
  standard briefings, 221
  up- and downslope, 187, 205
  venturi effect, 140
  wind field, 366
  wind profiler, 58
  zonal flow, 366
winds and temperatures aloft (FD), 133-144,
  233
  amendment criteria for, 137-139
  balloon launches for, 133-134
  flight planning with, 143
  forecast charts, 137-138

forecast periods of, 134, 135
freezing levels forecasted by, 143
frictional effect of winds and, 136, 143
fuel reserve requirements and, 139, 140
levels of, true altitude used in, 135
limitations, 135, 143
limited fine mesh (LFM) model for, 133
nested grid model (NGM) for, 133
sources of, 134
tabulated forecasts, 134-137
translation and use of, 139-144
transmission times of, 134, 135
tropopause prediction with, 143
updates, 135
wing loading, 45

world aeronautical charts (WAX), 42
World Meteorological Organization (WMO), 124
Wright brothers, 53
WST outlook, 66

X

X (sky obscured), 3, 4

Z

zero-zero conditions, 16, 86, 185
zonal flow, 366
ZULU time (*see* Coordinated Universal Time)

Other Bestsellers of Related Interest

ABCs OF SAFE FLYING—3rd Edition
—David Frazier

Take a step-by-step look at operational safety. This book presents a wealth of flight safety information in a fun-to-read format. The author's anecdotal episodes, as well as NTSB accident reports, lend both humor and sobering reality to the text. Detailed photographs, maps, and illustrations ensure you understand key concepts and techniques. 192 pages, illustrated. Book No. 3757, $14.95 paperback only

THE ART OF INSTRUMENT FLYING
—2nd Edition—J. R. Williams

". . . as complete and up-to-date as an instrument book can be." —Aero magazine

Williams has updated his comprehensive guide to include all elements of IFR flight—flight director, Loran-C, and Omega navigational systems. All en route, area, TCA, and SID/STAR charts reflect current designations. The first edition won the 1989 Best Technical Book award of the Western Region of the Aviation/Space Writers Association. 352 pages, 113 illustrations. Book No. 3654, $19.95 paperback, $31.95 hardcover

AVOIDING COMMON PILOT ERRORS: An Air Traffic Controller's View—John Stewart

This essential reference—written from the controller's perspective—interprets the mistakes pilots often make when operating in controlled airspace. It cites situations frequently encountered by controllers that show how improper training, lack of preflight preparation, poor communication skills, and confusing regulations can lead to pilot mistakes. 240 pages, 32 illustrations. Book No. 2434, $17.95 paperback only

MORE I LEARNED ABOUT FLYING FROM THAT—Editors of FLYING® magazine

What would you do if you lost half your wing in a midair collision or a strike force of wasps attacked you in the cockpit at 3,000 feet? What pilots have actually done in these nightmarish situations and in dozens of others is told by the fliers themselves in these accounts from Flying magazine's popular "I Learned About Flying From That" column. 196 pages. Book No. 3317, $12.95 paperback only

FLYING VFR IN MARGINAL WEATHER
—3rd Edition—Paul Garrison, Norval Kennedy, and Daryl E. Murphy

Here's an invaluable guide for every VFR pilot who must make cross-country flying decisions in the face of uncertain weather. You'll find specific information on determining what marginal weather is—ceiling, visibility, wind, turbulence, precipitation, and temperature. You'll also learn how to deal with situations ranging from flying VFR "on top" or between cloud layers to coping with thunderstorms, wind shear, and dust devils, to using an interstate highway to find your way in featureless terrain. 224 pages, 87 illustrations. Book No. 3699, $16.96 paperback only

STANDARD AIRCRAFT HANDBOOK
—5th Edition—Edited by Larry Reithmaier, originally compiled and edited by Stuart Leavell and Stanley Bungay

Now updated to cover the latest in aircraft parts, equipment, and construction techniques, this classic reference provides practical information on FAA-approved metal airplane hardware. Techniques are presented in step-by-step fashion and explained in shop terms without unnecessary theory and background. All data on materials and procedures is derived from current reports by the nation's largest aircraft manufacturers. 240 pages, 213 illustrations. Book No. 3634, $11.95 paperback only

GENERAL AVIATION LAW—Jerry A. Eichenberger

Although the regulatory burden that is part of flying sometimes seems overwhelming, it not need take the pleasure out of your flight time. This survey of aviation regulations gives you a solid understanding of FAA procedures and functions, airman ratings and maintenance certificates, the implications of aircraft ownership, and more. It allows you to recognize legal problems before they result in FAA investigations and potentially serious consequences. 240 pages. Book No. 3431, $16.95 paperback only

MASTERING INSTRUMENT FLYING
—Henry Sollman with Sherwood Harris

Perfect for pilots seeking an IFR rating, flight instructors developing lesson plans, and instrument pilots who want to brush up on their skills, this book introduces a course that's designed to meet or exceed the Instrument Flight Standards published by the FAA. The elements, techniques, procedures, and tolerances of instrument flight are addressed in precise detail. 336 pages, 256 illustrations. Book No. 2433, $18.95 paperback only

Prices Subject to Change Without Notice.

Look for These and Other TAB Books at Your Local Bookstore

To Order Call Toll Free 1-800-822-8158
(24-hour telephone service available.)

or write to TAB Books, Blue Ridge Summit, PA 17294-0840.

Title	Product No.	Quantity	Price

☐ Check or money order made payable to TAB Books

Charge my ☐ VISA ☐ MasterCard ☐ American Express

Acct. No. _____ Exp. _____

Signature: _____

Name: _____

Address: _____

City: _____

State: _____ Zip: _____

Subtotal $ _____

Postage and Handling
($3.00 in U.S., $5.00 outside U.S.) $ _____

Add applicable state and local
sales tax $ _____

TOTAL $ _____

TAB Books catalog free with purchase; otherwise send $1.00 in check or money order and receive $1.00 credit on your next purchase.

Orders outside U.S. must pay with international money order in U.S. dollars drawn on a U.S. bank.

TAB Guarantee: If for any reason you are not satisfied with the book(s) you order, simply return it (them) within 15 days and receive a full refund.   **BC**